Introduction to Modern Optics

Introduction to Modern Optics

GRANT R· FOWLES *University of Utah*

HOLT, RINEHART AND WINSTON, INC. *New York   Chicago
San Francisco Atlanta Dallas Montreal Toronto London*

Preface

The science of optics is very old, but in recent years there have been a number of new and far reaching developments. Perhaps the most notable among these, introduced in 1960, is the laser and its subsequent, rapidly growing list of striking applications. This, and other innovations have resulted in a remarkable upsurge in the importance of optics in both pure science and in technology.

It seems clear that there is a need for a modernized college textbook in optics at the intermediate level which brings to the student some of the new results that are presently available only in the research journals and highly specialized books. Hopefully, this book helps to fill such a need. It is intended to be a practical text for classroom use. The emphasis is on basic principles.

The first half of the book deals essentially with physical optics, that is, the propagation of light, its vectorial nature, coherence and interference, diffraction, and the optics of solids. The remainder of the book is devoted to the emission of light by atoms, molecules and solid bodies. The quantum aspect of light is, of course, taken up in this part of the book. The final chapter is concerned with the theory of optical amplification and the use of this principle in the making of the laser. The MKS rationalized system of units is employed throughout.

Recent developments, such as the applications of lasers to the study of optics, are integrated with the regular text material from the beginning. Thus in Chapter 2 there is a section on the Jones matrix and its application to the study of polarization.

Chapter 3 introduces the concepts of partial coherence, Fourier transform spectroscopy, and the theory of multilayer films, in addition to conventional interference theory. Chapter 4, besides the usual theory of diffraction, treats the theory of holography and the use of the Fourier transform in the study of diffraction. Chapter 5 contains a section on nonlinear optics.

In order to treat adequately the theory of light amplification, a brief introduction to quantum theory and optical spectra have been included (Chapters 6 and 7). These chapters deal with the emission of light by solid bodies (thermal radiation) and emission by atomic and molecular systems. They may be omitted in a short course if the student has taken a course in atomic physics.

The level is somewhat higher than that of older books in physical optics. It is assumed that the student has been introduced to Maxwell's equations in an intermediate course in electricity and magnetism. It is further expected that the student has had some advanced mathematics beyond calculus so that he is acquainted with such things as Fourier transforms, elementary matrix algebra, and so on. The level of mathematical proficiency is exemplified by texts such as Wylie's *Advanced Engineering Mathematics.*

In order to make the book useful for teaching, a list of problems is included at the end of each chapter. Answers to selected odd-numbered problems are given at the end of the book. A supplemental list of answers to all of the problems will be available to instructors.

The author wishes to express his thanks to the editorial staff of the publisher for their help and to C. Call for assistance in proofreading and preparation of the manuscript.

SALT LAKE CITY   *Grant R. Fowles*
SEPTEMBER 1967

Contents

CHAPTER I

The Propagation of Light

1.1 Elementary Optical Phenomena and the Nature of Light

"Rays of light," wrote Isaac Newton in his *Treatise on Opticks,* "are very small bodies emitted from shining substances." Newton probably chose to regard light as corpuscular chiefly because of the fact that, in a given uniform medium, light appears to travel in straight-line paths. This is the so-called law of *rectilinear propagation.* The formation of shadows is a familiar example cited to illustrate it.

A contemporary of Newton's, Christiaan Huygens (1629–1695), supported a different description, namely that light is a "wave motion" spreading out from the source in all directions. The reader will recall the time-honored use of Huygens' construction with primary waves and secondary wavelets to explain the elementary laws of reflection and refraction. Other optical facts that are well-explained by the wave picture are interference phenomena such as the formation of bright and dark bands by reflection of light from thin films, and diffraction, or the spreading of light around obstacles.

Owing mainly to the genius of James Clerk Maxwell (1831–1879), we know today that visible light is merely one form of electromagnetic energy, usually described as *electromagnetic waves,* the complete spectrum of which includes radio waves, infrared radiation, the visible spectrum of colors red through violet, ultraviolet radiation, x-rays, and gamma radiation. Furthermore, from the quantum theory of light pioneered by Planck, Einstein, and Bohr, we know that electromagnetic energy is *quantized,* that is, it can only be imparted to or taken from the electromagnetic field in discrete amounts called *photons.*

Thus the modern concept of light contains elements of both Newton's and Huygens' descriptions. Light is said to have a *dual* nature. Certain phenomena, such as interference, exhibit the wave character of light. Other phenomena, the photoelectric effect, for example, display the particle aspect of light.

If one were to ask the question "What is light, really?" there can be no simple answer. There is no familiar object or macroscopic model to employ as an analogy. But understanding need not be based on analogy. A consistent and unambiguous theoretical explanation of all optical phenomena is furnished jointly by Maxwell's electromagnetic theory and the quantum theory. Maxwell's theory treats the *propagation* of light, while the quantum theory describes the *interaction* of light and matter or the absorption and emission of light. Since electromagnetic theory and quantum theory also explain many other physical phenomena in addition to those related to electromagnetic radiation, it can be fairly assumed that the nature of light is well understood, at least within the context of a mathematical framework that accurately accounts for present experimental observations. The question as to the "true" or "ultimate" nature of light, although as yet unanswered, is quite irrelevant to our study of optics.

1.2   Electrical Constants and the Speed of Light

At a point in empty space the electromagnetic state of the vacuum is said to be specified by two vectors, the electric field $\mathbf{E}$, and the magnetic field $\mathbf{H}$. In the static case $\mathbf{E}$ and $\mathbf{H}$ are independent of one another and are determined, respectively, by the distribution of charges and currents in all space. In the dynamic case, however, the fields are not independent. Their space and time derivatives are interrelated in a manner expressed by the curl equations:

$$\boldsymbol{\nabla} \times \mathbf{E} = -\mu_0 \frac{\partial \mathbf{H}}{\partial t} \tag{1.1}$$

$$\boldsymbol{\nabla} \times \mathbf{H} = \varepsilon_0 \frac{\partial \mathbf{E}}{\partial t} \tag{1.2}$$

The divergence conditions:

$$\boldsymbol{\nabla} \cdot \mathbf{E} = 0 \tag{1.3}$$

$$\boldsymbol{\nabla} \cdot \mathbf{H} = 0 \tag{1.4}$$

indicate the absence of any charge at the point in question. They are true in either the static or the dynamic case.

The above four equations are generally referred to as Maxwell's equations for the vacuum. They can be regarded as the fundamental differential equations of the electromagnetic field in the absence of matter.

The constant μ_0 is known as the *permeability of the vacuum*. It has, by definition, the exact value $4\pi \times 10^{-7}$ henries per meter (H/m).[1]

---

[1] MKS rationalized units are generally used throughout the book. We have chosen to use $\mathbf{H}$ rather than $\mathbf{B}$ in all equations involving magnetic fields. Wherever it occurs, $\mathbf{H}$ can always be written $\mathbf{B}/\mu_0$ since nonmagnetic media only are considered in this text.

The constant ε_0 is called the *permittivity of the vacuum*. Its value must be determined by measurement. The value of ε_0 to four significant figures is 8.854×10^{-12} farads per meter (F/m).

Now the fields **E** and **H** in the two curl equations can be separated. This is done by taking the curl of one equation and the time derivative of the other and using the fact that the order of differentiation with respect to time or space can be reversed. The result is

$$\nabla \times (\nabla \times \mathbf{E}) = -\mu_0\varepsilon_0 \frac{\partial^2 \mathbf{E}}{\partial t^2} \tag{1.5}$$

$$\nabla \times (\nabla \times \mathbf{H}) = -\mu_0\varepsilon_0 \frac{\partial^2 \mathbf{H}}{\partial t^2} \tag{1.6}$$

Further, by using the divergence conditions (1.3) and (1.4) together with the vector identity

$$\nabla \times (\nabla \times \quad) \equiv \nabla (\nabla \cdot \quad) - \nabla^2(\quad) \tag{1.7}$$

we obtain

$$\nabla^2\mathbf{E} = \frac{1}{c^2} \frac{\partial^2 \mathbf{E}}{\partial t^2} \qquad \nabla^2\mathbf{H} = \frac{1}{c^2} \frac{\partial^2 \mathbf{H}}{\partial t^2} \tag{1.8}$$

where

$$c = (\mu_0\varepsilon_0)^{-1/2} \tag{1.9}$$

Thus the fields satisfy the same formal partial differential equation:

$$\nabla^2(\quad) = \frac{1}{c^2} \frac{\partial^2(\quad)}{\partial t^2}$$

This is called the *wave equation*. It occurs in connection with many different kinds of physical phenomena such as mechanical oscillations of a string, sound waves, vibrating membranes, and so forth [29].[2] The implication here is that *changes* in the fields **E** and **H** propagate through empty space with a speed equal to the value of the constant c. In MKS units, c is numerically equal to

$$1/\sqrt{4\pi \times 10^{-7}\, \varepsilon_0} \approx 3 \times 10^8 \text{ meters/sec (m/s)}$$

One of the most precise electrical determinations of the value of $(\mu_0\varepsilon_0)^{-1/2}$ was made at the National Bureau of Standards by Rosa and Dorsey [33]. They obtained by calculation, the capacitance of a condenser of accurately known physical dimensions. This gave the capacitance in electrostatic units. They then measured by means of a bridge, the capacitance of the same condenser in electromagnetic units. The

---

[2] Numbered references are listed at the end of the book.

ratio of the two values of the capacitance, when converted to MKS units, gives the value of $(\mu_0\varepsilon_0)^{-1/2}$. The Rosa and Dorsey result was $2.99784 \cdot 10^8$ m/s to a precision of about one part in 30,000. Other observers had previously measured $(\mu_0\varepsilon_0)^{-1/2}$ by purely electrical methods with similar but less precise results.

On the other hand, direct measurements of the speed of propagation of light have been carried out by many observers over the years since Römer's historic determination of the speed of light from eclipses of Jupiter's moons in 1676. A summary of measurements of the speed of electromagnetic radiation is given in Table 1.1. The results of all such measurements have always been the same when due account of experimental errors and reduction to vacuum have been made. The conclusion that light is an electromagnetic disturbance is inescapable.

The value of c as published by the National Bureau of Standards in 1963 is

$$c = (2.997925 \pm 0.000003) \times 10^8 \text{ m/s} \qquad \textbf{(1.10)}$$

An excellent review of recent measurements is given in the article "Velocity of Light" by Bergstrand in *The Encyclopedia of Physics* [2].

Speed of Light in a Medium   The Maxwell curl equations for the electric and magnetic fields in isotropic nonconducting media are precisely the same as those for the vacuum, except that the vacuum constants μ_0 and ε_0 are replaced by the corresponding constants for the medium, namely μ and ε. Consequently, the speed of propagation v of electromagnetic fields in a medium is given by

$$v = (\mu\,\varepsilon)^{-1/2} \qquad \textbf{(1.11)}$$

By introducing the two dimensionless ratios

$$K = \frac{\varepsilon}{\varepsilon_0} \qquad \textbf{(1.12)}$$

called the relative permittivity or the dielectric constant, and

$$K_m = \frac{\mu}{\mu_0} \qquad \textbf{(1.13)}$$

known as the relative permeability, we can write

$$v = (\mu\,\varepsilon)^{-1/2} = (K_m\mu_0 K\varepsilon_0)^{-1/2} = c(KK_m)^{-1/2} \qquad \textbf{(1.14)}$$

The index of refraction n is defined as the ratio of the speed of light in vacuum to its speed in the medium. Hence

$$n = (KK_m)^{1/2} \qquad \textbf{(1.15)}$$

Table 1.1. MEASUREMENTS OF THE SPEED OF ELECTROMAGNETIC RADIATION

A. SPEED OF LIGHT

Date	Investigator	Method	Result in km/sec	
1849	Fizeau	Rotating Toothed Wheel	313,000	± 5000*
1850	Foucault	Rotating Mirror	298,000	± 2000*
1875	Cornu	Rotating Mirror	299,990	± 200
1880	Michelson	Rotating Mirror	299,910	± 150
1883	Newcomb	Rotating Mirror	299,860	± 30
1883	Michelson	Rotating Mirror	299,853	± 60
1926	Michelson	Rotating Mirror	299,796	± 4
1928	Mittelstaedt	Kerr Cell Shutter	299,778	± 10
1932	Pease and Pearson	Rotating Mirror	299,774	± 2
1935	Michelson, Pease, and Pearson	Rotating Mirror	299,774	± 11
1940	Hüttel	Kerr Cell Shutter	299,768	± 10
1941	Anderson	Kerr Cell Shutter	299,776	± 6
1951	Bergstrand	Kerr Cell Shutter	299,793.1	± 0.3

B. SPEED OF RADIO WAVES

Date	Investigator	Method	Result in km/sec	
1923	Mercier	Standing Waves on Wires	299,782	± 30
1947	Jones and Conford	Oboe Radar	299,782	± 25
1950	Bol	Cavity Resonator	299,789.3	± 0.4
1950	Essen	Cavity Resonator	299,792.5	± 3.0
1951	Aslakson	Shoran Radar	299,794.2	± 1.9
1952	Froome	Microwave Interferometer	299,792.6	± 0.7

C. RATIO OF ELECTRICAL UNITS

Date	Investigator	Result	
1857	Weber and Kohlrausch	310,000	± 20,000*
1868	Maxwell	288,000	± 20,000*
1883	Thomson	282,000	± 20,000*
1907	Rosa and Dorsey	299,784	± 10

* Estimated error limits.

Most transparent optical media are nonmagnetic so that $K_m = 1$ in which case the index of refraction should be equal to the square root of the relative permittivity:

$$n = K^{1/2} \qquad \text{(1.16)}$$

Table 1.2 shows a number of examples in which the index of refraction is compared to the square root of the static permittivity. The agreement is good in the case of the gases, air, and carbon dioxide, and also for nonpolar solids, such as polystyrene. For media that contain polar molecules, such as water and alcohol, the agreement is poor. This is due to the high static polarizability of these substances.

Actually, the index of refraction is found to vary with the frequency of the radiation. This is true for all transparent optical media. The variation of the index of refraction with frequency is called *dispersion*. The dispersion of glass is responsible for the familiar splitting of light into its component colors by a prism.

In order to explain dispersion it is necessary to take into account the actual motion of the electrons in the optical medium through which the light is traveling. The theory of dispersion will be treated in detail later in Chapter 5.

Table 1.2. INDEX OF REFRACTION VERSUS THE SQUARE ROOT OF THE STATIC PERMITTIVITY [14].

SUBSTANCE	n (YELLOW LIGHT)	$\sqrt{K}$
Air (1 atm)	1.0002926	1.000295
CO_2 (1 atm)	1.00045	1.0005
Polystyrene	1.59	1.60
Glass*	1.5–1.7	2.0–3.0
Fused Quartz	1.46	1.94
Water	1.33	9.0
Ethyl Alcohol	1.36	5.0

* Approximate values.

1.3   Plane Harmonic Waves. Phase Velocity

If we employ rectangular coordinates and resolve the vector wave equations (1.8) and (1.9) into components, we observe that each component of **E** and **H** satisfies the general scalar[3] wave equation

$$\nabla^2 U = \frac{1}{v^2} \frac{\partial^2 U}{\partial t^2} \qquad \text{(1.17)}$$

Here the quantity U stands for any one of the field components E_x, E_y, E_z, H_x, H_y, H_z.

---

[3] The vectorial nature of electromagnetic waves is treated in Chapter 2.

Now, for the moment, let us consider the special case in which the spatial variation of U occurs only in some particular coordinate direction, say the z direction. In this case the operator ∇^2 reduces to $\partial^2/\partial z^2$, and Equation (1.17) becomes the one-dimensional wave equation

$$\frac{\partial^2 U}{\partial z^2} = \frac{1}{v^2}\frac{\partial^2 U}{\partial t^2} \tag{1.18}$$

By direct substitution, it is easy to verify that the function

$$U(z,t) = U_o \cos(kz - \omega t) \tag{1.19}$$

is, in fact, a solution of our wave equation (1.18) provided that the ratio of the constants ω and k is equal to the constant v, namely,

$$\frac{\omega}{k} = v \tag{1.20}$$

The particular solution given by Equation (1.19) is fundamental to the study of optics. It represents what is known as a *plane harmonic*

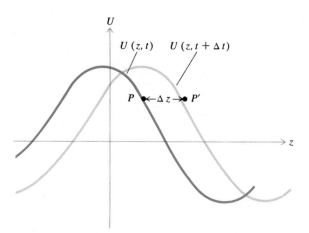

Figure 1.1.   Graph of U versus z at times t and $t + \Delta t$.

wave. A graph of the function $U(z,t)$ is shown in Figure 1.1. For a given value of z, the wave function $U(z,t)$ varies harmonically in time. The angular frequency of this time variation is the constant ω. At a given instant of time, the wave function also varies sinusoidally with z. The so-called "spatial frequency" of this variation is the constant k, also known as the *wavenumber*. This is not to be confused with the *spectroscopic wavenumber* which is $k/2\pi$. Thus k is the number of complete wave cycles in a distance of 2π units, whereas the spectroscopic wavenumber is the number of wave cycles in unit distance.

From a study of the graph of $U(z,t)$ we see that at a certain instant of time t, the curve is a certain cosine function. At a later instant, $t + \Delta t$, the whole curve is displaced in the z direction by a distance Δz where

$$\Delta z = v\Delta t$$

The distance Δz is the distance between any two points of corresponding phase, say PP', as indicated in the figure. This is the reason that v is called the *phase velocity*.

Returning now to the three-dimensional wave equation (1.17), it is readily verified that this equation is satisfied by a three-dimensional plane harmonic wave function as follows:

$$U(x,y,z,t) = U_o \cos(\mathbf{k} \cdot \mathbf{r} - \omega t) \tag{1.21}$$

where the position vector $\mathbf{r}$ is defined as

$$\mathbf{r} = \hat{\mathbf{i}}x + \hat{\mathbf{j}}y + \hat{\mathbf{k}}z \tag{1.22}$$

and the *propagation vector* or *wave vector* $\mathbf{k}$ is given in terms of its components by

$$\mathbf{k} = \hat{\mathbf{i}}k_x + \hat{\mathbf{j}}k_y + \hat{\mathbf{k}}k_z \tag{1.23}$$

In order to interpret Equation (1.21), consider the argument of the cosine, $\mathbf{k} \cdot \mathbf{r} - \omega t$. Constant values of this quantity define a set of planes in space called surfaces of constant phase, namely,

$$\mathbf{k} \cdot \mathbf{r} - \omega t = k_x x + k_y y + k_z z - \omega t = constant \tag{1.24}$$

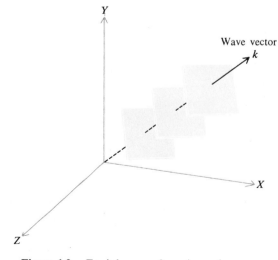

Figure 1.2. Equiphase surfaces in a plane wave.

It follows that the direction cosines of the planes of constant phase are proportional to the components of the propagation vector **k**. This means that **k** is normal to the wave surfaces, as shown in Figure 1.2. Furthermore, by virtue of the time factor in Equation (1.24), we see that these wave surfaces move in the direction of **k** at a rate equal to the phase velocity. Explicitly

$$v = \frac{\omega}{k} = \frac{\omega}{\sqrt{k_x{}^2 + k_y{}^2 + k_z{}^2}} \tag{1.25}$$

The *wavelength* λ is defined as the distance, measured along the direction of propagation, such that U goes through one complete cycle.

The *period* T is the time for one complete cycle. The reciprocal of the period, that is, the number of wave cycles per unit time, is called the *frequency f*. Since a wave travels a distance λ in time T, we have the following relations:

$$vT = \lambda = \frac{2\pi}{k} \tag{1.26}$$

$$T^{-1} = \frac{v}{\lambda} = f = \frac{\omega}{2\pi} \tag{1.27}$$

Sources of Electromagnetic Waves   Electromagnetic radiation is created by oscillating electric charges. The frequency of oscillation determines the kind of radiation that is emitted. The various portions of the electromagnetic spectrum, designated according to frequency and wavelength, are shown in Table 1.3. (The quantum energy of the radiation is also listed. Quantum theory is discussed later in Chapter 6.)

The units of wavelength commonly used for the optical region are the following:

UNIT	ABBREVIATION	EQUIVALENT
micron	μm	10^{-6} m
nanometer	nm	10^{-9} m
Ångstrom	Å	10^{-10} m

The unit of frequency is the cycle per second also called the *hertz*, Hz.

If, in a given source, the charges all oscillate in unison, the source is said to be *coherent*. If the charges oscillate independently and randomly, the source is called *incoherent*. Ordinary sources of radiation in the optical region are incoherent, for example, tungsten filament lamps, fluorescent lamps, flames, and so forth.

Table 1.3. THE ELECTROMAGNETIC SPECTRUM

TYPE OF RADIATION		FREQUENCY	WAVELENGTH	QUANTUM ENERGY
"Wave" Region	radio waves	10^9 Hz and less	300 mm and longer	0.000004 ev and less
	microwaves	10^9 Hz to 10^{12} Hz	300 mm to 0.3 mm	0.000004 ev to 0.004 ev
"Optical" Region	infrared	10^{12} Hz to 4.3×10^{14} Hz	300 μm to 0.7 μm	0.004 ev to 1.7 ev
	visible	4.3×10^{14} Hz to 5.7×10^{14} Hz	0.7 μm to 0.4 μm	1.7 ev to 2.3 ev
	ultraviolet	5.7×10^{14} Hz to 10^{16} Hz	0.4 μm to 0.03 μm	2.3 ev to 40 ev
"Ray" Region	x-rays	10^{16} Hz to 10^{19} Hz	300 Å to 0.3 Å	40 ev to 40,000 ev
	gamma rays	10^{19} Hz and above	0.3 Å and shorter	40,000 ev and above

Man-made sources of radio waves and microwaves are normally coherent. These low-frequency coherent sources are basically electronic oscillators that utilize amplifying devices such as vacuum tubes, transistors, klystrons, and so forth. The development of optical amplification—the laser—has extended the range of coherent sources to the optical region of the electromagnetic spectrum. The theory of the laser is treated in Chapter 8.

1.4   Alternative Ways of Representing Harmonic Waves

Let the unit vector $\hat{\mathbf{n}}$ denote the direction of the wave vector $\mathbf{k}$. Then $\mathbf{k} = \hat{\mathbf{n}}k$, and, accordingly, the expression for a plane harmonic wave, Equation (1.21) is equivalent to

$$U_o \cos[(\hat{\mathbf{n}} \cdot \mathbf{r} - vt)k]$$

It should be noted that the order of writing the factors in the argument of the cosine is immaterial, since $\cos u = \cos(-u)$. It is also immaterial whether one uses a cosine function or a sine function. Both represent the same thing, except for phase.

It is often convenient to make use of the identity

$$e^{iu} = \cos u + i \sin u$$

and write

$$U = U_o e^{i(\mathbf{k} \cdot \mathbf{r} - \omega t)} \tag{1.28}$$

to represent a plane harmonic wave. It is understood that the real part is the actual physical quantity being represented. The real part is identical with the previous expression, Equation (1.21). However, it is easy to verify that the complex expression (1.28) is itself a solution of the wave equation. The main reason for using the complex exponential expression is that it is algebraically simpler than the trigonometric expression. An example of the use of the complex exponential is given in the following section.

Spherical Waves   The functions $\cos(kr - \omega t)$ and $e^{i(kr - \omega t)}$ have constant values on a sphere of any given radius r at a given time t. As t increases, the functions would represent spherical expanding waves except for the fact that they are not solutions of the wave equation. However, it is easy to verify that the functions

$$\frac{1}{r} \cos(kr - \omega t) \qquad \text{and} \qquad \frac{1}{r} e^{i(kr - \omega t)}$$

are, indeed, solutions of the wave equation and represent, therefore, spherical waves propagating outward from the origin. See problem 1.2.

1.5   Group Velocity

Suppose we have two harmonic waves that have slightly different angular frequencies. Let us denote these frequencies by $\omega + \Delta\omega$ and $\omega - \Delta\omega$, respectively. The corresponding wavenumbers will, in general, also differ. We shall denote them by $k + \Delta k$ and $k - \Delta k$. Now suppose, in particular, that the two waves have the same amplitude, U_0, and are traveling in the same direction, say the z direction. Then the superposition of the two waves is given, in complex notation, by

$$U = U_0 e^{i[(k + \Delta k)z - (\omega + \Delta\omega)t]} + U_0 e^{i[(k - \Delta k)z - (\omega - \Delta\omega)t]} \tag{1.29}$$

By factoring and collecting terms, we get

$$U = U_0 e^{i(kz - \omega t)} [e^{i(\Delta kz - \Delta\omega t)} + e^{-i(\Delta kz - \Delta\omega t)}] \tag{1.30}$$

or

$$U = 2U_0 e^{i(kz - \omega t)} \cos(\Delta kz - \Delta\omega t) \tag{1.31}$$

The final expression can be interpreted as a single wave $2U_0 e^{i(kz - \omega t)}$, which has a modulation envelope $\cos(\Delta kz - \Delta\omega t)$, Figure 1.3. This

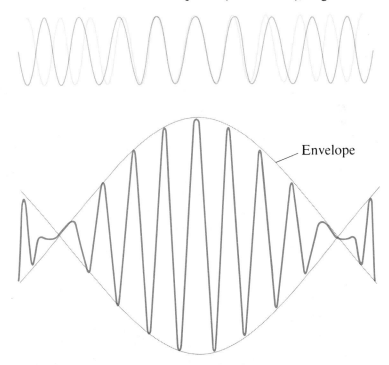

Figure 1.3.   Envelope of the combination of two harmonic waves.

modulation envelope does not travel at the phase velocity, ω/k, of the individual waves, but rather at a rate $\Delta\omega/\Delta k$, called the *group velocity*. We shall denote the group velocity by u. Then

$$u = \frac{\Delta\omega}{\Delta k} \tag{1.32}$$

or, in the limit

$$u = \frac{d\omega}{dk} \tag{1.33}$$

Although we have considered only two component waves in this example, it can be shown that the same thing happens in the case of more than two waves, that is, the overall wave envelope moves with a characteristic speed, which in general, differs from the speeds of the individual waves. If the wave group occupies a narrow range of frequencies, the group velocity is well defined and unique for the group. In a dispersive medium in which the index of refraction n varies in a known manner with the wavenumber k, we can write

$$\omega = kv = \frac{kc}{n} \tag{1.34}$$

Hence

$$u = \frac{d\omega}{dk} = \frac{c}{n} - \frac{c}{n^2}\frac{dn}{dk} = v\left(1 - \frac{1}{n}\frac{dn}{dk}\right) \tag{1.35}$$

which gives the relationship between u and v for a dispersive medium. For purposes of practical calculation of the group velocity, the following formulas, which are left as problems, are often used:

$$u = v - \lambda\frac{dv}{d\lambda} \tag{1.36}$$

$$\frac{1}{u} = \frac{1}{v} - \frac{\lambda_0}{c}\frac{dn}{d\lambda_0} \tag{1.37}$$

where λ_0 is the vacuum wavelength.

In the vacuum, $n = 1$, and therefore $dn/dk = 0$. Hence from Equation (1.35)

$$u = v = c \quad \text{(vacuum)} \tag{1.38}$$

so the group velocity in the vacuum is the same as the phase velocity.

For most optical media the index of refraction increases with increasing frequency so that dn/dk is positive. For such media the group velocity is therefore less than the phase velocity. Since any signal can be considered as a modulation of some type imposed on a continuous wave, then a signal travels at the group velocity, and is thus propagated at a slower rate, generally, than the phase velocity. This is also true for pulses. Michelson was one of the first to observe this experimentally. He found that the speed of light pulses in carbon disulfide was $c/1.76$, whereas the index of refraction is 1.64, so that the phase velocity is $c/1.64$.

In any determination of the velocity of light by a time-of-flight method, account must be taken of the difference between the phase velocity and the group velocity in a medium. Appropriate corrections must be made when computing the final result from the experimental data.

1.6 The Doppler Effect

If a source of waves and a receiver are in relative motion while the waves are being received, the observed frequency is changed compared with that in which there is no motion. This well-known phenomenon was first studied in connection with sound waves by J. C. Doppler. An elementary analysis proceeds as follows. If the source is moving away from the receiver with a velocity v, the number f of waves emitted per second will be expanded into a distance $c + v$ rather than c, where c is the speed of the waves in the medium. The medium is here considered to be at rest with respect to the receiver. The observed frequency f', being the number of waves reaching the receiver per second, will then be

$$f' = f\left(\frac{c}{c + v}\right) = f\left(1 - \frac{v}{c} + \frac{v^2}{c^2} - \cdots\right) \tag{1.39}$$

On the other hand, if the receiver is moving away from the source, the source considered to be stationary in the medium, then the speed of the waves relative to the receiver will be $c - v$, and therefore the observed frequency will be given by

$$f' = f\left(\frac{c - v}{c}\right) = f\left(1 - \frac{v}{c}\right)$$

or

$$\frac{f - f'}{f} = \frac{\Delta f}{f} = \frac{v}{c} \tag{1.40}$$

If the source and receiver are moving towards one another, then the sign of v is changed in each of the above formulas.

It can be seen from the series expansion of Equation (1.39) that if the value of v is very small in comparison with the wave velocity c, then the quadratic and higher terms can be neglected. The two cases then give the same result.

Measurable Doppler shifts in the case of light waves[4] can be observed in the laboratory by means of atomic beams. Another method is to reflect light from a moving mirror. With ordinary light sources it is necessary to have the mirror move at a very high speed, that is, by

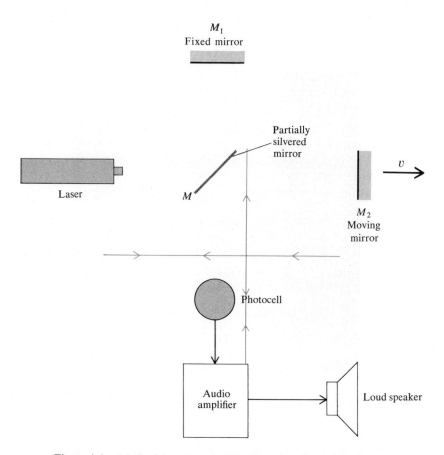

Figure 1.4.   Method for observing the Doppler effect with a laser.

attaching it to a rapidly rotating wheel. But by using a laser as the source, the Doppler effect can be observed with speeds of only a few centimeters per second. The experimental arrangement is shown in Figure 1.4. The light from the laser is split into two beams by means of a lightly silvered mirror M. One of the beams is reflected by a fixed mirror M_1 back through M to a photocell P. The other beam is reflected by a moving mirror M_2. The two beams combine at P to pro-

----

[4] Fizeau was one of the first to study the effect in connection with light waves. For this reason, the Doppler effect in light is also known as the *Doppler-Fizeau effect*.

duce a beat note whose frequency is equal to the difference Δf between the frequencies of the two beams. If v_m is the speed of the moving mirror, then $\Delta f/f = 2v_m/c$. The factor 2 arises from the fact that the apparent speed of the virtual source produced by the moving mirror is just twice the speed of the mirror.

Doppler shifts of spectral lines are well known in astronomy. The effect is used to determine the motion of astronomical objects. For

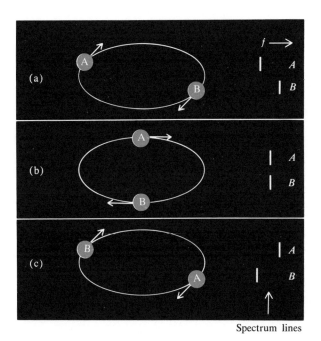

Figure 1.5.   Illustration of the motion of a binary star system and the Doppler shifts of a spectrum line.

example, in the case of binary stars, that is, two stars revolving about their common center of mass, the spectrum lines show a periodic doubling due to the fact that one star approaches the earth and the other recedes from the earth in a regular fashion as illustrated in Figure 1.5.

Typical astronomical velocities are of the order of 100 kilometers per second (km/s) so that v/c is of the order of 10^{-4}. In the case of the very distant galaxies however, the spectrum lines are shifted to lower frequencies by amounts that indicate recessional velocities up to half the speed of light. This shift, known as the galactic red shift, seems to be proportional to the distance and has, therefore, been interpreted as indicating an expansion of the universe. The recently discovered quasi stellar objects, or *quasars,* have even greater red shifts indicating velocities up to $0.8c$.

Doppler Broadening of Spectrum Lines   Another way in which the Doppler effect is manifest is the widening of the spectrum lines from a gaseous discharge. This widening is due to the random thermal motion of the radiating atoms. According to elementary kinetic theory [31], the value of the root mean square of a given component of the velocity of an atom in a gas is equal to $\sqrt{kT/m}$ where T is the absolute temperature, k is Boltzmann's constant, and m is the mass of the atom. At any instant, part of the atoms are going toward an observer, and part are going away. The "half-power" width Δf of a spectrum line of mean frequency f, due to thermal motion, is given by the relationship

$$\frac{\Delta f}{f} = \frac{2\sqrt{2\ln 2}}{c}\sqrt{\frac{kT}{m}} \tag{1.41}$$

The numerical factor $2\sqrt{2\ln 2}$ comes from the distribution of the velocities, which is a *Gaussian* function [39]. The intensity distribution, as a function of frequency, is also Gaussian.

We see that the width is proportional to the square root of the temperature and is inversely proportional to the square root of the mass of the atom. Thus hydrogen, the lightest atom, gives the widest spectrum lines at a given temperature. To obtain the narrowest lines, the discharge is cooled and heavy atoms are used. Thus the international standard of length is the wavelength of the orange krypton line emitted by a liquid-air-cooled discharge through krypton 86 gas. This provides a precise, highly reproducible source for interferometric measurements.

1.7   The Experiments of Sagnac and of Michelson and Gale to Detect Rotation

In 1911 the French physicist G. Sagnac performed an interesting experiment designed to detect rotation by means of light beams. His experiment is illustrated in Figure 1.6. A beam of light from a source S is divided into two beams by means of a half-silvered mirror M. The two beams are caused to traverse opposing paths around a circuit formed by mirrors M_1, M_2, and M_3 as shown. The beams recombine at M and are reflected into an observing telescope in which interference fringes are seen.

The apparatus is mounted on a rigid support that can be rotated about a vertical axis. The rotation causes a difference in the time required for the clockwise and counterclockwise beams to traverse the circuit. The result is a fringe shift that is proportional to the angular velocity of rotation. It is easy to show that the effective path difference Δs for the two beams is given approximately by

$$\Delta s = \frac{4A}{c}\Omega$$

where A is the area of the circuit and Ω is the angular velocity.

Sagnac was able to observe a fringe shift with a square light path about 1 m on a side and a speed of rotation of 120 revolutions per

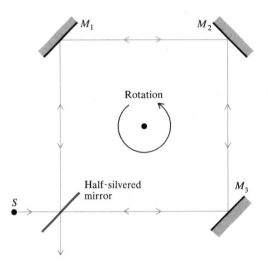

Figure 1.6.   Diagram of Sagnac's experiment.

minute (r/min). In order to detect small angular velocities, a larger loop is required. In 1925 Michelson and Gale set up the experiment with a large path, 2/5 mile by 1/5 mile, Figure 1.7. With this loop they were able to detect the expected fringe shift due to rotation of the earth. A smaller loop inside the larger one was used to provide a set of reference fringes.

1.8   The Michelson-Morley Experiment

This famous experiment, performed in 1887, was designed to measure the absolute velocity of the earth's motion in space by means of light waves.

A diagram of the optical arrangement is shown in Figure 1.8. The apparatus is essentially an optical interferometer. A beam of light from a source S is split into two beams by a half-silvered mirror M. One beam is reflected to a mirror M_1 which in turn, reflects the light directly back to M. The other beam is transmitted directly to the mirror M_2

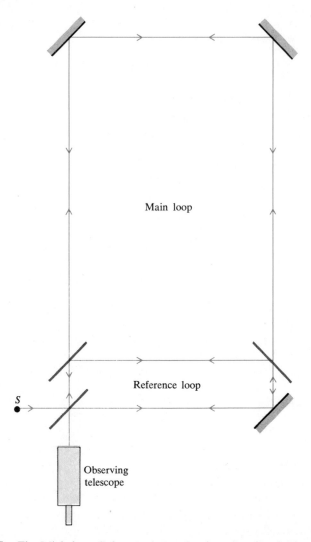

Main loop

Reference loop

S

Observing
telescope

Figure 1.7.   The Michelson-Gale experiment for detecting the absolute rotation
of the earth.

that also reflects the light back to M. The two partial beams then unite
at M, part of the combined light going to an observer O who sees an
interference pattern of bright and dark fringes.The interference pattern
can be made to shift by one fringe by displacing either of the two
mirrors M_1 or M_2 a distance of 1/4 wavelength.

If both mirrors M_1 and M_2 are located at precisely the same distance from M, and if the apparatus does not move during the time that
light is reflected back and forth, then the two waves return to M at the

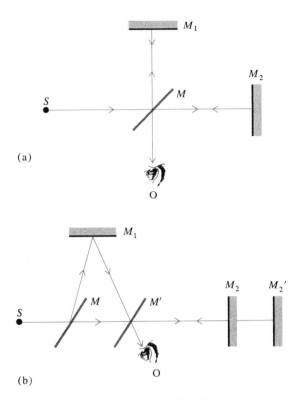

Figure 1.8. Simplified diagram of the Michelson-Morley experiment.

same phase so that a bright fringe is seen at O. Suppose, however, that the whole apparatus is moving in the direction of the initial beam SM. The paths of the beams will then be as shown by the blue lines in the figure. The times taken by the two partial waves in their respective journeys are no longer the same if it is assumed that light travels with a constant speed c in some medium. The situation is analogous to the case of two swimmers in a stream, one swimmer going upstream and back, the other going across the stream and returning.

To analyze the situation quantitatively, let us suppose that the speed of the apparatus through the medium is v. Then the wave moving toward M_2 travels with a speed $c - v$ relative to the apparatus. On its return, this wave travels with relative speed $c + v$. The total time for the round trip is therefore

$$t_2 = \frac{d}{c - v} + \frac{d}{c + v} = \frac{2cd}{c^2 - v^2} \tag{1.42}$$

in which d is the distance OM_2. On the other hand, the wave reflected by M_1 travels along the path $MM_1'O$, as shown. If we call t_1 the total time for the round trip in this case, then the distance MM_1' is equal to $\sqrt{d^2 + (1/4)v^2 t_1^2}$. Thus

$$t_1 = \left(\frac{2}{c}\right)\sqrt{d^2 + (1/4)v^2 t_1^2} \tag{1.43}$$

Solving for t_1, we get

$$t_1 = \frac{2d}{\sqrt{c^2 - v^2}} \tag{1.44}$$

The time difference Δt between the two paths is accordingly

$$\Delta t = t_2 - t_1 = 2d\left(\frac{c}{c^2 - v^2} - \frac{1}{\sqrt{c^2 - v^2}}\right) = \frac{dv^2}{c^3} + \cdots \tag{1.45}$$

This corresponds to a phase difference

$$\Delta\phi = \omega\Delta t = \frac{2\pi c}{\lambda}\Delta t \approx \frac{2\pi d}{\lambda}\frac{v^2}{c^2} \tag{1.46}$$

where λ is the wavelength of the light.

In their experiment, Michelson and Morley obtained an effective distance d of 10 m by multiple reflections as indicated in Figure 1.9. The experiment was performed by floating the entire apparatus in a pool of mercury and observing the fringes as the apparatus was rotated through an angle of 90 degrees. This would cause either of the two beams to be alternately parallel or perpendicular to the earth's motion. In its orbital motion around the sun, the earth's speed is about $10^{-4}\,c$. The expected shift with yellow light, 5900 angstroms (Å), was about one-third of a fringe. *Actually there was no observable shift at all.* This negative result came as a surprise to the scientific world. It was in contradiction to the (then) accepted idea concerning electromagnetic radiation, namely that such radiation must have a medium for its transmission through space. This medium, called the *ether,* was supposed to be an all-pervading substance, and numerous calculations concerning its properties had been carried out, including some by Maxwell.

The Michelson-Morley experiment has been repeated many times by different observers with essentially the same negative results. There have been some reports of measurable fringe shifts, but none anywhere near as large as should be predicted by the orbital speed of the earth. This is actually a minimum speed since the speed of the whole solar system, due to rotation of our galaxy, is about ten times the earth's orbital speed.

The idea of the ether had been so widely accepted that it was many

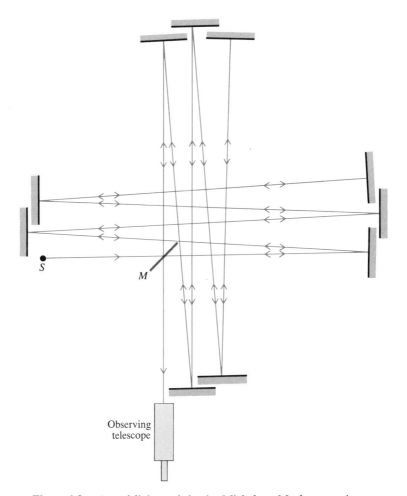

Figure 1.9. Actual light path in the Michelson-Morley experiment.

years before it was finally abandoned. In fact two physicists, Fitz-gerald and Lorentz, proposed to explain the null result of the Michel-son-Morley experiment by suggesting that a body *contracts* in the direction of its motion through the ether in precisely the ratio $\sqrt{1 - v^2/c^2}$. This amount of shortening, known as the Fitzgerald-Lorentz contraction, would just equalize the two light paths so that there would be no fringe shift. Now such an *ad hoc* explanation of the experiment is not very satisfactory, for the contraction is not capable of direct observation. Any attempt to measure it would fail, since the measuring apparatus contracts along with the object to be measured.

1.9   Einstein's Postulates of Special Relativity

In 1905 Albert Einstein formulated his special theory of relativity. This theory is based on two fundamental postulates:

(1) *All physical laws have the same form in all inertial coordinate systems.*

(2) *The speed of electromagnetic radiation in the vacuum is the same in all inertial systems.*

The first postulate is a statement concerning physical laws in general and is an extension of Newtonian relativity. It can be shown that Maxwell's equations obey this postulate, that is, the equations have the same general form in any inertial coordinate system. The proof is given in almost any textbook on relativity [32].

The second postulate is more specific. It is the one that is of immediate application to our study of optics. It says that any measurement of the speed of light must always yield the same result, even if the source of light is in motion relative to the observer, or if the observer is moving relative to the source. This postulate immediately explains the null result of the Michelson-Morley experiment, for it implies that the speed of propagation of each beam in the experimental arrangement is always c, whether the apparatus is moving or not. Hence there is no phase change and no fringe shift.[5]

1.10   Relativistic Optics

According to the second postulate of the special theory of relativity, the speed of light in vacuum is the same for any observer, regardless of the motion of the source relative to him or of his motion relative to the source. To examine the consequences of this postulate, let us consider two observers moving with constant relative speed v. We shall designate the coordinate systems of our two observers by $Oxyz$ and $O'x'y'z'$, respectively. For simplicity, we shall assume that the respective axes Ox, $O'x'$, and so forth, are parallel, and that the relative motion is in the xx' direction, Figure 1.10.

Suppose that the two origins O and O' are coincident at time $t = 0$. Then the distance OO' is equal to vt, and the equations of transformation, according to classical or Newtonian kinematics, are

---

[5] It should be noted that Einstein did not formulate the theory of relativity in order to account for the Michelson-Morley experiment. Rather, the Michelson-Morley experiment has merely been cited as one experiment that tends to confirm the second postulate. Other, more recent experiments have been performed to verify the constancy of the velocity of light when the source and the observer are in relative motion. An excellent discussion and review of these is given by J. G. Fox, *Am. J. Phys.*, **33**, 1 (1965).

$$x = x' + vt'$$
$$y = y'$$
$$z = z'$$ (1.47)
$$t = t'$$

The equation $t = t'$ expresses the assumed equality of the time scales of the two observers. They are using identical clocks. The above equa-

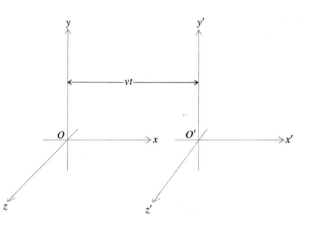

Figure 1.10. Coordinate systems of two observers moving with constant relative speed.

tions of transformation clearly contradict the second postulate, because from them we obtain $dx/dt = dx'/dt' + v$ so that anything moving with the speed of light c in, say, the primed system, moves with the speed $c + v$ in the unprimed system.

In order to find a coordinate transformation that agrees with the second postulate of relativity, let us consider the wave equation

$$\frac{\partial^2 U}{\partial x^2} - \frac{1}{c^2}\frac{\partial^2 U}{\partial t^2} = 0$$ (1.48)

This is the differential equation of a light wave propagating with velocity c in the x direction. The requirement of the second postulate is that the equation remains invariant when referred to the primed coordinate system. That is

$$\frac{\partial^2 U}{\partial x'^2} - \frac{1}{c^2}\frac{\partial^2 U}{\partial t'^2} = 0$$

This will be the case if

$$\frac{\partial^2 U}{\partial x^2} - \frac{1}{c^2}\frac{\partial^2 U}{\partial t^2} = \frac{\partial^2 U}{\partial x'^2} - \frac{1}{c^2}\frac{\partial^2 U}{\partial t'^2}$$ (1.49)

Now it turns out that a general linear transformation[6] of the form

$$x = a_{11}x' + a_{12}t'$$
$$t = a_{21}x' + a_{22}t'$$

(1.50)

with the proper choice of constants will make the wave equation invariant. By substituting the above transformation in (1.49) and requiring that the equation be an identity, we obtain three equations to solve for the coefficients a_{11}, a_{12}, and so forth. We also need the subsidiary condition that $x = 0$ transforms to $x' = -vt'$, so that $a_{12} = va_{11}$. The result is the famous Lorentz transformation:

$$x = \gamma(x' + vt')$$
$$y = y'$$
$$z = z'$$
$$t = \gamma\left(t' + \frac{vx'}{c^2}\right)$$

(1.51)

where

$$\gamma = \frac{1}{\sqrt{1 - v^2/c^2}}$$

(1.52)

It is assumed that the kinematic consequences of the Lorentz transformation, for example, length contraction and time dilatation, are already familiar to the reader [32].

The Relativistic Doppler Formula   Let us now consider a plane electromagnetic wave whose space-time dependence is of the form exp $i(kx - \omega t)$ when represented in the unprimed coordinate system. The observer in this system sees a wave of angular frequency $\omega = ck$ moving in the x direction. By applying the Lorentz transformation (1.51), we find that the observer in the primed coordinate system sees the space-time dependence of this same wave as

$$\exp i\left[k\gamma(x' + vt') - \omega\gamma\left(t' + \frac{vx'}{c^2}\right)\right]$$
$$= \exp i\left[\left(k\gamma - \frac{\omega\gamma v}{c^2}\right)x' - (\omega\gamma - k\gamma v)t'\right]$$

(1.53)

This must be identical with the expression

$$\exp i(k'x' - \omega't')$$

---

[6] A nonlinear transformation would be unrealistic because uniform motion in one coordinate system would appear as accelerated motion in the other.

Hence

$$\omega' = \omega\gamma\left(1 - \frac{kv}{\omega}\right) = \omega\gamma\left(1 - \frac{v}{c}\right) \qquad (1.54)$$

Also, since $\omega = 2\pi f$ and $\gamma = [1 - (v^2/c^2)]^{-1/2}$, we can write

$$f' = f\frac{1 - \frac{v}{c}}{\sqrt{1 - \frac{v^2}{c^2}}} = f\frac{\sqrt{1 - \frac{v}{c}}}{\sqrt{1 + \frac{v}{c}}} = f\left(1 - \frac{v}{c} + \frac{1}{2}\frac{v^2}{c^2} - \cdots\right) \qquad (1.55)$$

This is the relativistic Doppler formula. The series expansion shows that the relativistic Doppler shift differs from the nonrelativistic values, Equations (1.39) and (1.40), only in the second- and higher-order terms, and therefore, this difference becomes important only for large velocities. The relativistic formula has been verified by experiments with high speed hydrogen atoms in a specially designed discharge tube shown in Figure 1.11 [20].

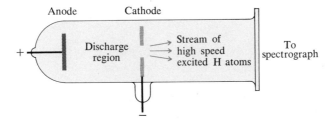

Figure 1.11. Discharge tube used to observe the relativistic Doppler effect.

The Transverse Doppler Shift Let us next suppose that we have a plane wave traveling in the negative y direction in the unprimed system. The space-time dependence of this wave is $\exp i(ky + \omega t)$. By applying the Lorentz transformation, Equation (1.51), we find that to an observer in the primed system moving with speed v in the x direction, the space-time dependence of the wave is

$$\exp i\left[ky' + \omega\left(\gamma t' + \frac{vx'\gamma}{c^2}\right)\right] = \exp i\left[\frac{\omega v\gamma x'}{c^2} + ky' + \omega\gamma t'\right] \qquad (1.56)$$

Since this must be the same as

$$\exp i(k_{x'}x' + k_{y'}y' + \omega't')$$

then, for the coefficient of t' we have

$$\omega' = \omega\gamma$$

or, equivalently

$$f = f' \sqrt{1 - \frac{v^2}{c^2}} = f'\left(1 - \frac{v^2}{2c^2} + \cdots\right) \qquad \text{(1.57)}$$

This is the formula for the *transverse Doppler shift,* giving the frequency change when the relative motion is at right angles to the direction of observation. The transverse Doppler shift is a second-order effect and is therefore very difficult to measure. It has been verified by using the Mossbauer effect with gamma radiation from radioactive atoms [11].

The Aberration of Starlight   Another consequence of the relativistic transformation of a plane wave, Equation (1.56), is the appearance of x' in the exponent. This implies that the wave vector $\mathbf{k}'$ has a component in the x' direction and consequently the direction of propagation is not exactly the same as the direction of the y' axis. The angle α of the inclination to the y' axis is given by $\tan \alpha = k_{x'}/k_{y'}$. Hence, from Equation (1.56),

$$\tan \alpha = \frac{\omega \gamma v/c^2}{k} = \frac{v}{c}\gamma = \frac{v}{c\sqrt{1 - v^2/c^2}} \qquad \text{(1.58)}$$

This effect is known as *aberration of light.* It was first observed experimentally by the English astronomer, Bradley in 1727. Bradley found

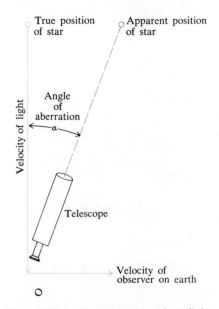

Figure 1.12.   The aberration of starlight.

an apparent shift in the positions of stars that was greatest for those stars whose line of sight was at right angles to the earth's orbital velocity around the sun. The maximum value of this stellar aberration is about 20 seconds of arc. Bradley's explanation is illustrated in Figure 1.12, which shows the change in apparent direction due to the observer's velocity v. The situation is similar to that of a person running through falling rain. If the rain is falling straight down, its velocity relative to the person is not vertical but has a horizontal component equal to the forward speed of the person. From the figure we have tan $\alpha = v/c$. This simple formula differs from the relativistic formula (1.58) by the factor γ. However, in the case of the earth, v/c is of the order of 10^{-4}, so the difference is entirely negligible.

It is interesting to note that the nonrelativistic transformation, Equation (1.47) gives zero aberration for plane waves, hence aberration is a relativistic effect in this context. The simple explanation is valid if light is considered to be a hail of photons, however.

PROBLEMS

1.1. Verify that Equation (1.21) is a solution of the wave equation, subject to the condition of Equation (1.25).

1.2. Prove that the spherical wave function

$$\frac{1}{r} e^{i(kr - \omega t)}$$

is a solution of the wave equation (1.17) where $r = (x^2 + y^2 + z^2)^{1/2}$. Do the problem using (a) rectangular coordinates, and (b) spherical coordinates.

1.3. Show that $f(\hat{\mathbf{n}} \cdot \mathbf{r} - vt)$ is a solution of the wave equation (1.17) where $\hat{\mathbf{n}}$ is any unit vector and f is any differentiable function of the argument $\hat{\mathbf{n}} \cdot \mathbf{r} - vt$.

1.4. Two harmonic waves have angular frequencies ω and $\omega + \Delta\omega$, respectively. Show that if $\Delta\omega \ll \omega$, then

$$\frac{\Delta\omega}{\omega} = \frac{\Delta f}{f} = \frac{\Delta k}{k} \approx \frac{|\Delta\lambda|}{\lambda}$$

1.5. Fill in the steps leading to Equations (1.36) and (1.37).

1.6. The *dispersive power* of glass is defined as the ratio $n_D/(n_F - n_C)$ where C, D, and F refer to the Fraunhoffer wavelengths: $\lambda_C = 6563$ Å, $\lambda_D = 5890$ Å, $\lambda_F = 4861$ Å. Find the approximate group velocity in glass whose dispersive power is 30, $n_D = 1.5$.

1.7. The dispersion curve of glass can be represented approximately by Cauchy's empirical equation $n = A + B\lambda^{-2}$. Find the phase and group velocities at $\lambda = 5000$ Å for a particular glass for which $A = 1.40$ and $B = 2.5 \times 10^6$ (Å)^2.

1.8. The dielectric constant K of a gas varies with angular frequency ω according to the formula

$$K = 1 + \frac{A}{\omega_0{}^2 - \omega^2}$$

where A and ω_0 are constants. Compute the phase velocity and the group velocity of light in this gas, assuming that the second term is very small compared to 1.

1.9. The group velocity of light in a certain substance is found to vary inversely with wavelength. How does the index of refraction vary with wavelength?

1.10. Show that the relativistic Doppler shift is the same whether the observer moves or the source moves.

1.11. Prove the general relativistic Doppler formula

$$f' = f \frac{1 - \frac{v}{c} \cos \theta}{\sqrt{1 - \frac{v^2}{c^2}}}$$

for the frequency observed from a source moving with velocity v in a direction making an angle θ with the direction of observation.

1.12. Derive a formula for the wavelength observed from the source of wavelength λ_0 for the cases (a) the source moves (nonrelativistic), (b) the observer moves (nonrelativistic), and (c) the relativistic case.

1.13. Show that the angle of aberration calculated by the relativistic formula differs from that calculated by the simple formula by approximately $(1/2)(v/c)^3$ if v is small compared to c.

1.14. What is the angle of aberration if $v = 0.9c$ as calculated (a) relativistically and (b) nonrelativistically.

1.15. Prove that the apparent velocity of light in a moving medium is $c/n + v_m(1 - 1/n^2)$, approximately, where v_m is the velocity of the medium relative to the observer, and n is the index of refraction of the medium. The result shows that light seems to be "dragged" along by the moving medium. The quantity $(1 - 1/n^2)$ is called the *Fresnel dragging coefficient*. Hint: Use the relativistic velocity transformation

$$\frac{dx}{dt} = \frac{\dfrac{dx'}{dt'} + v}{1 + \dfrac{v}{c^2} \dfrac{dx'}{dt'}}$$

1.16. It is found that the angle of aberration observed with a telescope filled with water is exactly the same as that observed with an ordinary telescope. Show that this is consistent with the assumption that the light traveling through the water is dragged forward with a speed $v[1 - (1/n^2)]$ as derived in Problem 1.15.

1.17. The milky-way galaxy rotates once in 200 million years, and our sun is located about 30,000 light years from the galactic center. As a result, the earth is moving through space relative to the other galaxies. What is the observed Doppler shift in Å of the hydrogen line at 6563 Å for light coming from other galaxies? Consider two cases: (a) the line of observation is in the direction of the earth's motion; (b) the line of observation is perpendicular to the direction of the earth's motion.

1.18. Compute the angle of abberation for case (b) in Problem 1.17.

1.19. Show that sinusoidal waves satisfy the *reduced wave equation* $\nabla^2 U + k^2 U = 0$ where k is the wavenumber.

1.20. Fill in the steps leading to the Lorentz transformation. Note:

$$\frac{\partial U}{\partial x'} = \frac{\partial U}{\partial x}\frac{\partial x}{\partial x'} + \frac{\partial U}{\partial t}\frac{\partial t}{\partial x'}$$

$$= \frac{\partial U}{\partial x}a_{11} + \frac{\partial U}{\partial t}a_{21}, \cdots$$

1.21. What is the Doppler width of the hydrogen line $H_\alpha(\lambda = 6563$ Å) in a laboratory discharge tube operating at a temperature of $200°C$? The value of the Boltzmann constant k is 1.38×10^{-23} joules per degree Kelvin (J/°K) and the mass of the H atom is 1.67×10^{-27} kilogram (kg). Give the result in both frequency units and in wavelength units.

CHAPTER **2**

The Vectorial Nature of Light

2.1 General Remarks

The various Cartesian components of the fields in an electromagnetic wave, as we have shown in the previous chapter, individually satisfy the same basic wave equation:

$$\nabla^2 U = \frac{1}{v^2} \frac{\partial^2 U}{\partial t^2} \tag{2.1}$$

The Maxwell curl equations require that for fields that vary in time and space, a magnetic field must always accompany an electric field and vice versa. In particular, for electromagnetic waves, there exists a very definite relationship between the two fields.

We wish to examine this relationship in detail. It will be useful at this juncture to establish some operator identities in connection with plane harmonic waves. Consider the complex exponential expression for a plane harmonic wave

$$\exp i(\mathbf{k} \cdot \mathbf{r} - \omega t)$$

Taking the time derivative, we have

$$\frac{\partial}{\partial t} \exp i(\mathbf{k} \cdot \mathbf{r} - \omega t) = -i\omega \exp i(\mathbf{k} \cdot \mathbf{r} - \omega t) \tag{2.2}$$

and taking the partial derivative with respect to one of the space variables, say x, we get

$$\frac{\partial}{\partial x} \exp i(\mathbf{k} \cdot \mathbf{r} - \omega t) = \frac{\partial}{\partial x} \exp i(k_x x + k_y y + k_z z - \omega t)$$

$$= ik_x \exp i(\mathbf{k} \cdot \mathbf{r} - \omega t) \tag{2.3}$$

Hence, upon application of the del operator

$$\nabla = \hat{\mathbf{i}} \frac{\partial}{\partial x} + \hat{\mathbf{j}} \frac{\partial}{\partial y} + \hat{\mathbf{k}} \frac{\partial}{\partial z}$$

it readily follows that

$$\nabla \exp i(\mathbf{k} \cdot \mathbf{r} - \omega t) = i\mathbf{k} \exp i(\mathbf{k} \cdot \mathbf{r} - \omega t) \tag{2.4}$$

Thus we have the following operator relations:

$$\frac{\partial}{\partial t} \rightarrow -i\omega \tag{2.5}$$

$$\nabla \rightarrow i\mathbf{k} \tag{2.6}$$

which are valid for plane harmonic waves. (The reader is here reminded that $\hat{\mathbf{i}}$, $\hat{\mathbf{j}}$, and $\hat{\mathbf{k}}$ are unit coordinate vectors, whereas i is the square root of -1, and $\mathbf{k}$ is the wave vector. This notation may be confusing, but it is standard.)

Let us return now to the Maxwell equations for isotropic nonconducting media:

$$\nabla \times \mathbf{E} = -\mu \frac{\partial \mathbf{H}}{\partial t} \tag{2.7}$$

$$\nabla \times \mathbf{H} = \varepsilon \frac{\partial \mathbf{E}}{\partial t} \tag{2.8}$$

$$\nabla \cdot \mathbf{E} = 0 \tag{2.9}$$

$$\nabla \cdot \mathbf{H} = 0 \tag{2.10}$$

From the operator relations, Equations (2.5) and (2.6), the Maxwell equations take the following form for plane harmonic waves:

$$\mathbf{k} \times \mathbf{E} = \mu\omega\mathbf{H} \tag{2.11}$$

$$\mathbf{k} \times \mathbf{H} = -\varepsilon\omega\mathbf{E} \tag{2.12}$$

$$\mathbf{k} \cdot \mathbf{E} = 0 \tag{2.13}$$

$$\mathbf{k} \cdot \mathbf{H} = 0 \tag{2.14}$$

A study of the above equations shows that the three vectors $\mathbf{k}$, $\mathbf{E}$, and $\mathbf{H}$ constitute a mutually orthogonal triad. The electric and magnetic fields are perpendicular to one another, and they are both perpendicular to the direction of propagation as illustrated in Figure 2.1. It follows that the magnitudes of the fields are related according to the equations

$$H = \frac{1}{\mu v}E = \varepsilon v E \tag{2.15}$$

where we have used the fact that the phase velocity $v = \omega/k$. Further, in terms of the index of refraction $n = c/v$, we have for nonmagnetic media ($\mu = \mu_o$):

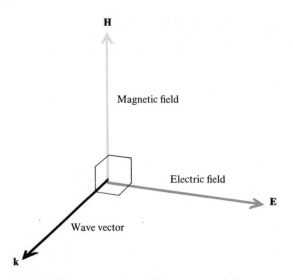

Figure 2.1. Relationships among the field vectors and the wave vector in an electromagnetic wave.

$$H = nE \sqrt{\frac{\varepsilon_o}{\mu_o}} \qquad (2.16)$$

The quantity $\sqrt{\varepsilon_o/\mu_o}$ is known as the admittance of free space. It is equal to about $1/377$ mho. Equation (2.16) shows that the greater the index of refraction of a medium, the greater is the magnetic field of an electromagnetic wave in the medium.

2.2   Energy Flow. The Poynting Vector

Poynting's theorem [16] states that the time rate of flow of electromagnetic energy per unit area is given by the vector **S**, called the Poynting vector, defined as the cross product of the electric and magnetic fields,

$$\mathbf{S} = \mathbf{E} \times \mathbf{H} \qquad (2.17)$$

This vector specifies both the direction and the magnitude of the energy flux. In the MKS system of units **S** is expressed in watts per square meter.[1]

---

[1] In Gaussian units $\mathbf{S} = \frac{c}{4\pi} \mathbf{E} \times \mathbf{H}$.

Consider now the case of plane harmonic waves in which the fields are given by the real expressions

$$\mathbf{E} = \mathbf{E_0} \cos(\mathbf{k} \cdot \mathbf{r} - \omega t) \qquad (2.18)$$

$$\mathbf{H} = \mathbf{H_0} \cos(\mathbf{k} \cdot \mathbf{r} - \omega t) \qquad (2.19)$$

We then have

$$\mathbf{S} = \mathbf{E_0} \times \mathbf{H_0} \cos^2(\mathbf{k} \cdot \mathbf{r} - \omega t) \qquad (2.20)$$

for the instantaneous value of the Poynting vector. Since the average value of the cosine squared is just $1/2$, then for the average value of the Poynting vector, we can write

$$<\mathbf{S}> = (1/2) \, \mathbf{E_0} \times \mathbf{H_0} \qquad (2.21)$$

Furthermore, from the relationships between $\mathbf{E}$ and $\mathbf{H}$ found in the previous section we find that the expression for the average energy flow can be expressed in another way:

$$<\mathbf{S}> = \frac{1}{2\mu\omega} | E_0 |^2 \, \mathbf{k} \qquad (2.22)$$

The magnitude of the average flux, or the *intensity,* is

$$I = <S> = \frac{1}{2\mu v} | E_0 |^2 \qquad (2.23)$$

I is also called the *irradiance.* Thus the rate of flow of energy is proportional to the square of the amplitude of the electric field. In isotropic media, the direction of the energy flow is specified by the direction of $\mathbf{S}$ and is the same as the direction of the wave vector $\mathbf{k}$. (In non-isotropic media, for example, crystals, $\mathbf{S}$ and $\mathbf{k}$ are not always in the same direction. This will be discussed later in Chapter 6.)

2.3   Linear Polarization

Consider a plane harmonic electromagnetic wave for which the fields $\mathbf{E}$ and $\mathbf{H}$ are given by the expressions

$$\mathbf{E} = \mathbf{E_0} \exp i \, (\mathbf{k} \cdot \mathbf{r} - \omega t) \qquad (2.24)$$

$$\mathbf{H} = \mathbf{H_0} \exp i \, (\mathbf{k} \cdot \mathbf{r} - \omega t) \qquad (2.25)$$

If the amplitudes $\mathbf{E_0}$ and $\mathbf{H_0}$ are constant real vectors, the wave is said to be *linearly polarized* or plane polarized. We know from the theory of the previous section that the fields $\mathbf{E}$ and $\mathbf{H}$ are mutually perpendicular. It is traditional in optics to designate the direction of

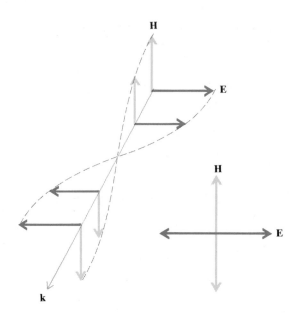

Figure 2.2.   Fields in a plane wave, linearly polarized.

the electric field as the direction of polarization. Figure 2.2 shows a diagram of the fields in a plane, linearly polarized wave.

In the case of natural or so-called unpolarized light, the instantaneous polarization fluctuates rapidly in a random manner. A linear polarizing device such as a sheet of polaroid, allows only the component of the electric field in a given direction to be transmitted [36]. Now the instantaneous electric field **E** can always be resolved into two mutually perpendicular components, E_1 and E_2, Figure 2.3, where

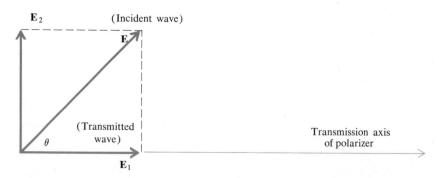

Figure 2.3   Relationship between the incident and the transmitted fields for a linear polarizer.

E_1 is along the transmission axis of the polarizer. If **E** makes an angle θ with the transmission axis, then the magnitude of the transmitted field is

$$E_1 = E \cos \theta \qquad (2.26)$$

The transmitted intensity I_1, being proportional to the square of the field, is therefore given by

$$I_1 = I \cos^2 \theta \qquad (2.27)$$

where I is the intensity of the incident beam. For unpolarized light all values of θ occur with equal probability. Therefore, the transmission of an ideal linear polarizer for unpolarized light is just the average value of $\cos^2 \theta$, namely $1/2$.

2.4   Circular and Elliptic Polarization

Let us return temporarily to the real representation for electromagnetic waves. Consider the special case of two linearly polarized waves of the same amplitude E_0 polarized at right angles to each other. Suppose the waves have a phase difference of $\pi/2$. To represent these waves we choose coordinate axes such that the electric vectors of the two waves are in the x and y directions, respectively. Accordingly, the electric fields are

$$\hat{\mathbf{i}} E_0 \cos(kz - \omega t)$$

$$\hat{\mathbf{j}} E_0 \sin(kz - \omega t)$$

The total electric field **E** is the vector sum of the two component fields, namely,

$$\mathbf{E} = E_0 [\hat{\mathbf{i}} \cos(kz - \omega t) + \hat{\mathbf{j}} \sin(kz - \omega t)] \qquad (2.28)$$

Now the above expression is a perfectly good solution of the wave equation. It can be interpreted as a single wave in which the electric vector at a given point, is constant in magnitude, but rotates with angular frequency ω. This type of wave is said to be *circularly polarized*. A drawing showing the electric field and associated magnetic field of circularly polarized waves is shown in Figure 2.4.

The signs of the terms in Equation (2.28) have been chosen such that the expression represents a wave in which the sense of rotation of the electric vector at a given point in space is *clockwise* when viewed against the direction of propagation. Such a wave is said to be *right* circularly polarized. If the sign of the second term were changed, the sense of rotation would be *counterclockwise* when viewed against the direction of propagation and would be *left* circularly polarized. (This

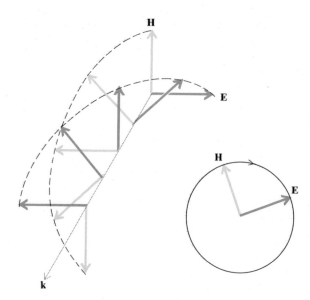

Figure 2.4.   Fields in a circularly polarized wave.

convention is common but, unfortunately, not universal. Some texts employ the opposite convention.)

Let us now return to the complex notation. The electric field for a circularly polarized wave can be written in complex form as

$$\mathbf{E} = \hat{\mathbf{i}} E_0 \exp i(kz - \omega t) + \hat{\mathbf{j}} E_0 \exp i(kz - \omega t \pm \pi/2) \qquad (2.29)$$

or, by employing the identity $e^{i\pi/2} = i$, we can write

$$\mathbf{E} = E_0(\hat{\mathbf{i}} \pm i\hat{\mathbf{j}})\exp i(kz - \omega t) \qquad (2.30)$$

It is easy to verify that the real part of the above expression is precisely that of Equation (2.28) where however, the minus sign must be used to represent right circular polarization and the plus sign for left circular polarization.

Elliptic Polarization   If the component (real) fields are not of the same amplitude, say $\hat{\mathbf{i}} E_0 \cos(kz - \omega t)$ and $\hat{\mathbf{j}} E_0' \sin(kz - \omega t)$ where $E_0 \neq E_0'$, the resultant electric vector, at a given point in space, rotates and also changes in magnitude in such a manner that the end of the vector describes an ellipse as illustrated in Figure 2.5. In this case the wave is said to be *elliptically polarized*.

It is sometimes convenient to employ a *complex vector amplitude* $\mathbf{E}_0$ defined as follows:

$$\mathbf{E}_0 = \hat{\mathbf{i}} E_0 + i\hat{\mathbf{j}} E_0' \qquad (2.31)$$

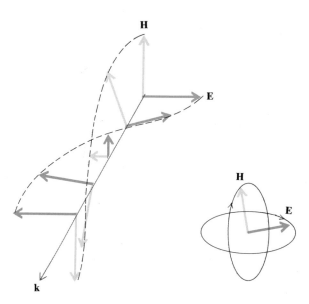

Figure 2.5.   Fields in an elliptically polarized wave.

The corresponding wave is

$$\mathbf{E} = \mathbf{E}_0 \exp i(kz - \omega t) \tag{2.32}$$

This expression can represent any type of polarization. Thus if $\mathbf{E}_0$ is real, we have linear polarization, whereas if it is complex, we have elliptic polarization. In the special case of circular polarization the real and imaginary parts of $\mathbf{E}_0$ are equal.

Quarter-Wave Plate   Circularly polarized light can be produced by introducing a phase shift of $\pi/2$ between two orthogonal components of linearly polarized light. One device for doing this is known as a *quarter-wave plate*. These plates are made of *doubly refracting* transparent crystals, such as calcite or mica.[2] Doubly refracting crystals have the property that the index of refraction differs for different directions of polarization. It is possible to cut a doubly refracting crystal into slabs in such a way that an axis of maximum index n_1 (the slow axis) and an axis of minimum index n_2 (the fast axis) both lie at right angles to one another in the plane of the slab. If the slab thickness is d, then the optical thickness is $n_1 d$ for light polarized in the direction of the slow axis and $n_2 d$ for light polarized in the direction of the fast axis. For a quarter-wave plate, d is chosen to make the

---

[2] The optics of crystals will be treated in detail in Chapter 5.

difference $n_1 d - n_2 d$ equal to 1/4 wavelength, so that d is given by the equation

$$d = \frac{\lambda}{4(n_1 - n_2)} \qquad (2.33)$$

The physical arrangement for producing circularly polarized light is shown in Figure 2.6. Incident unpolarized light is made linearly

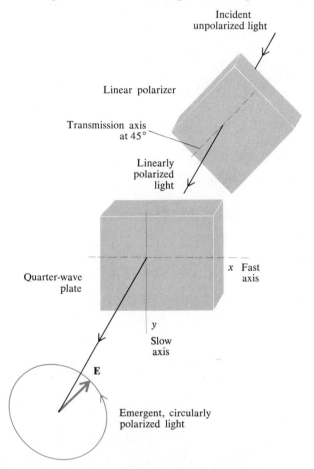

Figure 2.6. Arrangement for producing circularly polarized light.

polarized by means of a linear polarizer such as a sheet of polaroid. The quarter-wave plate is placed in the beam of linearly polarized light. The orientation of the quarter-wave plate is defined by the angle θ between the transmission axis of the polaroid and the fast axis of the quarter-wave plate. By choosing θ to be 45 degrees, the light entering the quarter-wave plate can be resolved into two orthogonal linearly polarized components of equal amplitude and equal phase. Upon emerging from the quarter-wave plate, these two components are out of phase by $\pi/2$. Hence the emerging light is circularly polarized.

The sense of rotation of the circularly polarized light depends on the value of θ and can be reversed by rotating the quarter-wave plate through an angle of 90 degrees so that θ is 135 degrees. If θ is any value other than 45 degrees or 135 degrees, the polarization of the emerging light will be elliptic rather than circular.

2.5 Matrix Representation of Polarization. The Jones Calculus

The complex vector amplitude given in the preceding section, Equation (2.31), is not the most general expression because it was assumed that the x component was real and the y component imaginary. A more general way of writing the complex amplitude of a plane harmonic wave is

$$\mathscr{E}_0 = \hat{\mathbf{i}}\mathscr{E}_{0x} + \hat{\mathbf{j}}\mathscr{E}_{0y} \qquad (2.34)$$

where $\mathscr{E}_{0x}$ and $\mathscr{E}_{0y}$ are both, possibly, complex. Accordingly, they can be expressed in exponential form as

$$\mathscr{E}_{0x} = E_{0x}e^{i\phi_x} \qquad (2.35)$$

$$\mathscr{E}_{0y} = E_{0y}e^{i\phi_y} \qquad (2.36)$$

A convenient notation for the above pair of complex amplitudes is the following matrix known as the Jones vector:

$$\begin{bmatrix} \mathscr{E}_{0x} \\ \mathscr{E}_{0y} \end{bmatrix} = \begin{bmatrix} E_{0x}e^{i\phi_x} \\ E_{0y}e^{i\phi_y} \end{bmatrix} \qquad (2.37)$$

The *normalized* form of the Jones vector is obtained by dividing by the appropriate complex number such that the sum of the squares of the absolute values of the two components is unity. A useful, not necessarily normalized, form is obtained by division of whatever quantity results in the simplest expression. In this way one can obtain a simple representation for the state of polarization of a plane harmonic wave. For example, $\begin{bmatrix} 1 \\ 0 \end{bmatrix}$ represents a beam linearly polarized in the x direction, and $\begin{bmatrix} 0 \\ 1 \end{bmatrix}$ a beam linearly polarized in the y direction. The vectors $\begin{bmatrix} 1/2 \\ 1/2 \end{bmatrix}$ or $\begin{bmatrix} 1 \\ 1 \end{bmatrix}$ represent a beam linearly polarized in a direction at 45 degrees with respect to the x axis.

Circular polarization is represented by $\begin{bmatrix} 1 \\ \pm i \end{bmatrix}$ where the minus sign is taken for right polarization and the plus sign is taken for left polarization.

One of the applications of the Jones notation is calculating the result of adding two or more waves of given polarizations. The result is obtained simply by adding the Jones vectors. As an example, suppose we want to know the result of adding two waves of equal amplitude, one being right circularly polarized, the other left circularly polarized. The calculation by means of the Jones vectors proceeds as follows:

$$\begin{bmatrix} 1 \\ -i \end{bmatrix} + \begin{bmatrix} 1 \\ i \end{bmatrix} = \begin{bmatrix} 1 + 1 \\ -i + i \end{bmatrix} = \begin{bmatrix} 2 \\ 0 \end{bmatrix} = 2\begin{bmatrix} 1 \\ 0 \end{bmatrix} \tag{2.38}$$

The last expression shows that the resultant wave is linearly polarized in the x direction and its amplitude is twice that of either of the circular components.

Another use of the matrix notation is that of computing the effect of inserting a linear optical element, or a train of such elements, into a beam of light of given polarization. The optical elements are represented by 2×2 matrices called *the Jones matrices*. The types of optical devices that can be so represented include linear polarizers, circular polarizers, phase retarders (quarter-wave plates, and so forth), isotropic phase changers, and isotropic absorbers. We give, without proof, the matrices for several optical elements in Table 2.1 [38].

The matrices are used as follows. Let the vector of the incident light be $\begin{bmatrix} A \\ B \end{bmatrix}$ and the vector of the emerging light be $\begin{bmatrix} A' \\ B' \end{bmatrix}$. Then

$$\begin{bmatrix} a & b \\ c & d \end{bmatrix}\begin{bmatrix} A \\ B \end{bmatrix} = \begin{bmatrix} A' \\ B' \end{bmatrix} \tag{2.39}$$

where $\begin{bmatrix} a & b \\ c & d \end{bmatrix}$ is the Jones matrix of the optical element. If light is sent through a train of optical elements, then the result is given by matrix multiplication:

$$\begin{bmatrix} a_n & b_n \\ c_n & d_n \end{bmatrix} \cdots \begin{bmatrix} a_2 & b_2 \\ c_2 & d_2 \end{bmatrix}\begin{bmatrix} a_1 & b_1 \\ c_1 & d_1 \end{bmatrix}\begin{bmatrix} A \\ B \end{bmatrix} = \begin{bmatrix} A' \\ B' \end{bmatrix} \tag{2.40}$$

To illustrate, suppose a quarter-wave plate is inserted into a beam of linearly polarized light as shown in Figure 2.6. Here the incoming beam is polarized at 45 degrees with respect to the horizontal (x axis), so that its vector, aside from an amplitude factor, is $\begin{bmatrix} 1 \\ 1 \end{bmatrix}$. From the table, the Jones matrix for a quarter-wave plate with the fast-axis horizontal is $\begin{bmatrix} 1 & 0 \\ 0 & -i \end{bmatrix}$. The vector of the emerging beam is then given by

Table 2.1.   JONES MATRICES FOR SOME LINEAR OPTICAL ELEMENTS

OPTICAL ELEMENT		JONES MATRIX
	Transmission axis horizontal	$\begin{bmatrix} 1 & 0 \\ 0 & 0 \end{bmatrix}$
Linear Polarizer	Transmission axis vertical	$\begin{bmatrix} 0 & 0 \\ 0 & 1 \end{bmatrix}$
	Transmission axis at 45 degrees	$1/2 \begin{bmatrix} 1 & 1 \\ 1 & 1 \end{bmatrix}$
Quarter-wave Plate	Fast axis horizontal	$\begin{bmatrix} 1 & 0 \\ 0 & -i \end{bmatrix}$
	Fast axis vertical	$\begin{bmatrix} 1 & 0 \\ 0 & i \end{bmatrix}$
Isotropic Phase Retarder		$\begin{bmatrix} e^{i\phi} & 0 \\ 0 & e^{i\phi} \end{bmatrix}$
Relative Phase Changer		$\begin{bmatrix} e^{i\phi_x} & 0 \\ 0 & e^{i\phi_y} \end{bmatrix}$
Circular Polarizer	Right	$1/2 \begin{bmatrix} 1 & i \\ -i & 1 \end{bmatrix}$
	Left	$1/2 \begin{bmatrix} 1 & -i \\ i & 1 \end{bmatrix}$

$$\begin{bmatrix} 1 & 0 \\ 0 & -i \end{bmatrix} \begin{bmatrix} 1 \\ 1 \end{bmatrix} = \begin{bmatrix} 1 \\ -i \end{bmatrix} \tag{2.41}$$

The emergent light is, therefore, right circularly polarized.

It should be noted that the Jones calculus is of use only for computing results with light that is initially polarized in some way. There is no Jones vector representation for unpolarized light.

Orthogonal Polarization   Two states of polarization represented by the complex vector amplitudes $\mathscr{E}_1$ and $\mathscr{E}_2$ are said to be *orthogonal* if

$$\mathscr{E}_1 \cdot \mathscr{E}_2{}^* = 0 \tag{2.42}$$

where the asterisk denotes the complex conjugate.

For linearly polarized light, orthogonality merely means that the fields are polarized at right angles to one another. In the case of circular polarization, it is readily seen that right circular and left circular polarizations are mutually orthogonal states. But, for any type of polarization, there is a corresponding orthogonal polarization.

In terms of Jones vectors, it is easy to verify that $\begin{bmatrix} A_1 \\ B_1 \end{bmatrix}$ and $\begin{bmatrix} A_2 \\ B_2 \end{bmatrix}$ are orthogonal if

$$A_1 A_2^* + B_1 B_2^* = 0 \qquad (2.43)$$

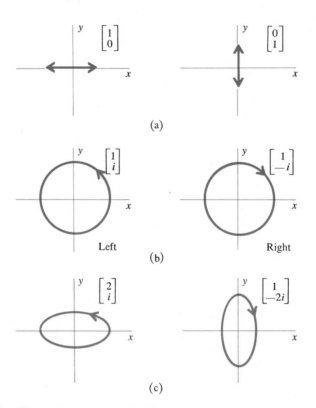

Figure 2.7.   Illustrations of some Jones vectors.

Thus, for example, $\begin{bmatrix} 2 \\ i \end{bmatrix}$ and $\begin{bmatrix} 1 \\ -2i \end{bmatrix}$ represent a particular pair of orthogonal states of elliptic polarization. These are shown in Figure 2.7.

2.6   Reflection and Refraction at a Plane Boundary

We now investigate the very basic phenomena of reflection and refraction of light from the standpoint of electromagnetic theory. It is assumed that the reader is already familiar with the elementary rules of reflection and refraction and how they are deduced from Huygens' principle. As we shall see, these rules can also be deduced from the application of boundary conditions for electromagnetic waves.

Consider a plane harmonic wave incident upon a plane boundary separating two different optical media, Figure 2.8. There will be a

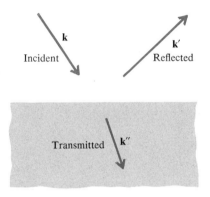

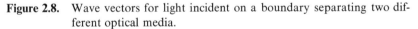

Figure 2.8.   Wave vectors for light incident on a boundary separating two different optical media.

reflected wave and a transmitted wave. The space-time dependence of these three waves, aside from constant amplitude factors, is given by the following complex expressions:

$\exp i(\mathbf{k} \cdot \mathbf{r} - \omega t)$ incident wave
$\exp i(\mathbf{k}' \cdot \mathbf{r} - \omega t)$ reflected wave
$\exp i(\mathbf{k}'' \cdot \mathbf{r} - \omega t)$ transmitted (refracted) wave

Now in order that any constant relation can exist for all points of the boundary and for all values of t, it is necessary that the arguments of the three exponential functions be equal at the boundary. Thus, since the time factors are already equal, we must have

$$\mathbf{k} \cdot \mathbf{r} = \mathbf{k}' \cdot \mathbf{r} = \mathbf{k}'' \cdot \mathbf{r} \quad \text{(at boundary)} \qquad (2.44)$$

These equations imply that all three wave vectors $\mathbf{k}$, $\mathbf{k}'$, and $\mathbf{k}''$ are coplanar, and that their projections onto the boundary plane are all equal. This can be argued by choosing a coordinate system $Oxyz$ such that one of the coordinate planes, say the xz plane, is the boundary,

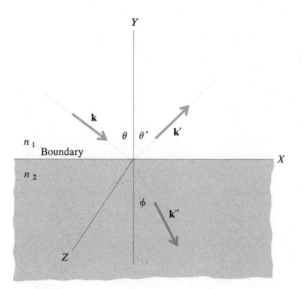

Figure 2.9.   Coordinate system for analyzing reflection and refraction at a plane boundary.

and also such that the vector **k** lies in the xy plane as shown in Figure 2.9. The angles between the boundary normal (y axis) and the wave vectors are labelled θ, θ', and ϕ, as shown. Equation (2.44) then becomes

$$k \sin \theta = k' \sin \theta' = k'' \sin \phi \qquad (2.45)$$

Now in the space of the incident and reflected waves ($y > 0$), the two waves are traveling in the same medium, hence the wave vectors have the same magnitude, that is, $k = k'$. The first equation then reduces to the familiar law of reflection

$$\theta = \theta' \qquad (2.46)$$

Taking the ratio of the propagation constants of the transmitted wave and the incident wave, we have

$$\frac{k''}{k} = \frac{\omega/v''}{\omega/v} = \frac{c/v''}{c/v} = \frac{n_2}{n_1} = n \qquad (2.47)$$

where n_1 and n_2 are the indices of refraction of the two media, and n is the relative index of refraction. The second part of Equation (2.45) therefore, is equivalent to Snell's law of refraction

$$\frac{\sin \theta}{\sin \phi} = n \qquad (2.48)$$

2.7 Amplitudes of Reflected and Refracted Waves. Fresnel's Equations

Let $\mathbf{E}$ denote the amplitude of the electric vector of a plane harmonic wave that is incident on a plane boundary separating two media, and let $\mathbf{E}'$ and $\mathbf{E}''$ denote the amplitudes of the reflected and transmitted waves, respectively. Then it follows from the Maxwell curl equations as applied to harmonic waves, Section 2.1, Equation (2.11), that the corresponding amplitudes of the magnetic vectors are given by

$$\mathbf{H} = \frac{1}{\mu\omega}\mathbf{k} \times \mathbf{E} \qquad \text{(incident)} \qquad (2.49)$$

$$\mathbf{H}' = \frac{1}{\mu\omega}\mathbf{k}' \times \mathbf{E}' \qquad \text{(reflected)} \qquad (2.50)$$

$$\mathbf{H}'' = \frac{1}{\mu\omega}\mathbf{k}'' \times \mathbf{E}'' \qquad \text{(transmitted)} \qquad (2.51)$$

It should be noted that the above equations apply either to the instantaneous values of the fields or to the amplitudes, since the exponential factors $\exp i(\mathbf{k} \cdot \mathbf{r} - \omega t)$, and so forth, are common to both the electric fields and associated magnetic fields.

It is convenient at this point to consider two different cases. The first case is that in which the electric vector of the incident wave is parallel to the boundary plane, that is, perpendicular to the plane of incidence. This case is called *transverse electric* or *TE* polarization. The second case is that in which the magnetic vector of the incident wave is parallel to the boundary plane. This is called *transverse magnetic* or *TM* polarization. The general case is handled by using appropriate linear combinations. The directions of the electric and associated magnetic vectors for the two cases are shown in Figure 2.10. As shown in the figure, the boundary is taken to be the xz plane so that the y axis is normal to the boundary. The xy plane is the plane of incidence.

We now apply the well-known boundary conditions [16] which require that the tangential components of the electric and magnetic fields be continuous as the boundary is crossed. This means that for *TE* polarization $E + E' = E''$, and for *TM* polarization $H - H' = H''$. The results are as follows:

$$\begin{aligned} E + E' &= E'' \\ -H\cos\theta + H'\cos\theta &= -H''\cos\phi \qquad (TE \text{ polarization}) \qquad (2.52) \\ -kE\cos\theta + k'E'\cos\theta &= -k''E''\cos\phi \end{aligned}$$

$$\begin{aligned} -H + H' &= -H'' \\ kE - k'E' &= k''E'' \qquad (TM \text{ polarization}) \qquad (2.53) \\ E\cos\theta + E'\cos\theta &= E''\cos\phi \end{aligned}$$

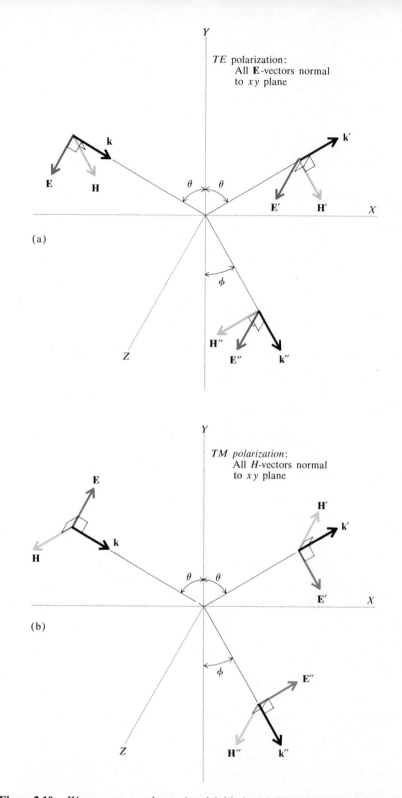

Figure 2.10. Wave vectors and associated fields for (a) *TE* and (b) *TM* polarization.

Here we have used Equation (2.16) to express the magnetic fields in terms of their associated electric fields.

We next eliminate E'' from the two sets of equations and use the relation $n = c/v = ck/\omega$ to obtain the following relations for the ratios of the reflected amplitudes to the incident amplitudes:

$$\frac{E'}{E} = \frac{\cos\theta - n\cos\phi}{\cos\theta + n\cos\phi} \qquad (TE\ \text{polarization}) \qquad (2.54)$$

$$\frac{E'}{E} = \frac{-n\cos\theta + \cos\phi}{n\cos\theta + \cos\phi} \qquad (TM\ \text{polarization}) \qquad (2.55)$$

Here

$$n = \frac{n_2}{n_1}$$

is the relative index of refraction of the two media. Ratios for the transmitted amplitudes can be obtained by eliminating E' in the two cases.

If one uses Snell's law $n = \sin\theta/\sin\phi$, the equations for the amplitudes of the reflected and refracted waves can be expressed in the form

$$\frac{E'}{E} = -\frac{\sin(\theta - \phi)}{\sin(\theta + \phi)}$$
$$\qquad\qquad\qquad\qquad (TE\ \text{polarization}) \qquad (2.56)$$
$$\frac{E''}{E} = \frac{2\cos\theta\sin\phi}{\sin(\theta + \phi)}$$

$$\frac{E'}{E} = -\frac{\tan(\theta - \phi)}{\tan(\theta + \phi)}$$
$$\qquad\qquad\qquad\qquad\qquad (TM\ \text{polarization}) \qquad (2.57)$$
$$\frac{E''}{E} = \frac{2\cos\theta\sin\phi}{\sin(\theta + \phi)\cos(\theta - \phi)}$$

The above equations are known as *Fresnel's equations*. Their derivation is left as a problem.

A third way of expressing the amplitude ratios for reflected light is to eliminate the variable ϕ in Equations (2.54) and (2.55) by use of Snell's law. The result is

$$\frac{E'}{E} = \frac{\cos\theta - \sqrt{n^2 - \sin^2\theta}}{\cos\theta + \sqrt{n^2 - \sin^2\theta}} \qquad (TE\ \text{polarization}) \qquad (2.58)$$

$$\frac{E'}{E} = \frac{-n^2\cos\theta + \sqrt{n^2 - \sin^2\theta}}{n^2\cos\theta + \sqrt{n^2 - \sin^2\theta}} \qquad (TM\ \text{polarization}) \qquad (2.59)$$

The reflectance R is defined as the ratio of the intensity of the reflected light to the intensity of the incident light, that is, the fraction of incident light energy that is reflected. Since the intensity is proportional to the square of the amplitude of the electric field, as shown in Section 2.2, we have

$$R = \left|\frac{E'}{E}\right|^2 \tag{2.60}$$

The reflectance as a function of the angle of incidence can then be obtained from the value of E'/E as given by any of the preceding equations.

Figure 2.11 shows the variation of E'/E and R with the angle of incidence, as calculated from the above theory.

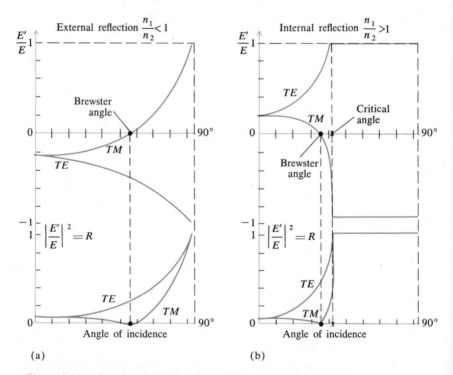

Figure 2.11. Graphs of E'/E and $|E'/E|^2$ versus angle of incidence for (a) external reflection and (b) internal reflection.

In the case of normal incidence ($\theta = 0$) we find that the ratio E'/E is the same for both types of polarization and has the value $(1 - n)/(1 + n)$. Hence the reflectance for normal incidence is

$$R = \left(\frac{1 - n}{1 + n}\right)^2 \tag{2.61}$$

Thus, for glass of index 1.5 the reflectance at normal incidence is 4 percent.

For grazing incidence ($\theta \sim 90$ degrees) the reflectance is also the same for both types of polarization, namely unity, and it is independent of n.

In order to discuss the reflection of light for intermediate values of θ, we must distinguish between two different possibilities. These are first, the case in which the relative index of refraction $n_2/n_1 = n$ is greater than unity. This is called *external reflection*. In the second case n is less than unity. This is known as *internal reflection*. In external reflection, the incident wave approaches the boundary from the side with the smaller index of refraction, whereas in internal reflection the incident wave is in the medium having the larger index of refraction.

In the case of external reflection, $n > 1$, the amplitude ratios as given by Equations (2.54) to (2.59) are real for all values of θ. The calculation of the reflectance R is then perfectly straightforward. For the case of internal reflection however, since $n < 1$, there will be values of θ such that $\sin \theta > n$, that is, $\theta > \sin^{-1} n$. The angle $\sin^{-1} n$ is called the *critical angle*. For ordinary glass it is about 41 degrees. For values of θ greater than the critical angle, the amplitude ratio E'/E is complex, which can be seen from Equations (2.58) and (2.59). For this range of values of θ we can express the amplitude ratios in the following form:

$$\frac{E'}{E} = \frac{\cos \theta - i \sqrt{\sin^2 \theta - n^2}}{\cos \theta + i \sqrt{\sin^2 \theta - n^2}} \qquad (TE \text{ polarization}) \qquad \text{(2.62)}$$

$$\frac{E'}{E} = \frac{-n^2 \cos \theta + i \sqrt{\sin^2 \theta - n^2}}{n^2 \cos \theta + i \sqrt{\sin^2 \theta - n^2}} \quad (TM \text{ polarization}) \qquad \text{(2.63)}$$

By multiplying by the complex conjugates, one can easily verify that the square of the absolute values of each of the above ratios is equal to unity. This means that $R = 1$, that is, we have *total reflection* when the internal angle of incidence is greater than the critical angle.

2.8   The Brewster Angle

From Equation (2.59), which gives the amplitude ratio for reflection in the *TM* case, we see that the reflection is zero for that particular angle of incidence θ such that

$$\theta = \tan^{-1} n \qquad \text{(2.64)}$$

This angle is called the *polarizing angle* or the *Brewster angle*. For glass it is about 57 degrees. Strictly speaking, the Brewster angle is a function of wavelength because of dispersion. The variation over the visible spectrum is very small, however.

If unpolarized light is incident on a surface at the Brewster angle, the reflected light is rendered linearly polarized with the electric vector transverse to the plane of incidence. This is one method, albeit inefficient, for producing polarized light.

Let a beam of light, linearly polarized in the *TM* mode, be incident at Brewster's angle on a glass plate with parallel faces as shown in Figure 2.12. Then no light is reflected from the first face. Neither is

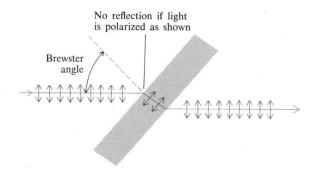

Figure 2.12.   A Brewster window.

there any reflection from the second face. (The proof of this statement is left as a problem.) The result is that the light is entirely transmitted, in other words, we have a perfect window. Such windows, known as *Brewster windows,* are used extensively in laser applications.

2.9   Penetration into the Rare Medium in Total Reflection

In spite of the fact that the incident energy is totally reflected for $\sin \theta > n$, there is still a wave that propagates into the region beyond the boundary. This can be shown theoretically by considering the complete wave function for the electric vector of the transmitted wave:

$$E'' \exp i(\mathbf{k}'' \cdot \mathbf{r} - \omega t) = E'' \exp i(k''x \sin \phi + k''y \cos \phi - \omega t) \quad \textbf{(2.65)}$$

There is no z dependence because of our choice of coordinate axes, Figure 2.10. From Snell's law $\sin \phi = \sin \theta / n$, we have

$$\cos \phi = \sqrt{1 - \frac{\sin^2 \theta}{n^2}} = i\sqrt{\frac{\sin^2 \theta}{n^2} - 1} \quad \textbf{(2.66)}$$

The expression for the transmitted wave can, therefore, be written as

$$E'' \exp\left(-k''y \sqrt{\frac{\sin^2 \theta}{n^2} - 1}\right) \exp i(k''x \sin \theta / n - \omega t)$$

$$\quad \textbf{(2.67)}$$

$$= E'' e^{-\alpha y} e^{i(k_1 x - \omega t)}$$

where $\alpha = k'' \sqrt{\sin^2 \theta / n^2 - 1}$ and $k_1 = k'' \sin \theta / n$

The first exponential function is real. It represents a rapid decrease of the amplitude of the wave as it penetrates into the rare medium. At first sight it may appear that the principle of conservation of energy is violated by the existence of the wave in the rare medium. However, a study of the direction of the energy flow by means of the Poynting vector diagram Figure 2.13, shows that the energy turns around and goes back into the dense medium as required from energy considerations.

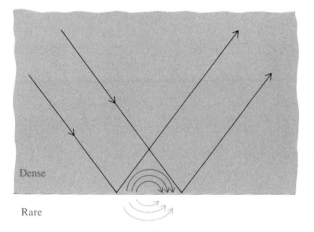

Figure 2.13.   Diagram showing the direction of the Poynting vector for the case of total internal reflection.

That the wave actually penetrates into the rare medium can be demonstrated experimentally by placing the long faces of two 45-degree prisms close together, but not touching, as shown in Figure 2.14. Light from a source S is found to be partially transmitted, the

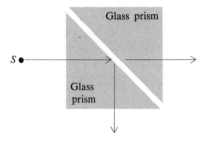

Figure 2.14.   A method for illustrating the penetration of light into the rare medium.

amount depending on the separation of the prism faces. This arrangement can be used to make such things as variable output couplers for lasers. In another experiment, first performed by Raman, reflection of light was obtained from a sharp metallic edge near but not in contact with the edge of a totally reflecting prism as shown in Figure 2.15.

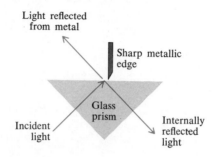

Figure 2.15. Raman's demonstration that light penetrates into the rare medium.

2.10 Phase Changes in Internal Reflection

In the case of total internal reflection the complex amplitude ratios, given by Equations (2.62) and (2.63), imply that a change of phase occurs that is a function of the angle of incidence. We now proceed to calculate this phase change. Since the absolute value of E'/E is unity, we can set

$$-\frac{E'}{E} = e^{-i\delta} = \frac{ae^{-i\alpha}}{ae^{+i\alpha}} \tag{2.68}$$

where δ is the phase change. The complex numbers $ae^{-i\alpha}$ and $ae^{+i\alpha}$ are equal to the numerators and denominators of the complex fractions in Equations (2.62) and (2.63). From Equation (2.68) above, we have $\delta = 2\alpha$, and accordingly, $\tan \alpha = \tan \delta/2$. We find, therefore, the following expressions for the phase changes occurring in internal reflection:

TE:
$$\tan(\delta_{TE}/2) = \frac{\sqrt{\sin^2 \theta - n^2}}{\cos \theta} \tag{2.69}$$

TM:
$$\tan(\delta_{TM}/2) = \frac{\sqrt{\sin^2 \theta - n^2}}{n^2 \cos \theta} \tag{2.70}$$

From these, the relative phase difference

$$\Delta = \delta_{TM} - \delta_{TE} \tag{2.71}$$

can be found. The result is expressible in the following form:

$$\tan(\Delta/2) = \frac{\cos\theta \sqrt{\sin^2\theta - n^2}}{\sin^2\theta} \tag{2.72}$$

Graphs of δ_{TE}, δ_{TM}, and Δ are shown in Figure 2.16.

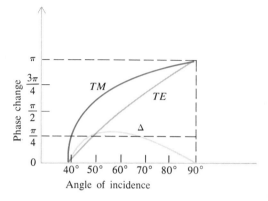

Figure 2.16.   Phase changes occurring in total internal reflection.

The phase change produced on internal reflection may be utilized to obtain circularly polarized light. The scheme, devised by Fresnel, is shown in Figure 2.17. The essential element is a glass prism made in

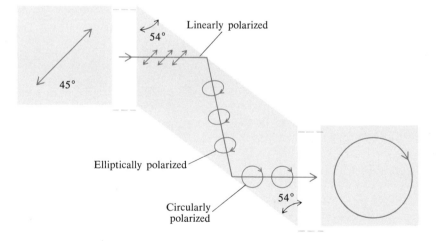

Figure 2.17.   The Fresnel rhomb.

the form of a rhomb having apex angles of 54 degrees. Linearly polarized light whose direction of polarization is at an angle of 45 degrees with respect to the face edge of the rhomb enters normally on one face as shown. The light undergoes two total internal reflections and emerges from the exit face. At each internal reflection a phase difference Δ is produced between the *TM* and *TE* polarizations. As indicated on the graph of Δ versus angle of incidence, Figure 2.16, Δ is equal to $\pi/4$ when the angle of incidence is 54 degrees. A total phase difference of $\pi/2$ is thereby obtained for the two internal reflections. The emerging light is thus circularly polarized.

PROBLEMS

2.1. Fill in the steps leading to Equation (2.4).

2.2. A light wave is traveling in glass of index of refraction 1.5. If the amplitude of the electric field of the light wave is 100 volts per meter (v/m), what is the amplitude of the magnetic field?

2.3. What is the magnitude of the Poynting vector of the wave in Problem 2.2?

2.4. What is the rms value of the electric field of the radiation
  (a) of a 60-watt(w) light bulb at a distance of 1 m?
  (b) of sunlight at the earth's surface? (The "solar constant" at the earth's surface is 1.94 calories per centimeter^2 (cal/cm^2) per minute.)
  (c) a 10-w laser beam focused to a spot 1 micrometer (μm) in diameter?

2.5. Draw diagrams to show the type of polarization of the waves whose electric vectors are given by the following equations:
  (a) $\mathscr{E} = \hat{\mathbf{i}}E_0 \cos(kz - \omega t) + \hat{\mathbf{j}}E_0 \cos(kz - \omega t + \pi/4)$
  (b) $\mathscr{E} = \hat{\mathbf{i}}E_0 \cos(kz - \omega t) + \hat{\mathbf{j}}2E_0 \sin(kz - \omega t)$
  (c) $\mathscr{E} = \hat{\mathbf{i}}E_0 e^{i(kz - \omega t)} + \hat{\mathbf{j}}2E_0 e^{i(kz - \omega t - 3\pi/4)}$
  (d) $\mathscr{E} = \mathscr{E}_0 e^{i(kz - \omega t)}$ where $\mathscr{E}_0 = (\hat{\mathbf{i}} + 2i\hat{\mathbf{j}})E_0$
  Also, express the amplitudes of (a), (b), and (c) as complex vectors like that given for (d).

2.6. Show that the average Poynting flux is given by the expression $(\frac{1}{2})Re(\mathscr{E}_0 \times \mathscr{H}_0^*)$ in which $\mathscr{E}_0$ and $\mathscr{H}_0$ are the complex field amplitudes of a light wave.

2.7. Give the equations for the electric fields for the following waves:
  (a) A linearly polarized wave traveling in the x direction. The electric vector makes an angle of 30 degrees with the y axis.
  (b) A right elliptically polarized wave traveling in the y direction. The major axis of the ellipse is in the z direction and is twice the minor axis.
  (c) A linearly polarized wave traveling in the xy plane in a direction making an angle of 45 degrees with the x axis. The direction of polarization is in the z direction.

2.8. Give the Jones vectors for the waves in Problem 2.7.

2.9. (a) Describe the type of polarization of the waves whose Jones vectors are the following:

$$\begin{bmatrix} 1 \\ 2 \end{bmatrix}, \begin{bmatrix} 1 \\ 2i \end{bmatrix}, \begin{bmatrix} 1 \\ 1+i \end{bmatrix}$$

(b) Give the orthogonal Jones vectors to each of the above and describe their polarizations.

2.10. Show that the wave represented by the Jones vector $\begin{bmatrix} A \\ B\,e^{i\phi} \end{bmatrix}$

is, in general, elliptically polarized and that the major axis of the ellipse makes an angle

$$\frac{1}{2}\tan^{-1}\left(\frac{2AB\cos\phi}{A^2 - B^2}\right)$$

with the x axis. Discuss the special cases: (a) $A = 0$, (b) $B = 0$, (c) $\phi = 0$, (d) $A = B, \phi = \pi/2$.

2.11. Show by means of the Jones calculus that circularly polarized light is produced by sending light through a linear polarizer and a quarter-wave plate only in the right order.

2.12. What is the direction of rotation of a circular polarizer whose Jones matrix is $\begin{bmatrix} 1 & i \\ -i & 1 \end{bmatrix}$? Show that it is transparent to one type of circularly polarized light and opaque to the opposite type.

2.13. Elliptically polarized light whose Jones vector is $\begin{bmatrix} 3 \\ i \end{bmatrix}$ is sent through a quarter-wave plate, the fast axis being in the x direction. What is the state of polarization of the emerging light?

2.14. Determine the reflectance of water ($n = 1.33$) for both TE and TM polarizations for the following angles of incidence: 0 degrees, 10 degrees, 45 degrees, 90 degrees.

2.15. Calculate the values of the critical angle and the Brewster angle for (a) water ($n = 1.33$) and (b) dense flint glass ($n = 1.75$).

2.16. A beam of circularly polarized light is incident on a glass surface ($n = 1.5$). The angle of incidence is 45 degrees. Describe precisely the state of polarization of the reflected light.

2.17. A beam of light is incident at an angle θ on a dielectric surface. Show that the sum of the energies in the reflected and refracted beams is equal to the energy in the incident beam.

2.18. The critical angle for total internal reflection in a certain piece of glass is exactly 45 degrees. What is the Brewster angle for (a) external reflection and (b) internal reflection?

2.19. The accompanying figure is a diagram of the Mooney rhomb for producing circularly polarized light. Show that if the index of refraction of the rhomb is 1.65, the apex angle A should be about 60 degrees.

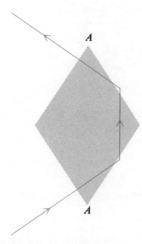

Figure 2.18. The Mooney rhomb.

2.20. Fill in the steps leading to Equation (2.72).

2.21. A beam of light is totally reflected in a 45–90–45-degree glass prism ($n = 1.5$) as shown in Figure 2.15. The wavelength of the light is 5000 Å. (a) What is the distance above the surface AB at which the amplitude of the external wave is $1/e$ of its value at the surface? (b) What is the ratio of the intensity of the external wave at a distance of 1 millimeter (mm) to that at the surface?

2.22. What thickness should a piece of quartz be in order to make a quarter-wave plate for $\lambda_{vac} = 6000$ Å. The two indices of refraction of quartz at this wavelength are 1.5442 and 1.5533.

CHAPTER *3*

Coherence and
Interference

3.1 The Principle of Linear Superposition

The theory of optical interference is based essentially on the principle of linear superposition of electromagnetic fields. According to this principle, the electric field **E** produced at a point in empty space jointly by several different sources is equal to the vector sum

$$\mathbf{E} = \mathbf{E}_{(1)} + \mathbf{E}_{(2)} + \mathbf{E}_{(3)} + \cdots \tag{3.1}$$

where $\mathbf{E}_{(1)}$, $\mathbf{E}_{(2)}$, $\mathbf{E}_{(3)}$, $\cdots$ are the fields produced at the point in question separately by the different sources. The same is true for magnetic fields.

In the presence of matter, the principle of linear superposition is only approximately true. (This does not mean that fields cannot be resolved into components. It merely means that the resultant total field produced in matter by several external sources acting simultaneously may not be the same as the sum of the fields produced by each source acting alone.) Deviations from linearity are observed at the high intensities produced by lasers and come under the heading of nonlinear optical phenomena.[1]

Let us consider two plane harmonic linearly polarized waves of the same frequency ω. The electric fields are then

$$\mathbf{E}_{(1)} = \mathbf{E}_1 \exp i(\mathbf{k}_1 \cdot \mathbf{r} - \omega t + \varphi_1)$$
$$\mathbf{E}_{(2)} = \mathbf{E}_2 \exp i(\mathbf{k}_2 \cdot \mathbf{r} - \omega t + \varphi_2) \tag{3.2}$$

Here the quantities φ_1 and φ_2 have been introduced to allow for any phase difference between the sources of the two waves. If the phase difference $\varphi_1 - \varphi_2$ is constant, the two sources are said to be *mutually coherent*. The resulting waves are also mutually coherent in this case.

For the present, we shall confine our discussion to mutually coherent monochromatic waves. The question of partial coherence and nonmonochromatic waves will be taken up later.

[1] Nonlinear optics will be treated later in Section 5.12.

We know from Section 2.2 that the intensity of radiation at a point is proportional to the square of the amplitude of the light field at the point in question. Thus, the superposition of our two monochromatic plane waves, aside from a constant proportionality factor, results in an intensity distribution given by

$$I = |\mathbf{E}|^2 = \mathbf{E} \cdot \mathbf{E}^* = (\mathbf{E}_{(1)} + \mathbf{E}_{(2)}) \cdot (\mathbf{E}^*_{(1)} + \mathbf{E}^*_{(2)})$$

$$= |\mathbf{E}_1|^2 + |\mathbf{E}_2|^2 + 2\mathbf{E}_1 \cdot \mathbf{E}_2 \cos \theta \qquad (3.3)$$

$$= I_1 + I_2 + 2\mathbf{E}_1 \cdot \mathbf{E}_2 \cos \theta$$

where

$$\theta = \mathbf{k}_1 \cdot \mathbf{r} - \mathbf{k}_2 \cdot \mathbf{r} + \varphi_1 - \varphi_2 \qquad (3.4)$$

The term $2\mathbf{E}_1 \cdot \mathbf{E}_2 \cos \theta$ is called the *interference term*. This term indicates that the intensity I can be greater than or less than the sum $I_1 + I_2$, depending on the value of θ. Since θ depends on $\mathbf{r}$, periodic spatial variations in the intensity occur. These variations are the familiar interference fringes that are seen when two mutually coherent beams of light are combined.

If the sources of the two waves are mutually incoherent, then the quantity $\varphi_1 - \varphi_2$ varies with time in a random fashion. The result is that the mean value of $\cos \theta$ is zero, and there is no interference. This is the reason interference fringes are not observed with two separate (ordinary) light sources.

In the event that the two waves are polarized, then the interference term also depends on the polarization. In particular, if the polarizations are mutually orthogonal, then $\mathbf{E}_1 \cdot \mathbf{E}_2 = 0$. Again there are no interference fringes. This is true not only for linearly polarized waves but for circularly and elliptically polarized waves as well. The proof of the latter statement is left as a problem.

3.2 Young's Experiment

The classic experiment that demonstrates interference of light was first performed by Thomas Young in 1802. In the original experiment sunlight was used as the source, but any bright source such as a tungsten filament lamp or an arc would be satisfactory. Light is passed through a pinhole S so as to illuminate an aperture consisting of two pinholes or narrow slits S_1 and S_2 as shown in Figure 3.1. If a white screen is placed in the region beyond the slits, a pattern of bright and dark interference bands can be seen. The key to the experiment is the use of a single pin hole S to illuminate the aperture. This provides the necessary mutual coherence between the light coming from the two slits S_1 and S_2.

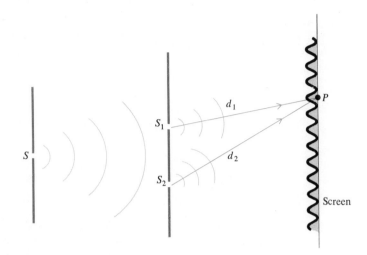

Figure 3.1.   Young's experiment.

The usual elementary analysis of the Young experiment involves finding the difference in phase between the two waves arriving at a given point P over the distances d_1 and d_2 as shown. Our approach will be to calculate the value of the interference term in the theory of the previous section. Assuming that the distance from the aperture to the screen is large enough, we can regard the fields produced by S_1 and S_2 to be approximately represented by the plane harmonic wave expressions

$$\mathbf{E}_1 \exp i(\mathbf{k}_1 \cdot \mathbf{r} - \omega t + \varphi_1)$$

$$\mathbf{E}_2 \exp i(\mathbf{k}_2 \cdot \mathbf{r} - \omega t + \varphi_2)$$

where $\mathbf{k}_1$ and $\mathbf{k}_2$ are the propagation vectors of the two component waves arriving from S_1 and S_2, respectively, and $\mathbf{r}$ is the position vector of a point in the region of space near the screen. The geometry of the arrangement is labeled as shown in Figure 3.2. From the figure it can be seen that the difference between the two propagation vectors is given approximately by

$$\mathbf{k}_1 - \mathbf{k}_2 = -\hat{\mathbf{j}}\frac{kh}{x} \tag{3.5}$$

provided that the distance x from P to the aperture is large compared to both y and slit separation h. Thus

$$(\mathbf{k}_1 - \mathbf{k}_2) \cdot \mathbf{r} = (\mathbf{k}_1 - \mathbf{k}_2) \cdot (\hat{\mathbf{i}}x + \hat{\mathbf{j}}y) = -\frac{kyh}{x} \tag{3.6}$$

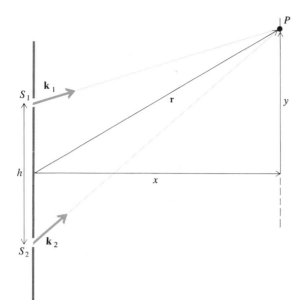

Figure 3.2. Geometry for analyzing interference in the case of the double slit.

The intensity distribution, from Equations (3.3) and (3.4) is

$$I = |\mathbf{E}|^2 = |\mathbf{E}_1|^2 + |\mathbf{E}_2|^2 + 2\mathbf{E}_1 \cdot \mathbf{E}_2 \cos{(\frac{kyh}{x} - \varphi)} \qquad (3.7)$$

Now if the slits are identical and the phase difference $\varphi = \varphi_1 - \varphi_2$ is zero, the above formula reduces to

$$I = 2I_0 \left[1 + \cos{(\frac{kyh}{x})} \right] \qquad (3.8)$$

where $I_0 = |\mathbf{E}_1|^2 = |\mathbf{E}_2|^2$. The intensity, therefore, varies between zero and $4I_0$ depending on the argument of the cosine.

Bright fringes occur when $kyh/x = 0, 2\pi, 4\pi, \cdots$, that is, when

$$y = 0, \frac{\lambda x}{h}, \frac{2\lambda x}{h}, \cdots \qquad (3.9)$$

which is the well-known result obtained by elementary methods. The angular separation between fringes is approximately λ/h.

If the slits are covered by optical devices such as phase retarders, polarizers, and so forth, the intensity distribution is easily calculated from the general formula, Equation (3.7). For example, if a relative phase difference φ is introduced by placing a thin piece of glass over one slit, then the whole pattern shifts accordingly. If polarizers are placed over the slits and oriented in such a manner that the component waves are orthogonally polarized, then $\mathbf{E}_1 \cdot \mathbf{E}_2 = 0$, and no interference fringes occur.

Alternative Methods of Demonstrating Interference Other experimental arrangements for demonstrating interference between two waves are illustrated in Figure 3.3. All of these make use of reflection or refraction to obtain two mutually coherent waves.

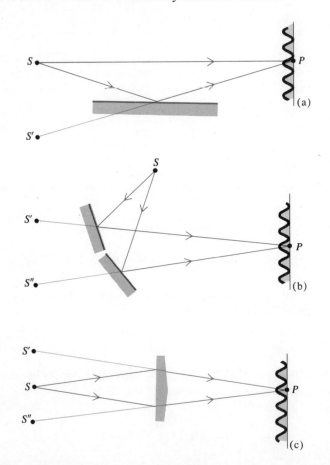

Figure 3.3. Arrangements for producing interference fringes with a single source. (a) Lloyd's single mirror; (b) Fresnel's double mirror; (c) Fresnel's biprism.

In Lloyd's single-mirror experiment, Figure 3.3(a), a pinhole source S is placed near a plane mirror as shown. That part of the light that is reflected by the mirror appears to come from a virtual source S'.

The field in the region of the screen is then equivalent to that in Young's experiment. In calculating the intensity at a point P, the phase change that occurs on reflection must of course be taken into account.

The Fresnel double-mirror arrangement, Figure 3.3(b), makes use of two mirrors to obtain two mutually coherent virtual sources S' and S'', as shown.

A glass prism is employed to obtain two mutually coherent sources in the Fresnel biprism arrangement, Figure 3.3(c). The apex angle of the prism should be nearly 180 degrees in order that the virtual sources are only slightly separated.

3.3 The Michelson Interferometer

Perhaps the best known and most versatile interferometric device is the interferometer developed by Michelson in 1880. The basic design is shown in Figure 3.4. Light from the source S falls on a lightly silvered-

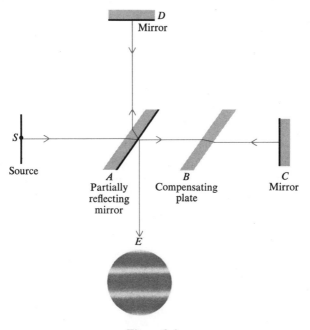

Figure 3.4.

glass plate A, which divides the beam into two parts. These separated beams are reflected back to A by mirrors C and D as shown. Usually, a compensating plate B is inserted in one beam in order that the two optical paths include the same thickness of glass. The compensating plate is necessary when observing fringes with white light.

The interference pattern is observed at E. Here the light appears to come from two virtual source planes H_1 and H_2 as indicated in Figure 3.5. The corresponding virtual point sources S' and S'' in these

Figure 3.5.   Virtual source planes in the Michelson interferometer.

planes are mutually coherent. If Δ is the optical path difference between the two rays reaching E, that is, the distance between S_1' and S_2'', then from Equations (3.3) and (3.4), the intensity is proportional to

$$1 + \cos\theta = 1 + \cos k\Delta = 1 + \cos\frac{2\pi\Delta}{\lambda} \qquad \text{(3.10)}$$

Now if the mirrors are slightly tilted so that the virtual source planes H_1 and H_2 are not quite parallel, then alternate bright and dark fringes appear across the field of view when the eye is placed at E. These fringes, called localized fringes, appear to come from the region of H_1 and H_2. On the other hand, if H_1 and H_2 are parallel, then the fringes are seen as circular and appear to come from infinity.

Several localized colored fringes can be observed with white light if H_1 and H_2 intersect at some point in the field of view. In this case the central fringe is dark owing to the fact that one ray is internally reflected in plate A, whereas the other ray is externally reflected in A, and accordingly, the two rays reaching E are 180 degrees out of phase for $\Delta = 0$.

One of the many uses of the Michelson interferometer is the determination of the index of refraction of gases. An evacuated optical cell is placed in one of the optical paths of the interferometer. The gas whose index is to be measured is then allowed to flow into the cell. This is equivalent to changing the lengths of the optical path and causes the interference fringes to move across the field of view. The number of such fringes gives the effective change in optical path from which the index of refraction of the gas can be calculated.

A modification of the Michelson interferometer known as the Twyman-Green interferometer is shown in Figure 3.6. This interfer-

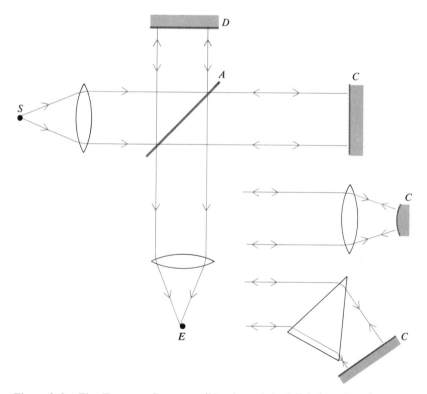

Figure 3.6. The Twyman-Green modification of the Michelson interferometer.

ometer is used for testing optical elements such as lenses, mirrors, and prisms. Collimated light is used in this case. The optical element to be tested is placed in one of the paths as shown. Imperfections are rendered visible by distortions in the fringe pattern.

A more complete discussion of various types of interferometers is given in references [7] and [40].

3.4   Theory of Partial Coherence. Visibility of Fringes

In the preceding discussions, it was assumed that the optical fields were completely coherent, monochromatic, and constant in amplitude. In the actual case of interference of two or more light waves, the amplitudes and phases usually vary with time in a random fashion. The instantaneous light intensity at a given point therefore fluctuates rapidly. It would seem more meaningful then, to define the intensity as a time average. In the case of two fields E_1 and E_2, the intensity I can be expressed accordingly, as

$$I = <\mathbf{E} \cdot \mathbf{E}^*> = <(\mathbf{E}_1 + \mathbf{E}_2) \cdot (\mathbf{E}_1{}^* + \mathbf{E}_2{}^*)>$$
$$= <|\mathbf{E}_1|^2 + |\mathbf{E}_2|^2 + 2Re(\mathbf{E}_1 \cdot \mathbf{E}_2{}^*)> \tag{3.11}$$

The sharp brackets denote the time average:

$$<f> = \lim_{T \to \infty} \frac{1}{T} \int_0^T f(t)dt \tag{3.12}$$

In the discussions to follow, it will be assumed that all quantities are *stationary*. By stationary is meant that the time average is independent of the choice of the origin of time. Also, for convenience, the optical fields will be assumed to have the same polarization so that their vectorial nature can be ignored. With these simplifying assumptions, Equation (3.11) can be written

$$I = I_1 + I_2 + 2\,Re <E_1 E_2{}^*> \tag{3.13}$$

where

$$I_1 = <|E_1|^2> \qquad I_2 = <|E_2|^2> \tag{3.14}$$

In the usual interference experiment, the two fields E_1 and E_2 originate from some common source. They differ because of a difference in their optical paths. A simplified schematic diagram is shown in Figure 3.7.

Let us call t the time for one light signal to traverse path 1 and $t + \tau$ the time for the other signal to traverse path 2. Then the interference term in Equation (3.13) may be written as

$$2\,Re\,\Gamma_{12}(\tau)$$

where

$$\Gamma_{12}(\tau) = <E_1(t)\,E_2{}^*(t + \tau)> \tag{3.15}$$

The function $\Gamma_{12}(\tau)$ is called the *mutual coherence function* or the

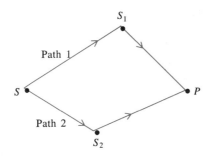

Figure 3.7. Generalized light paths in an interference experiment.

correlation function of two fields E_1 and E_2. From the definition, we see that $\Gamma_{11}(0) = I_1$, and $\Gamma_{22}(0) = I_2$.

It is sometimes convenient to use a normalized correlation function defined as

$$\gamma_{12}(\tau) = \frac{\Gamma_{12}(\tau)}{\sqrt{\Gamma_{11}(0)\,\Gamma_{22}(0)}} = \frac{\Gamma_{12}(\tau)}{\sqrt{I_1 I_2}} \qquad (3.16)$$

The intensity is then expressed as follows:

$$I = I_1 + I_2 + 2\sqrt{I_1 I_2}\, Re\, \gamma_{12}(\tau) \qquad (3.17)$$

The function $\gamma_{12}(\tau)$ is, in general, a periodic function of τ. Thus, an interference pattern results if $|\gamma_{12}(\tau)|$, called the *degree of coherence,* has a value other than zero. In terms of $|\gamma_{12}(\tau)|$, we have the following types of coherence:

$$|\gamma_{12}| = 1 \qquad \text{complete coherence}$$

$$0 < |\gamma_{12}| < 1 \qquad \text{partial coherence}$$

$$|\gamma_{12}| = 0 \qquad \text{complete incoherence}$$

In a pattern of interference fringes, the intensity varies between two limits I_{max} and I_{min}. From (3.17) we see that these are given by

$$I_{max} = I_1 + I_2 + 2\sqrt{I_1 I_2}|\gamma_{12}| \qquad I_{min} = I_1 + I_2 - 2\sqrt{I_1 I_2}|\gamma_{12}| \qquad (3.18)$$

The *fringe visibility* $\mathscr{V}$ is defined as the ratio

$$\mathscr{V} = \frac{I_{max} - I_{min}}{I_{max} + I_{min}} \qquad (3.19)$$

It follows that

$$\mathscr{V} = \frac{2\sqrt{I_1 I_2}\,|\gamma_{12}|}{I_1 + I_2} \qquad (3.20)$$

In particular, if $I_1 = I_2$, then

$$\mathscr{V} = |\gamma_{12}| \tag{3.21}$$

that is, the fringe visibility is equal to the degree of coherence. In the case of complete coherence ($|\gamma_{12}| = 1$) the interference fringes have the maximum contrast of unity, whereas for complete incoherence, $|\gamma_{12}| = 0$, the contrast is zero, that is, there are no interference fringes at all.

3.5   Coherence Time and Coherence Length

In order to see how the degree of coherence is related to the characteristics of the source, let us consider the case of a hypothetical "quasimonochromatic" source having the following property: The oscillation and the subsequent field varies sinusoidally for a certain time τ_0 and then changes phase abruptly. This sequence keeps repeating indefinitely. A graph is shown in Figure 3.8. We shall call τ_0 the *coherence*

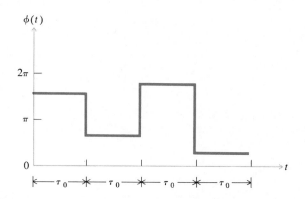

Figure 3.8.   Graph of the phase $\varphi(t)$ of a quasimonochromatic source.

time. The phase change that occurs after each coherence time is considered to be randomly distributed between 0 and 2π.

The time dependence of this quasimonochromatic field can be expressed as

$$E(t) = E_0 e^{-i\omega t} \, e^{i\varphi(t)} \tag{3.22}$$

where the phase angle $\varphi(t)$ is a random step function, illustrated in Figure 3.8. One can regard the above kind of a field as an approximation to that of a radiating atom the abrupt changes of phase being the result of collisions.

Suppose a beam of light, whose field is represented by Equation (3.22), is divided into two beams that are subsequently brought together to produce interference. The degree of coherence can be evaluated as follows: It is assumed that

$$|E_1| = |E_2| = |E|$$

Then

$$\gamma_{12}(\tau) = \frac{<E(t)\, E^*(t + \tau)>}{<|E|^2>} \tag{3.23}$$

From (3.22), we have

$$\gamma_{12}(\tau) = <e^{i\omega\tau}\, e^{i[\varphi(\tau) - \varphi(t + \tau)]}>$$
$$= e^{i\omega\tau} \lim_{T\to\infty} \frac{1}{T} \int_0^T e^{i[\varphi(t) - \varphi(t + \tau)]}\, dt \tag{3.24}$$

Consider the quantity $\varphi(t) - \varphi(t + \tau)$. This is plotted in Figure 3.9.

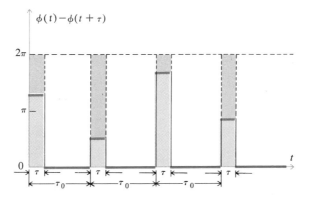

Figure 3.9.   Graph of the phase difference $\varphi(t) - \varphi(t + \tau)$.

In particular, for the first coherence time interval, $0 \leq t \leq \tau_0$, we observe that $\varphi(t) - \varphi(t + \tau)$ has the value zero if $\tau < t \leq \tau_0$, but for $0 < t < \tau$ it assumes some random value between 0 and 2π. The same is true for each succeeding coherence time interval.

The integral in Equation (3.24) is easily evaluated as follows: For the first interval, we have

$$\frac{1}{\tau_0} \int_0^{\tau_0} e^{i[\varphi(t) - \varphi(t + \tau)]}\, dt = \frac{1}{\tau_0} \int_0^\tau e^{i\Delta}\, dt + \frac{1}{\tau_0} \int_\tau^{\tau_0} dt$$

$$= \frac{e^{i\Delta}}{\tau_0}\tau + \frac{\tau_0 - \tau}{\tau_0} \tag{3.25}$$

where Δ is the random phase difference.

The same result is obtained for all subsequent intervals, except that

Δ is different for each interval. Since Δ is random, the terms involving $e^{i\Delta}$ will average to zero. The other term, $(\tau_0 - \tau)/\tau_0$, is the same for all intervals, hence it is equal to average value of the integral in question. Of course if $\tau > \tau_0$, then the phase difference $\varphi(t) - \varphi(t + \tau)$ is always random, and consequently, the whole integral averages to zero.

From the above result, we find that the normalized correlation function $\gamma_{12}(\tau)$ for a quasimonochromatic field is given by

$$\gamma_{12}(\tau) = (1 - \frac{\tau}{\tau_0}) e^{i\omega\tau} \qquad \tau < \tau_0$$

$$= 0 \qquad \tau \geqslant \tau_0$$

(3.26)

Accordingly, the degree of coherence is

$$|\gamma_{12}(\tau)| = 1 - \frac{\tau}{\tau_0} \qquad \tau < \tau_0$$

$$= 0 \qquad \tau \geqslant \tau_0$$

(3.27)

A graph of $|\gamma_{12}|$ is shown in Figure 3.10. We found in the previous section that the degree of coherence is equal to the fringe visibility $\mathscr{V}$

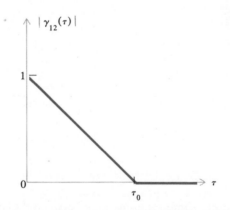

Figure 3.10. Graph of the degree of coherence of a quasimonochromatic source.

for the case of equal amplitudes in a two-beam interference arrangement. Evidently the fringe visibility drops to zero if τ exceeds the coherence time τ_0. This means that the path difference between the two beams must not exceed the value

$$c\tau_0 = l_c$$

in order to obtain interference fringes. The quantity l_c is called the *coherence length*. It is essentially the length of an uninterrupted wave train.

In the actual case of radiating atoms, the time between collisions is not constant but varies randomly from one collision to the next. Consequently, the wave trains vary in length in a similar random fashion. In this more realistic situation we can define the coherence time as the *average* value of all the individual coherence times and similarly for the coherence length. The actual mathematical form of the degree of coherence and of the fringe visibility will then depend on the precise statistical distribution of the lengths of the wave trains. In any case, the fringe visibility will be large (of the order of unity) for path differences that are small compared to the average coherence length. Conversely, the fringe visibility will become small and approach zero as the path difference becomes larger than the average coherence length.

For further reading on the subject of coherence, references [1] and [5] may be consulted.

3.6 Spectral Resolution of a Finite-Wave Train.
Coherence and Line Width

In practice, no source of light is ever strictly monochromatic. Even in the best so-called monochromatic sources there is always some finite spread of frequency centered about some mean frequency. We now proceed to investigate the relationship between the frequency spread, or line width, and the coherence of a light source. To do this we make use of the Fourier integral theorem [27].

According to the theorem, stated here without proof, a function $f(t)$ can be expressed as an integral over the variable ω in the following way:

$$f(t) = \int_{-\infty}^{+\infty} g(\omega)e^{-i\omega t}d\omega$$

$$g(\omega) = \frac{1}{2\pi}\int_{-\infty}^{+\infty} f(t)e^{i\omega t}dt$$

(3.28)

The functions $f(t)$ and $g(\omega)$ are called *Fourier transforms* of each other and are said to constitute a Fourier transform pair. In our present application, the variables t and ω are time and frequency, respectively. The function $g(\omega)$ then constitutes a frequency resolution of the time dependent function $f(t)$, or stated in another way, $g(\omega)$ represents the function in the frequency domain.

Let us consider now the particular case in which the function $f(t)$ represents a single wave train of finite duration τ_0. The time variation of this wave train is given by the function:

$$f(t) = e^{-i\omega_0 t} \qquad -\tfrac{1}{2}\tau_0 < t < \tfrac{1}{2}\tau_0$$
$$= 0 \qquad \text{otherwise} \tag{3.29}$$

Taking the Fourier transform, we have

$$g(\omega) = \frac{1}{2\pi} \int_{-\tau_0/2}^{+\tau_0/2} e^{i(\omega - \omega_0)t}\, dt$$
$$= \frac{1}{\pi} \frac{\sin[\tfrac{1}{2}\tau_0(\omega - \omega_0)]}{\omega - \omega_0} \tag{3.30}$$

A plot of the real part of the function $f(t)$ is shown in Figure 3.11.

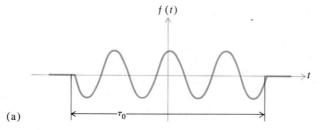

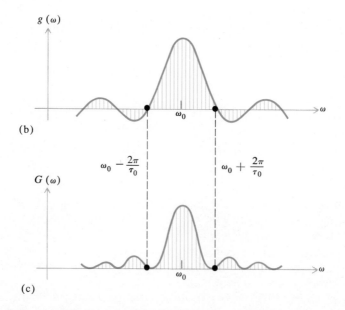

Figure 3.11.   (a) A finite wave train, (b) its Fourier transform, and (c) the power spectrum.

Also plotted is a graph of the *power spectrum:*

$$G(\omega) = |g(\omega)|^2$$

This function, in the case of a finite-wave train, is given by

$$G(\omega) = |g(\omega)|^2 = \frac{1}{\pi^2} \frac{\sin^2[\frac{1}{2}(\omega - \omega_0)\tau_0]}{(\omega - \omega_0)^2} \tag{3.31}$$

We see that the spectral distribution is maximum for $\omega = \omega_0$, and drops to zero for $\omega = \omega_0 \pm 2\pi/\tau_0$. Secondary maxima and minima also occur as shown in the diagram. Most of the energy is contained in the region between the first two minima on either side of the central maximum at ω_0. The "width" $\Delta\omega$ of the frequency distribution is therefore given by

$$\Delta\omega = \frac{2\pi}{\tau_0} \tag{3.32}$$

or

$$\Delta f = \frac{1}{\tau_0} \tag{3.33}$$

Now if we have a sequence of wave trains, each lasting for a time τ_0 but occurring at random times, then the power spectrum is exactly the same as that of the single pulse given above. On the other hand, if the pulses are not all of the same duration, that is, if τ_0 varies from pulse to pulse, then we can think of an average time $\langle\tau_0\rangle$. The precise form of the spectral distribution is different from that of the single pulse, but the width of the corresponding frequency spectrum is approximately $\langle\tau_0\rangle^{-1}$. Suppose we now take the reverse reasoning, namely, that if a spectral source has a line width Δf, then the corresponding coherence time $\langle\tau_0\rangle$ is given by

$$\langle\tau_0\rangle = \frac{1}{\Delta f} \tag{3.34}$$

and the coherence length l_c is

$$l_c = c\langle\tau_0\rangle = \frac{c}{\Delta f} \tag{3.35}$$

We can also express the coherence length in terms of wavelength. Using the fact that $\Delta f/f = |\Delta\lambda|/\lambda$, we obtain

$$l_c = \frac{\lambda^2}{\Delta\lambda} \tag{3.36}$$

where $\Delta\lambda$ is the width of the spectrum line on the wavelength scale.

As a specific example, ordinary spectral sources, such as discharge tubes, have line widths of the order of an angstrom in the visible region of the spectrum, $\sim$ 5000 Å. The corresponding coherence length, from Equation (3.36), is of the order of 5000 wavelengths or about 2 mm. In an interference experiment, the fringe visibility would become vanishingly small for path differences much larger than this distance.

In the case of an interference experiment with white light in which the eye is used to detect the interference fringes, we must consider the spectral sensitivity of the eye. This is maximum at about 5500 Å, and falls to zero at approximately 4000 Å and 7000 Å.

Therefore, as far as the eye is concerned, the spectral "width" of a white-light source is about 1500 Å, and the corresponding coherence length is about 3 or 4 wavelengths. This is about the number of fringes that can be seen on either side of the zero fringe in the Michelson interferometer when using a source of white light such as a tungsten lamp.

At the other extreme, the line width of a laser is of the order of 10^3 cycles per second (c/s). This corresponds to a coherence length of $f/\Delta f \approx 10^{14}/10^3 = 10^{11}$ wavelengths, which is the order of 50 km! Not only can interference effects be produced over very long distances with lasers, but interference fringes can be produced by using two different lasers as sources. However, if two sources are used, the fringe pattern is not steady but fluctuates in a random fashion. A given fringe pattern persists for a time interval of the order of the coherence time of the laser sources. Typically this is about 10^{-3} s.

3.7   Spatial Coherence

In the previous section we treated the problem of coherence between two fields arriving at the same point in space over different optical paths. We now wish to discuss the more general problem of coherence between two fields at different points in space. This will be of importance in studying the coherence of the radiation fields of extended sources.

Suppose, first, that we have a single quasimonochromatic point source S, Figure 3.12. Three receiving points P_1, P_2, P_3 are located as shown. The corresponding fields are E_1, E_2, and E_3, respectively. The two points P_1 and P_3 lie in the same direction from the source. They differ only in their distances from S. Accordingly, the coherence be-

Figure 3.12.   Diagram to illustrate lateral and longitudinal coherence.

tween the fields E_1 and E_3 measures the *longitudinal spatial coherence* of the field. On the other hand, the receiving point P_2 is located at the same distance from S as P_1. In this case, the coherence between E_1 and E_2 measures the *lateral spatial coherence* of the field.

It is evident that the longitudinal coherence will merely depend on how large r_{13} is in comparison with the coherence length of the source, or equivalently, on the value of $t_{13} = r_{13}/c$ compared to the coherence time τ_0. For whatever $E_1(t)$ is, E_3 will vary with t in the same way but at a time t_{13} later. If $t_{13} \ll \tau_0$, there will be a high coherence between E_1 and E_3, whereas if $t_{13} \gg \tau_0$, there will be little or no coherence.

Regarding the lateral coherence, if S is a true point source, then the time dependence of the two fields E_1 and E_2 will be precisely the same. That is, they will be completely mutually coherent. Incoherence between E_1 and E_3 will occur if the source has spatial extension rather than being a point. We shall now proceed to find how the lateral coherence of the field is related to the size of the source.

Since an extended source can be considered to be made up of many independent point sources, it will be convenient to study the case of two point sources before discussing the more general case of finite extended sources. The geometry is shown in Figure 3.13. The two quasi-

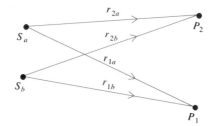

Figure 3.13. Geometry for analyzing the lateral coherence of two sources.

monochromatic point sources S_a and S_b are considered to be identical with one another, except of course, that their phases vary randomly and independently. In other words, they are mutually incoherent.

We have

$$E_1 = E_{1a} + E_{1b}$$
$$E_2 = E_{2a} + E_{2b}$$

where E_{1a} is the contribution to the field at P_1 from the source S_a, and similarly for E_{1b}, and so forth.

The degree of coherence between the two receiving points P_1 and P_2 is then the modulus of the quantity:

$$\gamma_{12}(\tau) = \frac{\langle E_1(t)\, E_2^*(t + \tau)\rangle}{\sqrt{I_1 I_2}}$$

$$= \frac{\langle [E_{1a}(t) + E_{1b}(t)]\,[E_{2a}^*(t + \tau) + E_{2b}^*(t + \tau)]\rangle}{\sqrt{I_1 I_2}} \qquad (3.37)$$

$$= \frac{\langle E_{1a}(t)\, E_{2a}^*(t + \tau)\rangle}{\sqrt{I_1 I_2}} + \frac{\langle E_{1b}(t)\, E_{2b}^*(t + \tau)\rangle}{\sqrt{I_1 I_2}}$$

In the second step we have used the fact that S_a and S_b are mutually incoherent so the cross terms $\langle E_{1a} E_{2b}^*\rangle$ and $\langle E_{1b} E_{2a}^*\rangle$ both vanish.

If it is assumed that the fields are both of the type given by Equation (3.22) in the previous section, then the two time averages in the above equation can be evaluated in exactly the same way that was done in arriving at Equation (3.25). It is necessary, however, to take into account the different times for the optical fields to travel from their respective sources to the receiving points. If this is done, the result can be expressed as follows:

$$\gamma_{12}(\tau) = \tfrac{1}{2}\gamma(\tau_a) + \tfrac{1}{2}\gamma(\tau_b) \qquad (3.38)$$

where

$$\gamma(\tau) = e^{i\omega\tau}\left(1 - \frac{\tau}{\tau_0}\right)$$

$$\tau_a = \frac{r_{1a} - r_{2a}}{c} \qquad \tau_b = \frac{r_{1b} - r_{2b}}{c}$$

The modulus is then approximately given by

$$|\gamma_{12}(\tau)| \approx \left(\frac{1 + \cos[\omega(\tau_b - \tau_a)]}{2}\right)\left(1 - \frac{\tau_a}{\tau_0}\right) \qquad (3.39)$$

In arriving at the above result, it has been assumed that $\tau_a - \tau_b$ is small in comparison with τ_a and with τ_b.

Our result shows that the coherence between the fields E_1 and E_2 depends critically on the value of the quantity $\tau_a - \tau_b$. This is given by

$$\tau_b - \tau_a = \frac{r_{1b} - r_{2b}}{c} - \frac{r_{1a} - r_{2a}}{c}$$

$$= \frac{r_{1b} - r_{1a}}{c} - \frac{r_{2b} - r_{2a}}{c} \qquad (3.40)$$

$$\approx \frac{s}{c}\frac{l}{r}$$

Here s is the distance between the two sources, l is the lateral distance between the two receiving points, and r is the mean distance from the sources to the receiving points. It has been assumed that r is large compared to either s or l.

Suppose we take the point P_1 to be symmetrically located with respect to the two sources. Then a plot of $|\gamma_{12}|$ as a function of the distance to P_2, Figure 3.14, shows that the lateral coherence is similar to

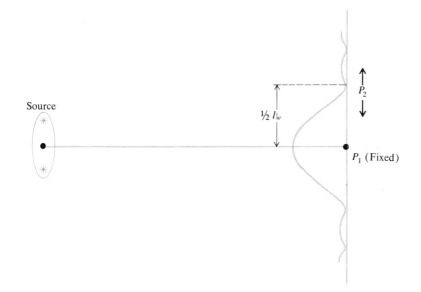

Figure 3.14.   Diagram illustrating the lateral coherence of a broad source.

a system of interference fringes. The coherence is, of course, maximum at the center where P_1 and P_2 are close together. The coherence drops to zero on either side of the central line at a distance l such that $\cos \omega(\tau_a - \tau_b) = -1$, that is

$$\omega(\tau_b - \tau_a) = \frac{\omega s l}{cr} = \pi \qquad (3.41)$$

This gives

$$l = \frac{r\lambda}{2s} \qquad (3.42)$$

Twice this value or

$$\frac{r\lambda}{s} = \frac{\lambda}{\theta_s} = l_w \qquad (3.43)$$

is then approximately the width of the region of high lateral coherence.

We shall call it the *lateral coherence width*, l_w. In the above formula θ_s is the angular separation between the two sources as seen from the receiving position.

Extended Sources. Measurement of Stellar Diameters   In the case of an extended source, the same result as that of Equation (3.43) is obtained for the lateral coherence width except that there is a numerical factor that depends on the shape of the source. If the source is circular, the lateral coherence width is given by

$$l_w = \frac{1.22\lambda}{\theta_s} \tag{3.44}$$

According to the above result, if one were to perform an interference experiment in which a double-slit aperture was used, as in Young's experiment, then the distance between the slits would have to be less than the lateral coherence width in order to obtain distinct interference fringes. As a numerical example, let a pinhole of 1-mm diameter be the source, and let the wavelength be, say 5000 Å. Then at a distance of 1 m, the lateral coherence width, l_w, from Equation (3.43) turns out to be about 0.5 mm. For a 0.1-mm pinhole, it is about 5 mm.

Suppose that one wanted to know the angular diameter of a distant object, such as a star. By using a variable double-slit interference arrangement as shown in Figure 3.15, the lateral coherence width is easily

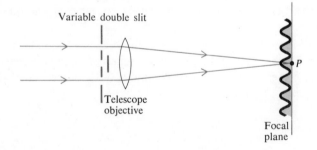

Figure 3.15.   Method for producing interference fringes from a distant source.

found. It is merely the slit separation that results in the disappearance of interference fringes. The angular diameter is then given by Equation (3.44).

Due to their enormous distances, the angular diameters of stars are extremely small, of the order of hundredths of a second of arc, even for the nearby stars. Hence, the lateral coherence width for starlight of the order of several meters.

Michelson was the first to determine stellar diameters by interferometry. He employed mirrors to increase the distance between the slits, Figure 3.16. One of the largest stars measured, Betelguese, was found to have an angular diameter of 0.047 seconds. From the known distance, this corresponds to a linear diameter of about 280 times that of the sun!

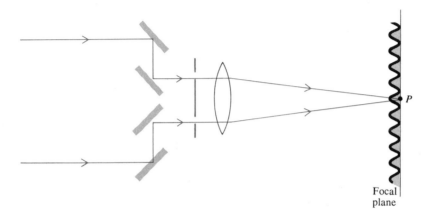

Figure 3.16.   Michelson's stellar interferometer.

3.8   Intensity Interferometry

A method of interferometry based on intensity correlations between two points has been devised by Hanbury-Brown and Twiss. This method, known as *intensity interferometry*, makes it possible to determine much smaller stellar angular diameters than those measureable by Michelsons' method.

The essential features of the Hanbury-Brown–Twiss arrangement are shown in Figure 3.17. M_1 and M_2 are two mirrors that need not

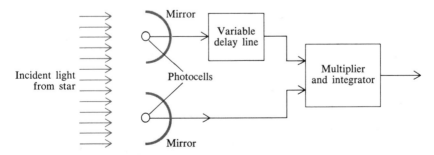

Figure 3.17.   The Hanbury-Brown–Twiss intensity interferometer.

be of high optical quality. (Searchlight mirrors were actually used.) The light is focused onto photocells the outputs of which are proportional to the instantaneous intensities, $|E_1|^2$ and $|E_2|^2$, at the two mirrors. The signals from the photocells are fed to a delay line and an electronic multiplier and integrater M as shown. The output of M is proportional to the average of the product $\langle|E_1|^2 \, |E_2|^2\rangle$. This quantity is known as the *second-order coherence function* of the two fields.

It can be shown that the second-order coherence function exhibits an interference effect similar to the interference effect shown by the ordinary (first-order) function already discussed. In particular, for a distant extended source, a measurement of the second-order coherence between two receiving points P_1 and P_2 yields the lateral coherence width and hence, the angular diameter of the source. The main advantage of the method of intensity interferometry is that high quality optical components and rigid mountings are not necessary. For more information on this subject, the reader should consult the references [10] [15] listed at the end of the book.

3.9   Fourier Transform Spectroscopy

Suppose that a beam of light is divided into two mutually coherent beams, as in the Michelson interferometer, and these beams are reunited after traversing different optical paths, Figure 3.18. If the light

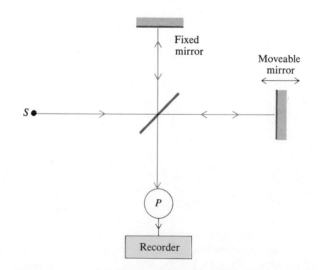

Figure 3.18.   Arrangement for Fourier transform spectroscopy.

is not monochromatic but has a spectral composition given by the function $G(\omega)$, then the intensity at P varies in a manner that depends on the particular spectrum. By recording the intensity as a function of the path difference, the power spectrum $G(\omega)$ can be deduced. This method of obtaining a spectrum is called *Fourier transform spectroscopy*.

For the present application it is convenient to represent the spectral distribution in terms of the wavenumber k, rather than the angular frequency ω. Since ω and k are proportional to one another ($\omega = ck$ in vacuum), then we can just as well use $G(k)$ as $G(\omega)$. Now, referring to Equation (3.3), which gives the intensity at P for monochromatic light, we see that the intensity for nonmonochromatic light will be given by a summation over the complete spectrum, namely,

$$I(x) = \int_0^\infty (1 + \cos kx)\, G(k)dk$$

$$= \int_0^\infty G(k)dk + \int_0^\infty G(k)\, \frac{e^{ikx} + e^{-ikx}}{2}\, dk$$

$$= \tfrac{1}{2}I(0) + \tfrac{1}{2}\int_{-\infty}^\infty G(k)\, e^{ikx}dk$$

or

$$W(x) = 2I(x) - I(0) = \int_{-\infty}^\infty e^{ikx}\, G(k)dk \qquad \textbf{(3.45)}$$

where $I(0)$ is the intensity for zero path difference. Therefore, $W(x)$ and $G(k)$ constitute a Fourier transform pair. Accordingly, we can write

$$G(k) = \frac{1}{2\pi} \int_{-\infty}^\infty W(x)e^{-ikx}dx \qquad \textbf{(3.46)}$$

That is, the power spectrum $G(k)$ is the Fourier transform of the intensity function $W(x) = 2I(x) - I(0)$.

The above technique of spectrum analysis is particularly useful for analyzing the infrared absorption of gases where the spectra are extremely complicated. A second advantage is the efficient utilization of the available light. This makes the Fourier transform method invaluable for the study of very weak sources.

The actual calculation of the Fourier transform of the intensity function is often done by means of high speed electronic computers. Examples of some intensity functions and the corresponding spectra are shown in Figure 3.19.

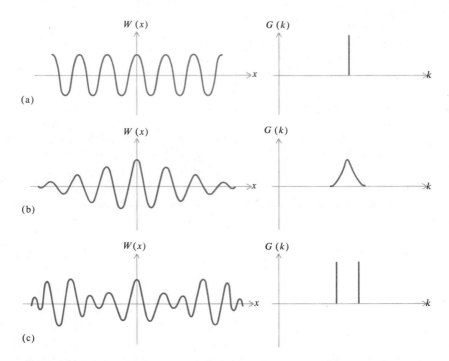

Figure 3.19. Intensity functions and their spectra. (a) A single monochromatic line. (b) A single broad line. (c) Two narrow lines.

3.10 Multiple-Beam Interference

In our study of interference thus far we have been concerned only with interference between two beams. We now proceed to treat the more general problem of multiple-beam interference.

One method of producing a large number of mutually coherent beams, that is, beams having a constant phase difference between successive components, is by multiple reflection between two parallel, partially reflecting plane surfaces, Figure 3.20. These surfaces may be semitransparent mirrors, or merely the two sides of a film or slab of glass, and so forth. The primary beam is partially reflected and partially transmitted at the first surface. The transmitted part is subsequently reflected back and forth between the two surfaces as shown. Let r be the coefficient of reflection and t the coefficient of transmission. Then, from the diagram we see that the amplitudes of the successive internally reflected rays are E_0t, E_0tr, E_0tr^2, $\cdots$, where E_0 is the amplitude of the primary beam. It follows that the amplitudes of the successive transmitted rays are E_0t^2, $E_0t^2r^2$, $E_0t^2r^4$, $\cdots$, as indicated. Now it is easily shown that the geometric path difference between any two suc-

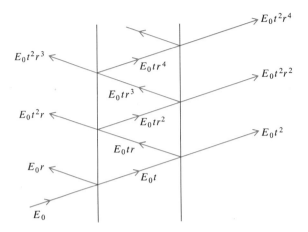

Figure 3.20. Paths of light rays in multiple reflection between two parallel mirrors.

cessive transmitted rays is $2d \cos \theta$ where d is the separation between the reflecting surfaces, and θ is the angle either ray makes with the surface normal, Figure 3.21. The corresponding phase difference δ between two successive rays is then given by

$$\delta = 2kd\cos\theta = \frac{4\pi}{\lambda}d\cos\theta \tag{3.47}$$

Taking this phase difference into account as a factor $e^{i\delta}$ and adding the amplitudes of all of the transmitted rays, we obtain

$$E_T = E_0t^2 + E_0t^2r^2e^{i\delta} + E_0t^2r^4e^{2i\delta} + \cdots = \frac{E_0t^2}{1 - r^2e^{i\delta}} \tag{3.48}$$

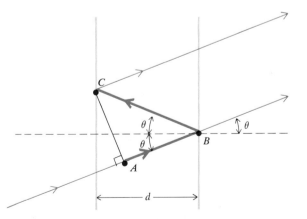

Figure 3.21. Diagram showing the path difference between two successive rays.

The intensity $I_T = |E_T|^2$ of the transmitted light is thus given by

$$I_T = I_0 \frac{|t|^4}{|1 - r^2 e^{i\delta}|^2} \tag{3.49}$$

where $I_0 = |E_0|^2$ is the intensity of the incident beam.

Now a phase change may occur on reflection, hence r is, in general, a complex number. We can express it, accordingly, as

$$r = |r| \, e^{i\delta_r/2} \tag{3.50}$$

where $\delta_r/2$ is the phase change for one reflection. Furthermore, if R denotes the reflectance and T the transmittance of one surface, then in terms of r and t, we have

$$R = |r|^2 \qquad T = |t|^2 \tag{3.51}$$

Equation (3.49) can then be written in the following alternative form

$$I_T = I_0 \frac{T^2}{(1 - R)^2} \frac{1}{1 + \dfrac{4R}{(1 - R)^2} \sin^2 (\Delta/2)} \tag{3.52}$$

Here

$$\Delta = \delta + \delta_r \tag{3.53}$$

is the total phase difference between two successive transmitted beams.

The intensity thus varies with Δ according to the function:

$$\frac{1}{1 + \dfrac{4R}{(1 - R)^2} \sin^2 (\Delta/2)} = \frac{1}{1 + F \sin^2 (\Delta/2)} \tag{3.54}$$

known as the *Airy function*. The quantity F is

$$F = \frac{4R}{(1 - R)^2} \tag{3.55}$$

It is a measure of the sharpness of the interference fringes.

The general behavior of the Airy function is shown in Figure 3.22. Curves are drawn for various values of the reflectance R. These curves show the intensity distribution of the fringes in multiple beam interference.

If the argument of the sine is an integral multiple of π, that is, if $\Delta/2 = n\pi$, then the Airy function $(1 + F \sin^2 \Delta/2)^{-1}$ is equal to unity for all values of R. If R is very small, the interference fringes are broad and indistinct, whereas if R is close to 1, the fringes are very sharp.

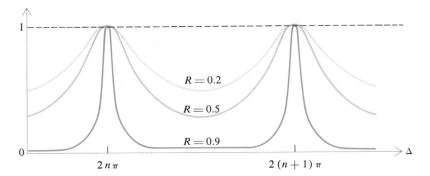

Figure 3.22. Graphs of the Airy function giving the intensity distribution of fringes in multiple-beam interference.

The maximum and minimum values of I_T are

$$I_{T(max)} = I_0 \frac{T^2}{(1 - R)^2} \tag{3.56}$$

$$I_{T(min)} = I_0 \frac{T^2}{(1 + R)^2} \tag{3.57}$$

If A is the fraction of incident energy that is absorbed at each reflection, then by conservation of energy, we must have

$$A + R + T = 1 \tag{3.58}$$

If there were no absorption, then we would have $R + T = 1$. According to Equation (3.56), this would give $I_{T(max)} = I_0$. This means that the peak intensity of the transmitted fringes would be equal to the intensity of the incident light, even if R were very close to 1. In actual practice A is never zero, and the maximum intensity of the transmitted fringes is always somewhat less than I_0.

3.11 The Fabry-Perot Interferometer

This instrument, devised by C. Fabry and A. Perot in 1899, employs multiple-beam interference. It is used to measure wavelengths with high precision and to study the fine structure of spectrum lines. A Fabry-Perot interferometer consists essentially of two optically flat, partially reflecting plates of glass or quartz with their reflecting surfaces held accurately parallel. If the plate spacing can be mechanically varied, the device is called an *interferometer,* whereas if the plates are held fixed by spacers, it is called an *etalon.* The surfaces must be extremely flat and parallel in order to obtain the maximum fringe sharpness. An ordinary optical flat of 1/4-wavelength flatness is not good enough for precise Fabry-Perot applications. Rather, a flatness of the order of 1/20 to 1/100 wavelength is required.

In use, the interferometer is usually mounted between a collimating lens and a focusing lens as shown in Figure 3.23(a). If a broad source of light is used, interference fringes in the form of concentric circular rings appear in the focal plane of the focusing lens, Figure 3.24. These rings may be observed visually or photographed. Another way of using the interferometer, called the *scanning method,* employs a point source or a pinhole. The source is placed so that only one spot, the center of the ring system, appears at the exit focal plane, Figure 3.23(b). Scanning may be accomplished by changing the spacing either mechanically or optically, say by changing the air pressure. The intensity at the ring center is usually recorded photoelectrically. This gives a graph of the interference pattern. The graphical record is essentially a plot of the Airy function $(1 + F \sin^2 \Delta/2)^{-1}$ or rather, a sum of such functions for each component frequency. A typical record is shown in Figure 3.23(b).

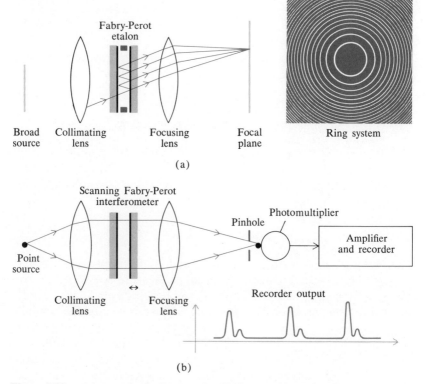

Figure 3.23. Arrangements for (a) the Fabry-Perot etalon; (b) the scanning interferometer.

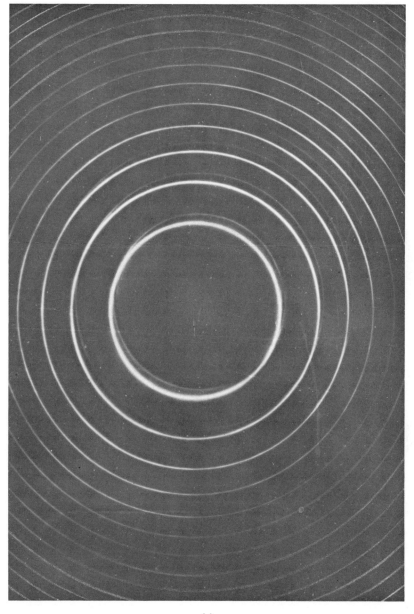

(a)

Figure 3.24. Fabry-Perot interference fringes. (a) Monochromatic source (a laser). (b) (following page) Non-monochromatic source.

Figure 3.24 (b)

The *free spectral range* is the difference in frequency (or wavelength) corresponding to two adjacent orders of interference. From the form of the Airy function, we see that this is given by setting

$$\Delta_{n+1} - \Delta_n = 2\pi$$

Thus, from Equations (3.47) and (3.53), the free spectral range is given by

$$\omega_{n+1} - \omega_n = \frac{\pi c}{d \cos \theta} \tag{3.59}$$

or

$$f_{n+1} - f_n = \frac{c}{2d \cos \theta} \tag{3.60}$$

For small θ, the free spectral range, in frequency units, is approximately $c/2d$.

3.12 Resolving Power of Fabry-Perot Instruments

Suppose a spectrum consisting of two closely-spaced frequencies, ω and ω', is to be analyzed with a Fabry-Perot interferometer. The intensity distribution in the fringe pattern will be a combination of two fringe systems as shown in Figure 3.25. Here the two component lines

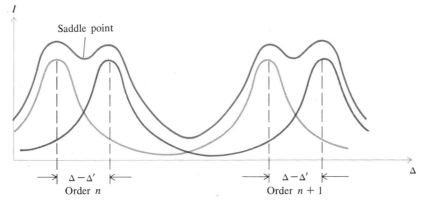

Figure 3.25. Graph of intensity distribution for two monochromatic lines in Fabry-Perot interferometry.

are assumed to be of equal intensity. The fringe pattern is then given by the sum of two Airy functions, namely,

$$\frac{I}{I_0} = \left[1 + \frac{4R}{(1-R)^2} \sin^2 (\Delta/2) \right]^{-1}$$

$$+ \left[1 + \frac{4R}{(1-R)^2} \sin^2 (\Delta'/2) \right]^{-1} \tag{3.61}$$

where
$$\Delta \approx \delta_r + 2kd = \delta_r + \frac{2\omega d}{c}$$

and similarly

$$\Delta' \approx \delta_r + 2k'd = \delta_r + \frac{2\omega'd}{c}$$

We assume that θ is small so that $\cos\theta \approx 1$.

Now in order that the two lines be resolved, there must be a dip in the intensity distribution. A generally accepted convention for resolution of two lines is the Rayleigh criterion. According to this criterion, two equal lines are considered to be resolved if the intensity at the saddle point is not greater than $8/\pi^2$ times the intensity at the two maxima. Thus, at the midpoint between two lines that are barely resolved

$$\frac{I}{I_0} = 2\left[1 + \frac{4R}{(1-R)^2}\sin^2\left(\frac{\Delta-\Delta'}{2}\right)\right]^{-1} = \frac{8}{\pi^2} \qquad \text{(3.62)}$$

Solving the above equation for $\Delta - \Delta'$, we find approximately

$$\Delta - \Delta' \approx 2.4\left(\frac{1-R}{\sqrt{R}}\right) \qquad \text{(3.63)}$$

Here we have assumed that the difference $\Delta' - \Delta$ is small enough so that the sine term can be replaced by its argument. Finally, in terms of ω and ω', we obtain

$$\omega - \omega' = \frac{1.2c}{d}\left(\frac{1-R}{\sqrt{R}}\right) \qquad \text{(3.64)}$$

for the minimum angular frequency difference that can be resolved with a plate separation d and reflectance R.

The *resolving power,* abbreviated R.P., of any spectroscopic instrument is defined at the reciprocal of the minimum fractional resolution. For the Fabry-Perot interferometer we then have

$$\text{R.P.} = \frac{\omega}{\omega - \omega'} = \frac{\omega d}{1.2c}\left(\frac{\sqrt{R}}{1-R}\right) \qquad \text{(3.65)}$$

This is seen to depend critically on the reflectance, as expected, because the fringes become very sharp as R approaches unity. A good Fabry-Perot instrument may easily have a resolving power of 1 million, which is 10 to 100 times greater than the resolving power of prism or small grating spectroscopes. For a more complete discussion of Fabry-Perot interferometry, and other instruments used for interference spectroscopy, see references [7] and [40] listed at the end of the book.

3.13   Theory of Multilayer Films

Multilayer films are widely used in science and industry for control of light. Optical surfaces having virtually any desired reflectance and transmittance characteristics may be produced by means of thin film coatings. These films are usually deposited on glass or metal substrates by high-vacuum evaporation. The well-known use of antireflecting coatings for camera lenses and other optical instruments is only one of the many practical applications of thin films. Other applications include such things as heat reflecting and heat transmitting mirrors ("hot" and "cold" mirrors), one-way mirrors, optical filters, and so forth.

First consider the case of a single layer of dielectric of index n_1 and thickness l between two infinite media of indices n_0 and n, Figure 3.26.

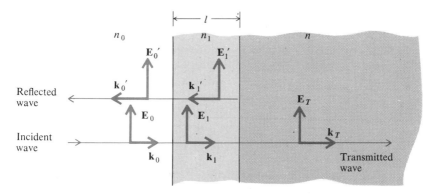

Figure 3.26.   Wave vectors and their associated electric fields for the case of normal incidence on a single dielectric layer.

For simplicity we shall develop the theory for normally incident light. The modifications for the general case of oblique incidence are easily made. The amplitude of the electric vector of the incident beam is E_0. That of the reflected beam is E_0', and that of the transmitted beam is E_T. The electric-field amplitudes in the film are E_1 and E_1' for the forward and backward traveling waves, respectively, as indicated in the figure.

The boundary conditions require that the electric and magnetic fields be continuous at each interface. These conditions are expressed as follows:

	First Interface	*Second Interface*	
Electric:	$E_0 + E_0' = E_1 + E_1'$	$E_1 e^{ikl} + E_1' e^{-ikl} = E_T$	**(3.66)**
Magnetic:	$H_0 - H_0' = H_1 - H_1'$	$H_1 e^{ikl} - H_1'^{-ikl} = H_T$	**(3.67)**
or	$n_0 E_0 - n_0 E_0' = n_1 E_1 - n_1 E_1'$	$n_1 E_1 e^{ikl} - n_1 E_1' e^{-ikl} = n E_T$	**(3.68)**

The relations for the magnetic fields follow from the theory developed in Section 2.7. The phase factors e^{ikl} and e^{-ikl} result from the fact that the wave travels through a distance l from one interface to the other.

If we eliminate the amplitudes E_1 and E_1' we obtain

$$1 + \frac{E_0'}{E_0} = (\cos kl - i\frac{n}{n_1} \sin kl)\frac{E_T}{E_0}$$

$$n_0 - n_0\frac{E_0'}{E_0} = (-in_1\sin kl + n \cos kl)\frac{E_T}{E_0}$$

(3.69)

or, in matrix form,

$$\begin{bmatrix} 1 \\ n_0 \end{bmatrix} + \begin{bmatrix} 1 \\ -n_0 \end{bmatrix}\frac{E'}{E_0} = \begin{bmatrix} \cos kl & \dfrac{-i}{n_1} \sin kl \\ -in_1 \sin kl & \cos kl \end{bmatrix}\begin{bmatrix} 1 \\ n \end{bmatrix}\frac{E_T}{E_0}$$

which can be abbreviated as

$$\begin{bmatrix} 1 \\ n_0 \end{bmatrix} + \begin{bmatrix} 1 \\ -n_0 \end{bmatrix}r = M\begin{bmatrix} 1 \\ n \end{bmatrix}t$$

(3.70)

We have here introduced the reflection coefficient

$$r = \frac{E_0'}{E_0}$$

(3.71)

and the transmission coefficient

$$t = \frac{E_T}{E_0}$$

(3.72)

The matrix

$$M = \begin{bmatrix} \cos kl & -\dfrac{i}{n_1} \sin kl \\ -in_1 \sin kl & \cos kl \end{bmatrix}$$

(3.73)

is called the *transfer matrix* of the film.

Now suppose that we have N layers numbered $1,2,3,\cdots N$ having indices of refraction $n_1,n_2,n_3,\cdots n_N$ and thicknesses $l_1,l_2,l_3,\cdots l_N$, respectively. In the same way that we derived Equation (3.70), we can show that the reflection and transmission coefficients of the multilayer film are related by a similar matrix equation:

$$\begin{bmatrix} 1 \\ n_0 \end{bmatrix} + \begin{bmatrix} 1 \\ -n_0 \end{bmatrix}r = M_1M_2M_3\cdots M_N\begin{bmatrix} 1 \\ n \end{bmatrix}t = M\begin{bmatrix} 1 \\ n \end{bmatrix}t$$

(3.74)

where the transfer matrices of the various layers are denoted by M_1,

$M_2, M_3, \cdots M_N$. Each transfer matrix is of the form given by Equation (3.73) with appropriate values of n, l, and k. The overall transfer matrix M is the product of the individual transfer matrices. Let the elements of M be A, B, C, and D, that is

$$M_1 M_2 M_3 \cdots M_N = M = \begin{bmatrix} A & B \\ C & D \end{bmatrix} \tag{3.75}$$

We can then solve Equation (3.74) for r and t in terms of these elements. The result is

$$r = \frac{A n_0 + B n n_0 - C - D n}{A n_0 + B n n_0 + C + D n} \tag{3.76}$$

$$t = \frac{2 n_0}{A n_0 + B n n_0 + C + D n} \tag{3.77}$$

The reflectance R and the transmittance T are then given by $R = |r|^2$ and $T = |t|^2$, respectively.

Antireflecting Films   The transfer matrix for a single film of index n_1 and thickness l is given by Equation (3.73). Suppose this film is placed on a glass substrate of index n. The coefficient of reflection of the combination, in air, is then given by Equation (3.76) with $n_0 = 1$. The result is

$$r = \frac{n_1(1 - n)\cos kl - i(n - n_1^2)\sin kl}{n_1(1 + n)\cos kl - i(n + n_1^2)\sin kl} \tag{3.78}$$

If the optical thickness of the film is ¼ wavelength, then $kl = \pi/2$. The reflectance for a quarter-wave film is therefore

$$R = |r|^2 = \frac{(n - n_1^2)^2}{(n + n_1^2)^2} \tag{3.79}$$

In particular, the reflectance is zero if

$$n_1 = \sqrt{n} \tag{3.80}$$

Magnesium fluoride, whose index is 1.35, is commonly used for coating lenses. Although this does not exactly satisfy the above requirement for ordinary glass, $n \approx 1.5$, the reflectance of glass coated with a quarter-wave layer of magnesium fluoride is reduced to about 1 percent, which is one-fourth that of uncoated glass. This can result in a considerable saving of light in the case of optical instruments having many elements, such as high-quality camera lenses that may have as many as five or six components, that is, ten or twelve reflecting surfaces.

By using two layers, one of high index and one of low, it is possible to obtain zero reflectance (at one wavelength) with available coating materials. More layers obviously afford greater latitude and more extensive possibilities. Thus with three suitably chosen layers the reflectance can be reduced to zero for 2 wavelengths and can be made to average less than ¼ percent over almost the entire visible spectrum. Some curves are shown in Figure 3.27.

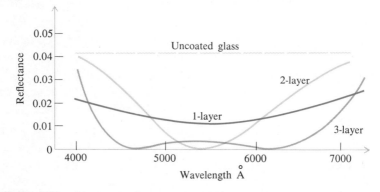

Figure 3.27. Curves of reflectance versus wavelength of antireflecting films.

High-Reflectance Films   In order to obtain a high value of reflectance in a multilayer film, a stack of alternate layers of high index, n_H, and low index, n_L, materials is used, the thickness of each layer being ¼ wavelength, Figure 3.28. In this case the transfer matrices are all of the same form, and the product of two adjacent ones is

$$\begin{bmatrix} 0 & \dfrac{-i}{n_H} \\ -in_H & 0 \end{bmatrix} \begin{bmatrix} 0 & \dfrac{-i}{n_L} \\ -in_L & 0 \end{bmatrix} = \begin{bmatrix} \dfrac{-n_H}{n_L} & 0 \\ 0 & \dfrac{-n_L}{n_H} \end{bmatrix} \tag{3.81}$$

If the stack consists of $2N$ layers, then the transfer matrix of the complete multilayer film is

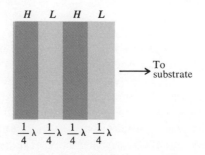

Figure 3.28. Multilayer stack for producing high reflectance. The stack consists of alternate quarter-wave layers of high and low index material.

$$M = \begin{bmatrix} \dfrac{-n_H}{n_L} & 0 \\ 0 & \dfrac{-n_L}{n_H} \end{bmatrix}^N = \begin{bmatrix} \left(\dfrac{-n_H}{n_L}\right)^N & 0 \\ 0 & \left(\dfrac{-n_L}{n_H}\right)^N \end{bmatrix} \qquad (3.82)$$

Assuming, for simplicity, that n_0 and n are both unity, the reflectance of a multilayer stack is given by Equation (3.76) as follows:

$$R = |r|^2 = \left[\frac{(-n_H/n_L)^N - (-n_L/n_H)^N}{(-n_H/n_L)^N + (-n_L/n_H)^N}\right]^2 = \left[\frac{(n_H/n_L)^{2N} - 1}{(n_H/n_L)^{2N} + 1}\right]^2 \qquad (3.83)$$

The reflectance thus approaches unity for large N. For instance, an eight-layer stack ($N = 4$) of zinc sulfide ($n_H = 2.3$) and magnesium fluoride ($n_L = 1.35$) gives a reflectance of about 0.97, which is higher than the reflectance of pure silver in the visible region of the spectrum. A thirty-layer stack results in a reflectance of better than 0.999. This maximum reflectance, of course, occurs only at one wavelength, but it is possible to broaden the region of high reflectance by combinations of different thicknesses. Figure 3.29 shows some approximate curves of reflectance as a function of wavelength for multilayer films such as are used in laser work.

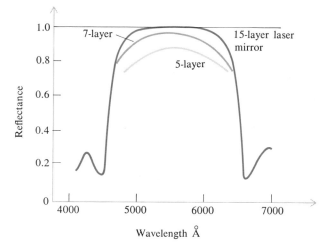

Figure 3.29. Reflectance curves for some multilayer high reflectance films.

Fabry-Perot Interference Filter   This type of filter consists of a layer of dielectric having a thickness of 1/2 wavelength (for some wavelength λ_0) and bounded on both sides by partially reflecting surfaces.

In effect, this is a Fabry-Perot etalon with a very small spacing. The result is a filter that has a transmission curve given by the Airy function, Equation (3.54), where the peak occurs at the wavelength λ_0. Higher order peaks also occur for wavelengths $\frac{1}{2}\lambda_0$, $\frac{1}{3}\lambda_0$, $\frac{1}{4}\lambda_0$, $\cdots$, and so forth. The spectral width of the transmission band depends on the reflectance of the bounding surfaces. Fabry-Perot filters were first made with silver films to produce the necessary high reflectance, but now they are usually made entirely of multilayer dielectric films. The latter are superior to the metal films because of their higher reflectance and lower absorption. Figure 3.30 shows a typical design of a multilayer Fabry-Perot interference filter together with a transmission curve.

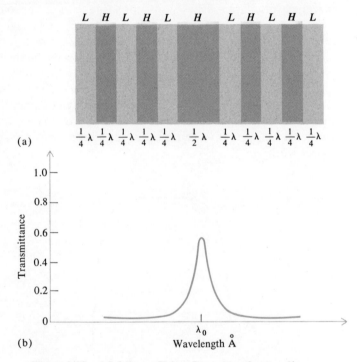

Figure 3.30.   Multilayer Fabry-Perot interference filter.

PROBLEMS

3.1.   Calculate the form of the interference term in the case of three mutually coherent plane waves.

3.2.   Prove that the interference term is zero for two mutually orthogonal, elliptically polarized beams of light.

3.3. Calculate and plot the interference pattern that would be obtained if three slits instead of two were used in Young's experiment. (Assume equal spacing of the slits.)

3.4. A Michelson interferometer is used to measure the index of refraction of a gas. The gas flows into an evacuated glass cell of length l placed in one arm of the interferometer. The wavelength is λ.

  (a) If N fringes are counted as the gas flows in from vacuum to atmospheric pressure, what is the index of refraction n in terms of N, λ, and l?

  (b) How many fringes would be counted if the gas were carbon dioxide ($n = 1.00045$) for a 10-cm cell length using sodium light ($\lambda = 5890$ Å)?

3.5. In an interference experiment of the Young type, the distance between the slits is $1/2$ mm. The wavelength of the light is 6000 Å. If it is desired to have a fringe spacing of 1 mm at the screen, what is the corresponding screen distance?

3.6. In the experiment of Problem 3.5, a thin plate of glass ($n = 1.5$) of thickness 0.1 mm is placed over one of the slits. What is the resulting lateral fringe displacement at the screen?

3.7. In a Lloyd's single-mirror interference experiment, the angle of incidence is 89 degrees. What is the fringe spacing for light of wavelength 6000 Å?

3.8. A Fresnel biprism of apex angle $\alpha = 179$ degrees is made of glass of index n. The wavelength is λ. The distance from the source to the biprism is D and the distance from the biprism to the observing plane is D'. Find the fringe spacing. Use appropriate approximations.

3.9. A linearly polarized, monochromatic plane wave is incident at 45 degrees on a plane mirror. Calculate the total intensity I at a point P located a distance y from the mirror. Show that I varies periodically with y for TE polarization, but is constant for TM polarization.

3.10. What is the fringe visibility v if ordinary unpolarized light is used in the arrangement of Problem 3.9?

3.11. A monochromator is used to obtain approximately monochromatic light from a white source. The linear dispersion of the monochromator is 20 Å/mm and an exit slit of 0.2 mm is used. What is the coherence time and coherence length of the light from the monochromator when the mean wavelength is 5000 Å?

3.12. What is the line width in angstroms and in hertz of the light from a laser whose coherence length is 10 km? The mean wavelength is 6328 Å.

3.13. What is the lateral coherence width of sunlight? (Take the effective wavelength as 6000 Å.) The apparent angular diameter of the sun is ½ degree.

3.14. A pinhole of 1-mm diameter is used as a source for a double slit interference experiment using a sodium lamp. ($\lambda = 5890$ Å). If the distance from the pinhole to the slits is 2 m, what is the maximum slit spacing such that interference fringes are just observable?

3.15. Calculate the power spectrum of a damped wave train:

$$f(t) = A \exp(at - i\omega_o t) \qquad t \geqslant 0$$
$$= 0 \qquad t < 0$$

3.16. Show that the degree of coherence of a field is given by the normalized Fourier transform of the power spectrum, namely

$$|\gamma_{12}(\tau)| = \frac{\left| \int_{-\infty}^{\infty} G(\omega) e^{-i\omega\tau} d\omega \right|}{\left| \int_{-\infty}^{\infty} G(\omega) d\omega \right|}$$

3.17. Using the results of Problems 13.15 and 13.16, find the degree of coherence of the damped wave of Problem 13.14.

3.18. Show that the power spectrum of a Gaussian pulse:

$$f(t) = A \exp(-at^2 - i\omega_o t)$$

is also a Gaussian function centered at the frequency ω_o.

3.19. A Fabry-Perot interferometer has a plate spacing d and plate reflectance R. Find the minimum frequency difference, $f - f'$ and the corresponding minimum wavelength difference, $\lambda - \lambda'$, between two barely resolvable spectrum lines.

3.20. The reflectance of the plates of a Fabry-Perot interferometer is 0.9. (a) Find the plate separation d required to resolve the $H\alpha$ doublet: $\lambda = 6563$ Å, $\lambda - \lambda' = 0.14$ Å. (b) What is the resulting free spectral range in angstroms?

3.21. A collimated beam of light of wavelength λ falls at normal incidence on a plate of glass of index n and thickness d. Give a formula for the fraction of the incident intensity that is transmitted. Find the numerical value of the transmission for $\lambda_{vac} = 5000$ Å exactly, and $\lambda_{vac} = 5000.0416$ Å, $n = 1.5, d = 1$ cm.

3.22. Develop an explicit expression for the reflectance in air ($n_0 = 1$) of a thin double-layer film deposited on a glass plate of index n. Let n_1 and n_2 denote the indices of the layers, and l_1 and l_2 be their respective thicknesses.

3.23. A "solid" Fabry-Perot interferometer consists merely of a 2-cm slab of high-index material ($n = 4.5$). Calculate (a) the fringe contrast and (b) the resolving power. (The faces of the slab are uncoated.) Fringe contrast $= I_{max}/I_{min}$.

3.24. Find the peak reflectance of a high-reflecting stack consisting of (a) 4, and (b) 16 layers of high-low index material when $n_L = 1.4$ and $n_H = 2.8$.

3.25. A Fabry-Perot interferometer is to be used to resolve the mode structure of a He-Ne laser operating at 6328 Å. The frequency separation between the modes is 150 megahertz (MHz). What plate spacing is required if (a) $R = 0.9$, (b) $R = 0.999$?

CHAPTER 4
Diffraction

4.1 General Description of Diffraction

If an opaque object is placed between a point source of light and a white screen, it is found that the shadow that is cast by the object departs from the perfect sharpness predicted by geometrical optics. Close examination of the shadow edge reveals that some light goes over into the dark zone of the geometrical shadow and that dark fringes appear in the illuminated zone. This "smearing" of the shadow edge is closely related to another phenomenon, namely, the spreading of light after passing through a very small aperture, such as a pinhole or a narrow slit, as in Young's experiment. The collective name given to these departures from geometrical optics is *diffraction*.

The essential features of diffraction phenomena can be explained qualitatively by Huygens' principle. This principle in its original form states that the propagation of a light wave can be predicted by assuming that each point of the wave front acts as the source of a secondary wave that spreads out in all directions. The envelope of all the secondary waves is the new wave front.

We shall not attempt to treat diffraction by a direct application of Huygens' principle. We want a more quantitative approach. Our strategy will be to cast Huygens' principle into a precise mathematical form known as the *Fresnel-Kirchhoff formula*. This formula will then be applied to various specific cases of diffraction of light by obstacles and apertures.

4.2 Fundamental Theory

Let us recall Green's theorem that states that if U and V are any two scalar-point functions that satisfy the usual conditions of continuity and integrability, then the following equality holds:

$$\int \int (V \operatorname{grad}_n U - U \operatorname{grad}_n V)d\mathscr{A} = \int \int \int (V \nabla^2 U - U \nabla^2 V)d\mathscr{V} \quad (4.1)$$

The left-hand integral extends over any closed surface $\mathscr{A}$, and the right-hand integral includes the volume $\mathscr{V}$ within that surface. By "grad_n" is meant the normal component of the gradient at the surface of integration.

In particular, if both U and V are wave functions, that is, if they satisfy the regular wave equations

$$\nabla^2 U = \frac{1}{v^2} \frac{\partial^2 U}{\partial t^2} \qquad \nabla^2 V = \frac{1}{v^2} \frac{\partial^2 V}{\partial t^2}$$

and if they both have a harmonic time dependence of the form $e^{\pm i\omega t}$, then it is straightforward to show that the volume integral in Green's theorem is identically zero. The theorem then reduces to

$$\iint (V \, \text{grad}_n \, U - U \, \text{grad}_n \, V) \, d\mathscr{A} = 0 \qquad (4.2)$$

Now suppose that we take V to be the wave function

$$V = V_0 \frac{e^{i(kr + \omega t)}}{r} \qquad (4.3)$$

This particular function represents spherical waves converging to the point P $(r = 0)$. We let the volume enclosed by the surface of integration include the point P. Since V becomes infinite at P, we must exclude that point from the integration. This is accomplished by the standard method of subtracting an integral over a small sphere of radius ρ centered at P, as indicated in Figure 4.1. Over this small sphere, $r = \rho$ and $\text{grad}_n = -\partial/\partial r$. Hence we can write

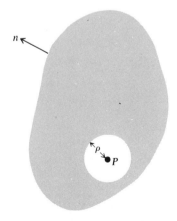

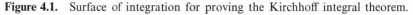

Figure 4.1. Surface of integration for proving the Kirchhoff integral theorem.

$$\int \int \left(\frac{e^{ikr}}{r} \, \text{grad}_n \, U - U \, \text{grad}_n \, \frac{e^{ikr}}{r} \right) d\mathscr{A}$$

$$- \int \int \left(\frac{e^{ikr}}{r} \frac{\partial U}{\partial r} - U \frac{\partial}{\partial r} \frac{e^{ikr}}{r} \right)_{r = \rho} \rho^2 d\Omega = 0 \qquad (4.4)$$

where $d\Omega$ is the element of solid angle on the sphere centered at P, and $\rho^2 d\Omega$ is the corresponding element of area. The common factor $V_0 e^{i\omega t}$ has been cancelled out.

We now let ρ shrink to zero. Then, in the limit as ρ approaches zero, the integrand of the second integral approaches the value that U has at the point P, namely U_p. This is easily verified by performing the indicated operations. Consequently, the second integral itself approaches the value

$$\int \int U_p d\Omega = 4\pi U_p \qquad (4.5)$$

Equation (4.4) then becomes, upon rearranging terms,

$$U_p = -\frac{1}{4\pi} \int \int \left(U \, \text{grad}_n \, \frac{e^{ikr}}{r} - \frac{e^{ikr}}{r} \, \text{grad}_n \, U \right) d\mathscr{A} \qquad (4.6)$$

This equation is known as the *Kirchhoff integral theorem*. It relates the value of any scalar wave function at any point P *inside* an arbitrary closed surface, to the value of the wave function *at* the surface.

In the application of Kirchhoff's theorem to diffraction, the wave function U is known as the "optical disturbance." Being a scalar quantity, it cannot accurately represent an electromagnetic field. However, in this so-called "scalar approximation," the square of the absolute value of U may be regarded as a measure of the light intensity at a given point.

The more rigorous theory of diffraction, which takes into account the vectorial nature of light, is beyond the scope of this book. Owing to the mathematical complexity of the rigorous theory, complete calculations have been carried out for only a relatively few simple cases [5].

The Fresnel-Kirchhoff Formula   We now proceed to apply the Kirchhoff integral theorem to the general problem of diffraction of light. The diffraction is produced by an aperture of arbitrary shape in an otherwise opaque partition. This partition separates a light source from a receiving point, Figure 4.2.

Our task is to determine the optical disturbance reaching the receiving point P from the source S. In applying the Kirchhoff integral, we choose a surface of integration such that it encloses the receiving point, and includes, as a part of it, the aperture opening as indicated in the figure.

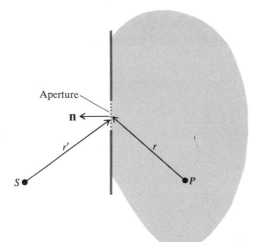

Figure 4.2. Geometry for the Fresnel-Kirchhoff formula.

Two basic simplifying assumptions are introduced:
(1) The wave function U and its gradient contribute negligible amounts to the integral except at the aperture opening itself.
(2) The values of U and grad U at the aperture are the same as they would be in the absence of the partition.

Although the validity of these assumptions is open to considerable debate, the results are generally in good agreement with experimental observations.

If r' denotes the position of a point on the aperture, relative to the source S, then the wave function at the aperture is given by the expression

$$U = U_{\mathrm{o}} \frac{e^{i(kr' - \omega t)}}{r'} \tag{4.7}$$

which represents spherical monochromatic waves traveling outward from S. The Kirchhoff integral theorem then yields

$$U_{\mathrm{p}} = \frac{U_{\mathrm{o}} e^{-i\omega t}}{4\pi} \int\int \left(\frac{e^{ikr}}{r} \operatorname{grad}_{\mathbf{n}} \frac{e^{ikr'}}{r'} - \frac{e^{ikr'}}{r'} \operatorname{grad}_{\mathbf{n}} \frac{e^{ikr}}{r} \right) d\mathscr{A} \tag{4.8}$$

where the integration extends only over the aperture opening.
The operations indicated in the integrand are carried out as follows:

$$\operatorname{grad}_{\mathbf{n}} \frac{e^{ikr}}{r} = \cos(\mathbf{n},\mathbf{r}) \frac{\partial}{\partial r} \frac{e^{ikr}}{r} = \left(\frac{ike^{ikr}}{r} - \frac{e^{ikr}}{r^2} \right) \cos(\mathbf{n},\mathbf{r}) \tag{4.9}$$

$$\text{grad}_n \frac{e^{ikr'}}{r'} = \cos(\mathbf{n},\mathbf{r}') \frac{\partial}{\partial r'} \frac{e^{ikr'}}{r'} = \left(\frac{ike^{ikr'}}{r'} - \frac{e^{ikr'}}{r'^2} \right) \cos(\mathbf{n},\mathbf{r}') \quad \text{(4.10)}$$

where $(\mathbf{n},\mathbf{r}')$ and $(\mathbf{n},\mathbf{r}')$ denote the angles between the vectors and the normal to the surface of integration. Thus, neglecting small quantities,

$$U_p = - \frac{ikU_o e^{-i\omega t}}{4\pi} \int\int \frac{e^{ik(r+r')}}{rr'} [\cos(\mathbf{n},\mathbf{r}) - \cos(\mathbf{n},\mathbf{r}')] \, d\mathscr{A} \quad \text{(4.11)}$$

This equation is known as the *Kirchhoff integral formula*. It is, in effect, a mathematical statement of Huygens' principle. This is most easily seen by applying the formula to a specific case, namely that of a circular aperture with the source symmetrically located as shown in Figure 4.3. The surface of integration is taken to be a spherical cap

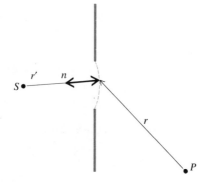

Figure 4.3. Diagram to show how Huygens' principle follows from the Kirchhoff integral formula.

bounded by the aperture opening. In this case r' is constant and $\cos(\mathbf{n},\mathbf{r}') = -1$. The Fresnel-Kirchhoff formula then reduces to

$$U_p = - \frac{ik}{4\pi} \int\int \frac{U_\mathscr{A} e^{i(kr-\omega t)}}{r} [\cos(\mathbf{n},\mathbf{r}) + 1] \, d\mathscr{A} \quad \text{(4.12)}$$

where

$$U_\mathscr{A} = \frac{U_o e^{ikr'}}{r'}$$

Equation (4.12) can be given the following simple interpretation: $U_\mathscr{A}$ is the complex amplitude of the incident primary wave at the aperture. From this primary wave, each element $d\mathscr{A}$ of the aperture gives rise to a secondary spherical wave

$$\frac{U_\mathscr{A} e^{i(kr-\omega t)}}{r} \, d\mathscr{A}$$

The total optical disturbance at the receiving point P is obtained by summing the secondary waves from each element. However, in the summation it is necessary to take into account the factor $\cos(\mathbf{n,r})$ − $\cos(\mathbf{n,r'})$ known as the *obliquity factor*. In the case under discussion, the obliquity factor is $\cos(\mathbf{n,r})$ + 1. In the forward direction $\cos(\mathbf{n,r})$ = 1, and the obliquity factor is then equal to 2, its maximum value. On the other hand, in the backward direction $\cos(\mathbf{n,r})$ = −1, so the obliquity factor is zero. This explains why there is no backward-progressing wave created by the original-wave front. Huygens' principle, as originally proposed, did not include the obliquity factor and thus could not account for the absence of a backward wave. The presence of the factor $-i$ means that the diffracted waves are shifted in phase by 90 degrees with respect to the primary incident wave. This feature was also lacking in the original form of Huygens' principle.

Complementary Apertures. Babinet's Principle   Consider a diffracting aperture $\mathscr{A}$ that produces a certain optical disturbance U_p at a given observing point P. Suppose, now, that the aperture is divided into two portions $\mathscr{A}_1$ and $\mathscr{A}_2$ such that $\mathscr{A} = \mathscr{A}_1 + \mathscr{A}_2$. The two apertures $\mathscr{A}_1$ and $\mathscr{A}_2$ are then said to be *complementary*. An example is shown in Figure 4.4.

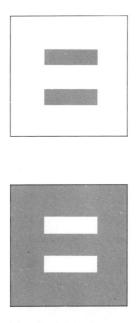

Figure 4.4.   Complementary apertures.

From the form of the Fresnel-Kirchhoff formula, it is clear that

$$U_\mathrm{p} = U_\mathrm{1p} + U_\mathrm{2p} \qquad (4.13)$$

where U_1p is the optical disturbance at P produced by aperture $\mathscr{A}_1$ alone, and U_2p is the optical disturbance produced by aperture $\mathscr{A}_2$ alone. The above equation is one form of a theorem known as *Babinet's principle*.

Babinet's principle is useful in certain special cases. For instance, if $U_\mathrm{p} = 0$, then $U_\mathrm{1p} = -U_\mathrm{2p}$. The complementary apertures, in this case, yield identical optical disturbances, except that they differ in phase by 180 degrees. The intensity at P, being equal to the absolute square of the optical disturbance, is therefore the same for the two apertures.

4.3   Fraunhofer and Fresnel Diffraction

In the detailed treatment of diffraction, it is customary to distinguish between two general cases. These are known as *Fraunhofer diffraction* and *Fresnel diffraction*. Qualitatively speaking, Fraunhofer diffraction occurs when both the incident and diffracted waves are effectively plane. This will be the case when the distances from the source to the diffracting aperture and from the aperture to the receiving point are both large enough so that the curvatures of the incident and diffracted waves can be neglected, Figure 4.5 (a).

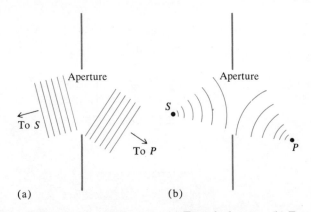

Figure 4.5.   Diffraction by an aperture. (a) Fraunhofer case. (b) Fresnel case.

If either the source or the receiving point is close enough to the diffracting aperture so that the curvature of the wave front is significant, then one has Fresnel diffraction, Figure 4.5(b). There is, of course, no sharp line of distinction between the two cases. However, a quantitative criterion can be obtained as follows. Consider Figure 4.6, which shows the general geometry of the diffraction problem. The receiving point P is located a distance d from the plane of the diffracting aperture, and the source S is a distance d' from this plane. One edge of the aperture

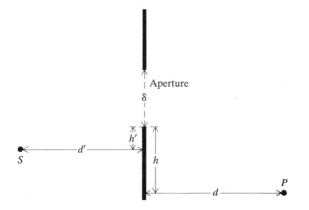

Figure 4.6. Geometry to show distinction between Fraunhofer diffraction and Fresnel diffraction.

is located a distance h from the foot of the perpendicular drawn from P to the plane of the aperture. The corresponding distance for the source is h' as shown. The size of the aperture opening is δ. From the figure it is seen that the variation Δ of the quantity $r + r'$ from one edge of the aperture to the other is given by

$$\Delta = \sqrt{d'^2 + (h' + \delta)^2} + \sqrt{d^2 + (h + \delta)^2} - \sqrt{d'^2 + h'^2} - \sqrt{d^2 + h^2}$$

$$= \left(\frac{h'}{d'} + \frac{h}{d}\right)\delta + \frac{1}{2}\left(\frac{1}{d'} + \frac{1}{d}\right)\delta^2 + \cdots \tag{4.14}$$

The quadratic term in the above expansion is essentially a measure of the curvature of the wave front. The wave is effectively plane over the aperture if this term is negligibly small compared to the wavelength of the light, that is if

$$\frac{1}{2}\left(\frac{1}{d'} + \frac{1}{d}\right)\delta^2 \ll \lambda \tag{4.15}$$

This is the criterion for Fraunhofer diffraction. If this condition does not obtain, the curvature of the wave front becomes important and the diffraction is of the Fresnel type.

Examples of Fraunhofer and Fresnel diffraction by various types of apertures are treated in the sections to follow. Since the Fraunhofer case is, in general, mathematically simpler than the Fresnel case, Fraunhofer diffraction will be discussed first.

4.4   Fraunhofer Diffraction Patterns

The usual experimental arrangement for observing Fraunhofer diffraction is shown in Figure 4.7. Here the aperture is *coherently illuminated* by means of a point monochromatic source and a collimating

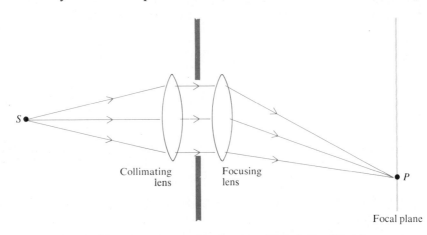

Figure 4.7.   Arrangement for observing Fraunhofer diffraction.

lens. A second lens is placed behind the aperture as shown. The incident and diffracted wave fronts are, therefore, strictly plane, and the Fraunhofer case is rigorously valid. In applying the Fresnel-Kirchhoff formula, Equation (4.11), to the calculation of the diffraction patterns of various apertures, it is assumed, for simplicity, that the angular spread of the diffracted light is small enough so that the obliquity factor is essentially constant over the aperture. A further simplification results by noting that the variation due to the radial factors in the denominator is negligibly small compared to the variation of the exponential function. Accordingly, the Fresnel-Kirchhoff formula reduces to the very simple equation

$$U_{\mathrm{p}} = C \int\int_{\mathscr{A}} e^{ikr} d\mathscr{A} \qquad (4.16)$$

where all constant factors have been lumped into one constant C. The above formula states that the distribution of the diffracted light is obtained simply by integrating the phase factor e^{ikr} over the aperture.

The Single Slit   The case of diffraction by a single narrow slit is here treated as a one dimensional problem. Let the slit be of length L and

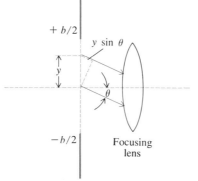

Figure 4.8.   Definition of the variables for Fraunhofer diffraction by a single slit.

of width b. The element of area is then $d\mathcal{A} = L dy$ as indicated in Figure 4.8. Furthermore, we can express r as

$$r = r_0 + y \sin \theta \tag{4.17}$$

where r_0 is the value of r for $y = 0$, and where θ is the angle shown. The diffraction formula (4.16) then yields

$$U = C e^{ikr_0} \int_{-b/2}^{+b/2} e^{iky \sin \theta} L dy$$

$$= 2C e^{ikr_0} L \frac{\sin (\frac{1}{2} kb \sin \theta)}{k \sin \theta} = C' \left(\frac{\sin \beta}{\beta} \right) \tag{4.18}$$

where $\beta = \frac{1}{2} kb \sin \theta$, and $C'(= e^{ikr_0} CbL)$ is merely another constant. Thus $C'(\sin \beta / \beta)$ is the total amplitude of the light diffracted in a given direction defined by β. This light is brought to a focus by the second lens, and the corresponding intensity distribution in the focal plane is given by the expression

$$I = |U|^2 = I_0 \left(\frac{\sin \beta}{\beta} \right)^2 \tag{4.19}$$

where $I_0 = \langle CLb \rangle^2$ which is the intensity for $\theta = 0$. The distribution is plotted in Figure 4.9. The maximum value occurs at $\theta = 0$, and zero values occur for $\beta = \pm\pi, \pm 2\pi, \cdots$, and so forth. Secondary maxima

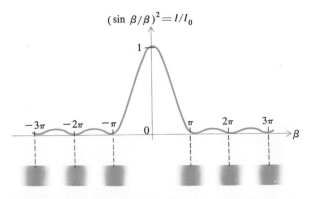

Figure 4.9.   Fraunhofer diffraction pattern of a single slit.

of rapidly diminishing intensity occur between these zero values. Thus the diffraction pattern at the focal plane consists of a central bright band. On either side there are alternating bright and dark bands. Table 4.1 gives the relative intensities of the first three secondary maxima. The first minimum, $\beta = \pi$, corresponds to

$$\sin \theta = \frac{2\pi}{kb} = \frac{\lambda}{b} \qquad (4.20)$$

Thus, for a given wavelength, the angular width of the diffraction pattern varies inversely with the slit width, and the amplitude of the central maximum is proportional to the area of the slit. For very narrow slits the pattern is dim but wide. It shrinks and becomes brighter as the slit is widened.

The Rectangular Aperture   The case of diffraction by a single aperture of rectangular shape is treated in the same way as the single slit, except that one must now integrate in two dimensions, say x and y as shown in Figure 4.10. It is left as a problem to show that the intensity distribution is given by the product of two single-slit distribution functions, namely,

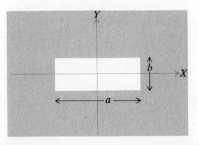

Figure 4.10.   Rectangular aperture.

$$I = I_o \left(\frac{\sin \alpha}{\alpha}\right)^2 \left(\frac{\sin \beta}{\beta}\right)^2 \qquad \textbf{(4.21)}$$

where $\alpha = \frac{1}{2}ka \sin \phi$, $\beta = \frac{1}{2}kb \sin \theta$. The dimensions of the aperture are a and b and the angles ϕ and θ define the direction of the diffracted ray. The resulting diffraction pattern, Figure 4.11, has lines of zero intensity defined by $\alpha = \pm\pi, \pm2\pi, \cdots$, and $\beta = \pm\pi, \pm2\pi \cdots$. As with the slit, the scale of the diffraction pattern bears an inverse relationship to the scale of the aperture.

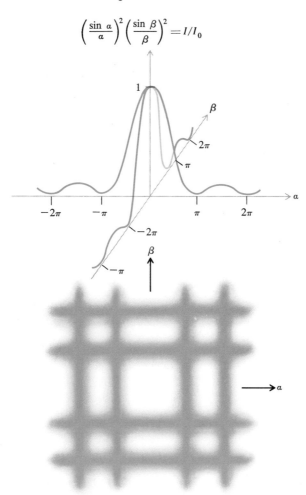

Figure 4.11. Fraunhofer diffraction pattern of a rectangular aperture.

The Circular Aperture   To calculate the diffraction pattern of a circular aperture, we choose y as the variable of integration, as in the case of the single slit. If R is the radius of the aperture, then the element of area is taken to be a strip of width dy and length $2\sqrt{R^2 - y^2}$, Figure 4.12.

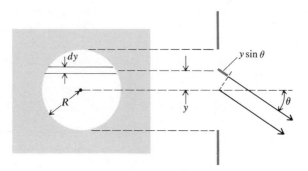

Figure 4.12.   Circular aperture.

The amplitude distribution of the diffraction pattern is then given by

$$U = C\,e^{ikr_0} \int_{-R}^{+R} e^{iky\,\sin\theta}\, 2\sqrt{R^2 - y^2}\, dy \qquad (4.22)$$

We introduce the quantities u and ρ defined by $u = y/R$ and $\rho = kR\sin\theta$. The integral in the above equation then becomes

$$\int_{-1}^{+1} e^{i\rho u\sqrt{1 - u^2}}\, du \qquad (4.23)$$

This is a standard integral. Its value is $\pi J_1(\rho)/\rho$ where J_1 is the Bessel function of the first kind, order one [27]. The ratio $J_1(\rho)/\rho \to 1/2$ as $\rho \to 0$. The intensity distribution is, therefore, given by

$$I = I_0 \left[\frac{2J_1(\rho)}{\rho}\right]^2 \qquad (4.24)$$

where $I_0 = (C\pi R^2)^2$, which is the intensity for $\theta = 0$.

A graph of the intensity function is shown in Figure 4.13. The diffraction pattern is circularly symmetric and consists of a bright central disk surrounded by concentric circular bands of rapidly diminishing intensity. The bright central area is known as the *Airy disk*. It extends to the first dark ring whose size is given by the first zero of the Bessel function, namely, $\rho = 3.832$. The angular radius of the first dark ring is thus given by

$$\sin\theta = \frac{3.832}{kR} = \frac{1.22\lambda}{D} \approx \theta \qquad (4.25)$$

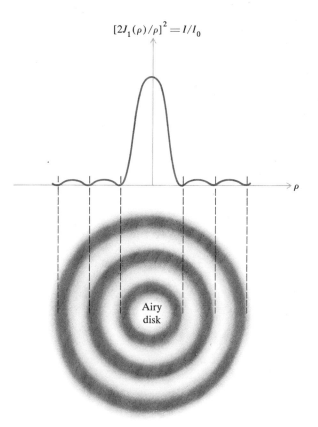

$$[2J_1(\rho)/\rho]^2 = I/I_0$$

Figure 4.13.   Fraunhofer diffraction pattern of a circular aperture.

which is valid for small values of θ. Here $D = 2R$ is the diameter of the aperture.

The angular size of the Airy disk is thus slightly larger than the corresponding value λ/b for the bright central band of the diffraction pattern of the rectangular aperture or slit. In Table 4.1 are listed the values of the first few maxima of the diffraction patterns of rectangular and circular apertures.

Table 4.1.   RELATIVE INTENSITIES OF THE MAXIMA OF DIFFRACTION PATTERNS OF RECTANGULAR AND CIRCULAR APERTURES

	Rectangular	Circular
Central Max	1	1
1st Max	0.0496	0.0174
2d Max	0.0168	0.0042
3rd Max	0.0083	0.0016

Optical Resolution   The image of a distant point source formed at the focal plane of an optical-telescope lens or a camera lens is actually a Fraunhoffer diffraction pattern for which the aperture is the lens opening. Thus the image of a composite source is a superposition of many Airy disks. The resolution of detail in the image, therefore, depends on the size of the individual Airy disks. If D is the diameter of the lens opening, then the angular radius of an Airy disk is approximately $1.22 \lambda/D$. This is also the approximate minimum angular separation between two equal point sources such that they can be just barely resolved, because at this angular separation, the central maximum of the image of one source falls on the first minimum of the other, Figure 4.14. This condition for optical resolution is the Rayleigh criterion mentioned earlier. The Rayleigh criterion does not give an absolute minimum separation for resolution, but it is almost always used because of its simplicity.

In the case of the rectangular aperture, the minimum angular separation according to the Rayleigh criterion is just λ/b, where b is the width of the aperture. The intensity at the saddle point in this case is $8/\pi^2 = 0.81$ times the maximum intensity. The proof of this statement is left as an exercise.

The Double Slit   Let us consider a diffracting aperture consisting of two parallel slits, each of width b and separated by a distance h, Figure 4.15. As with the single slit, we treat this case as a one-dimensional problem. The relevant diffraction integral is evaluated as follows:

$$
\int_{\mathscr{A}} e^{iky \sin \theta} \, dy = \int_0^b e^{iky \sin \theta} \, dy + \int_h^{h+b} e^{iky \sin \theta} \, dy
$$

$$
= \frac{1}{ik \sin \theta} \left(e^{ikb \sin \theta} - 1 + e^{ik(h+b) \sin \theta} - e^{ikh \sin \theta} \right)
$$

$$
= \left(\frac{e^{ikb \sin \theta} - 1}{ik \sin \theta} \right) \left(1 + e^{ikh \sin \theta} \right) \tag{4.26}
$$

$$
= 2b \, e^{i\beta} \, e^{i\gamma} \, \frac{\sin \beta}{\beta} \cos \gamma
$$

where $\beta = \frac{1}{2}kb \sin \theta$ and $\gamma = \frac{1}{2}kh \sin \theta$. The corresponding intensity distribution function is

$$
I = I_o \left(\frac{\sin \beta}{\beta} \right)^2 \cos^2\gamma \tag{4.27}
$$

The factor $(\sin \beta/\beta)^2$ is the previously found distribution function for a single slit. This factor here constitutes an envelope for the interference fringes given by the term $\cos^2\gamma$. A plot is shown in Figure 4.16.

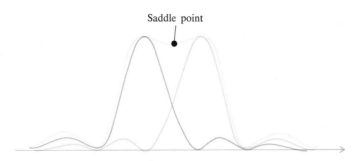

Figure 4.14. Rayleigh criterion.

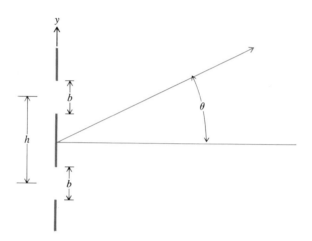

Figure 4.15. Double-slit aperture.

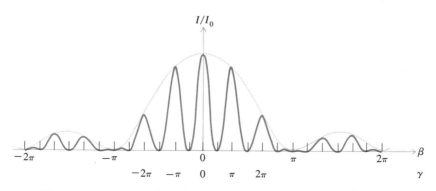

Figure 4.16. Fraunhofer diffraction pattern of a double-slit aperture.

Bright fringes occur for $\gamma = 0, \pm\pi, \pm2\pi$, and so forth. The angular separation between fringes is given by $\Delta\gamma = \pi$, or approximately, in terms of the angle θ

$$\Delta\theta \approx \frac{2\pi}{kh} = \frac{\lambda}{h} \tag{4.28}$$

It is interesting to note that this is equivalent to the result of the analysis of Young's experiment, Equation (3.9).

Multiple Slits. Diffraction Gratings   Let the aperture consist of a grating, that is, a large number N of identical parallel slits of width b and separation h, Figure 4.17. The evaluation of the diffractional integral is carried out in a manner similar to that of the double slit:

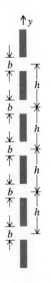

Figure 4.17.   Multiple-slit aperture or diffraction grating.

$$\int_{\mathcal{A}} e^{iky \sin\theta}\, dy = \int_0^b + \int_h^{h+b} + \int_{2h}^{2h+b} + \cdots + \int_{(N-1)h}^{(N-1)h+b} e^{iky \sin\theta}\, dy$$

$$= \frac{e^{ikb \sin\theta} - 1}{ik \sin\theta}\left[1 + e^{ikh \sin\theta} + \cdots + e^{ik(N-1)h \sin\theta}\right]$$

$$= \frac{e^{ikb \sin\theta} - 1}{ik \sin\theta} \cdot \frac{1 - e^{ikNh \sin\theta}}{1 - e^{ikh \sin\theta}} \tag{4.29}$$

$$= 2b\, e^{i\beta} e^{i(N-1)\gamma}\left(\frac{\sin\beta}{\beta}\right)\left(\frac{\sin N\gamma}{\sin\gamma}\right)$$

where $\beta = \tfrac{1}{2}kb \sin \theta$ and $\gamma = \tfrac{1}{2}kh \sin \theta$. This yields the following intensity distribution function:

$$I = I_0 \left(\frac{\sin \beta}{\beta}\right)^2 \left(\frac{\sin N\gamma}{N \sin \gamma}\right)^2 \tag{4.30}$$

The factor N has been inserted in order to normalize the expression. This makes $I = I_0$ when $\theta = 0$.

Again the single-slit factor $(\sin \beta/\beta)^2$ appears as the envelope of the diffraction pattern. Principal maxima occur within the envelope at $\gamma = n\pi, n = 0, 1, 2 \cdots$, that is

$$n\lambda = h \sin \theta \tag{4.31}$$

which is the grating formula giving the relation between wavelength and angle of diffraction. The integer n is called the *order of diffraction*.

Secondary maxima occur for $\gamma = 3\pi/2N, 5\pi/2N$, and so forth, and zeros occur at $\gamma = \pi/N, 2\pi/N, 3\pi/N \cdots$ A graph is shown in Figure 4.18(a). If the slits are very narrow, then the factor $\sin \beta/\beta \approx 1$. The first few primary maxima then all have approximately the same value, namely I_0.

Resolving Power of a Grating   The angular width of a principal fringe, that is, the separation between the peak and the adjacent minimum, is found by setting the *change* of the quantity $N\gamma$ equal to π, that is, $\Delta\gamma = \pi/N = \tfrac{1}{2}kh \cos \theta \, \Delta\theta$. This corresponds to

$$\Delta\theta_N = \frac{\lambda}{Nh \cos \theta} \tag{4.32}$$

Thus if N is made very large, then $\Delta\theta$ is very small, and the diffraction pattern consists of a series of sharp fringes corresponding to the different orders $n = 0, \pm1, \pm2$, and so forth, Figure 14.18(b), (c). For a given order the dependence of θ on the wavelength, Equation (4.31), gives by differentiation

$$\Delta\theta_\lambda = \frac{n\Delta\lambda}{h \cos \theta} \tag{4.33}$$

This is the angular separation between two spectral lines differing in wavelength by $\Delta\lambda$. Combining Equation (4.32) and (4.33), we obtain the *resolving power* of a grating spectroscope according to the Rayleigh criterion, namely

$$\text{R.P.} = \frac{\lambda}{\Delta\lambda} = nN \tag{4.34}$$

Diffraction gratings used for optical spectroscopy are made by ruling grooves on a transparent surface (transmission type) or on a

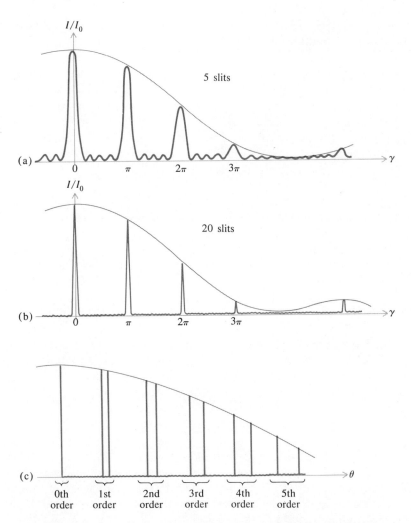

Figure 4.18.   Fraunhofer diffraction pattern of a multiple-slit aperture.

metal surface (reflection type). A typical grating may have, say, 600
lines/mm ruled over a total width of 10 cm. This would give a total of
60,000 lines and a theoretical resolving power of 60,000 n where n is
the order of diffraction used. In practice, resolving powers up to 90
percent of the theoretical values are obtainable with good gratings.

If the grooves are suitably shaped, usually of a sawtooth profile,
most of the diffracted light can be made to appear in one order, thus
increasing the efficiency of the grating. The essential requirement is
that the spacing be uniform, within a fraction of a wavelength. This
places extreme requirements on the mechanical rigidity of the ruling

machine. High-quality replica gratings can be produced by a plastic moulding process. These are much less expensive than original gratings.

Most of the gratings used in practical spectroscopy are of the reflection type. Reflection gratings are made with the ruled surface either plane or concave, Figure 4.19. Plane gratings require the use of col-

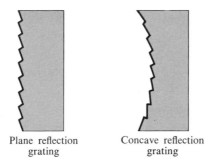

Plane reflection
grating

Concave reflection
grating

Figure 4.19.   Reflection gratings.

limating and focusing lenses or mirrors, whereas concave gratings can perform the collimating and focusing functions as well as disperse the light into a spectrum. For more information on the subject of diffraction gratings and their use, the reader should consult references [17] and [35].

4.5   Fresnel Diffraction Patterns

According to the criteria discussed in Section 4.3, diffraction is of the Fresnel-type when either the light source or the observing screen, or both, are so close to the diffracting aperture that the curvature of the wave front becomes significant. Since one is no longer dealing with plane waves, Fresnel diffraction is mathematically more difficult to treat than Fraunhoffer diffraction but is actually simpler to observe experimentally because all that is needed is a source of light, an observing screen, and the diffracting aperture. The previously mentioned fringe effects seen around shadows are examples of Fresnel diffraction. In this section we shall discuss only a few relatively simple cases of Fresnel diffraction, which can be handled by elementary mathematical methods.

Fresnel Zones   Consider a plane aperture illuminated by a point source S, Figure 4.20, such that a straight line connecting S to the receiving point P is perpendicular to the plane of the aperture. Let O

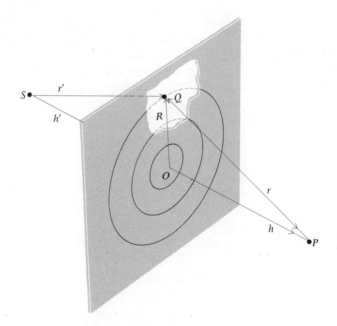

Figure 4.20.   Fresnel zones in a plane aperture.

be the point of intersection of the line SP with the aperture plane, and call R the distance from O to any point Q in the aperture. Then the distance $PQS = r + r'$ can be expressed in terms of R as follows:

$$r + r' = (h^2 + R^2)^{1/2} + (h'^2 + R^2)^{1/2} \tag{4.35}$$
$$= h + h' + \tfrac{1}{2}R^2\left(\frac{1}{h} + \frac{1}{h'}\right) + \cdots$$

where h and h' are the distances OP and OS, respectively. Now suppose that the aperture is divided up into regions bounded by concentric circles, $R = constant$, defined such that $r + r'$ differs by $\frac{1}{2}$ wavelength from one boundary to the next. These regions are called *Fresnel zones*. From (4.35) the successive radii are $R_1 = \sqrt{\lambda L}$, $R_2 = \sqrt{2\lambda L}$, $\cdots$ $R_n = \sqrt{n\lambda L}$, where λ is the wavelength, and

$$L = \left(\frac{1}{h} + \frac{1}{h'}\right)^{-1} \tag{4.36}$$

If R_n and R_{n+1} are the inner and outer radii of the nth zone, then the area is $\pi R_{n+1}^2 - \pi R_n^2 = \pi R_1^2$. This is independent of n. The areas of the complete zones are, therefore, all equal.

The optical disturbance at P can be evaluated in terms of the contributions from the various Fresnel zones, U_1, U_2, U_3, $\cdots$. Since the mean phase changes by exactly 180 degrees from one zone to the next, the sum of the contributions to the amplitude $|U_p|$ can be expressed as

$$|U_p| = |U_1| - |U_2| + |U_3| - \cdots \tag{4.37}$$

Consider for example the case of a circular aperture centered at O. If the aperture includes precisely n complete zones, then, since the areas are equal, the $|U|$'s are all approximately the same. Hence the sum will be very nearly zero if n is even, and approximately the value of $|U_1|$ alone if n is odd.

Consideration of the obliquity factor and the radial distance factor in the Fresnel-Kirchhoff formula, Equation (4.11), shows that the value of $|U_n|$ decreases slowly with increasing n. As a result, as $n \to \infty$, the total optical disturbance at P for the case of an infinitely large aperture, that is, *no aperture at all,* is approximately one-half the contribution from the first Fresnel zone alone! To show this (at least qualitatively) we group the terms in Equation (4.37) in the following way:

$$|U_p| = \tfrac{1}{2}|U_1| + (\tfrac{1}{2}|U_1| - |U_2| + \tfrac{1}{2}|U_3|) + \\ (\tfrac{1}{2}|U_3| - |U_4| + \tfrac{1}{2}|U_5|) + \cdots \tag{4.38}$$

If the decrease with increasing n is very slow, the value of any $|U_n|$ is approximately equal to the mean value of the two adjacent $|U|$'s, so that the terms in parentheses very nearly cancel. Thus, $\tfrac{1}{2}|U_1|$ is the optical disturbance at P when there is no aperture at all.

Suppose we have a circular obstacle instead of an aperture. The construction of the Fresnel zones is now started at the edge of the obstacle. The value of $|U_p|$ is then, as above, just half the contribution from the first unobstructed zone. As a result, the center of the shadow of a circular opaque object shows a bright spot of very nearly the same intensity as if the object were not there.

In the case of an irregular obstacle or aperture, the appearance of the Fresnel zones as seen from the receiving point P is shown in Figure 4.21. In the illuminated region (a) the outer zones are partially blocked. Thus the higher terms in Equation (4.37) diminish more rapidly than if there were no obstacle, but the beginning terms are unaffected. As a result, the value of $|U_p|$ is hardly changed. On the other hand, in (b) the central zones are completely blocked and the outer zones are partially obstructed. Accordingly, the terms in the summation diminish at both ends and the result is almost complete cancellation. Thus if P is in the illuminated region the presence of the obstacle makes little or no difference, but if it is in the shadow region the optical disturbance is very small, which is roughly in agreement with geometrical optics. Diffraction fringes appear around the shadow only if the irregularities

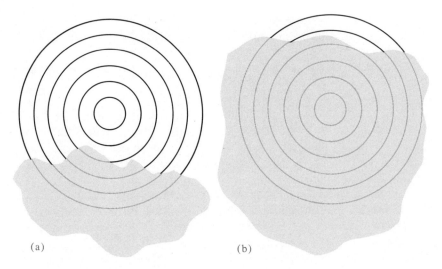

Figure 4.21. Fresnel zones of a point source behind an irregular obstacle.

at the edge of the obstacle are small compared to the radius of the first Fresnel zone.

Zone Plate If an aperture is constructed so as to obstruct alternate Fresnel zones, say the even numbered ones, then the remaining terms in the summation are all of the same sign. Thus

$$|U_p| = |U_1| + |U_3| + |U_5| + \cdots \qquad (4.39)$$

Such an aperture is called a *zone plate*. It acts very much like a lens, because $|U_p|$, and hence the intensity at P, is now much larger than if there were no aperture. The equivalent focal length is L in (4.36). It is given by

$$L = \frac{R_1{}^2}{\lambda} \qquad (4.40)$$

Zone plates can be made by photographing a drawing similar to that of Figure 4.22. The resulting photographic transparency can focus light and form images of distant objects. It is a very chromatic lens, however, since the focal length is inversely proportional to the wavelength.

Rectangular Aperture Fresnel diffraction by an aperture of rectangular shape is treated by using the Fresnel-Kirchhoff formula, Equation (4.11). We shall employ Cartesian coordinates x,y in the aperture

Figure 4.22.   A zone plate.

plane as shown in Figure 4.23. Then $R^2 = x^2 + y^2$, and therefore, referring to Equations (4.35) and (4.36) we have approximately

$$r + r' = h + h' + \frac{1}{2L}(x^2 + y^2) \qquad \textbf{(4.41)}$$

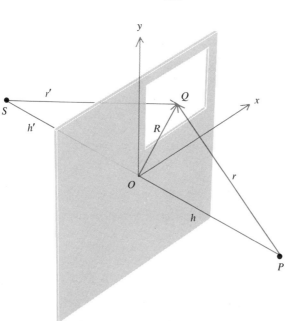

Figure 4.23.   Geometry of a rectangular aperture.

Again, as in the treatment of Fraunhofer diffraction, we shall assume that the obliquity factor $\cos(\mathbf{n},\mathbf{r}) - \cos(\mathbf{n},\mathbf{r}')$ and the radial factor $1/rr'$ vary so slowly compared to the exponential factor $e^{ik(r + r')}$ that they can be taken outside the integrand. The Fresnel-Kirchhoff formula then becomes

$$U_p = C \int_{x_1}^{x_2} \int_{y_1}^{y_2} e^{ik(x^2 + y^2)/2L} dx \, dy$$

(4.42)

$$= C \int_{x_1}^{x_2} e^{ikx^2/2L} dx \int_{y_1}^{y_2} e^{iky^2/2L} dy$$

where C includes all other factors. Upon introducing the dimensionless variables u and v defined as

$$u = x\sqrt{\frac{k}{\pi L}} \qquad v = y\sqrt{\frac{k}{\pi L}}$$

(4.43)

we can write

$$U_p = U_1 \int_{u_1}^{u_2} e^{i(1/2)\pi u^2} du \int_{v_1}^{v_2} e^{i(1/2)\pi v^2} dv$$

(4.44)

where $U_1 = C\pi L/k$.

The integrals in Equation (4.44) are evaluated in terms of the integral

$$\int_0^w e^{i(1/2)\pi w^2} dw = C(w) + iS(w)$$

(4.45)

where

$$C(w) = \int_0^w \cos(\tfrac{1}{2}\pi w^2) dw \qquad S(w) = \int_0^w \sin(\tfrac{1}{2}\pi w^2) \, dw$$

(4.46)

$C(w)$ and $S(w)$ are known as *Fresnel integrals*. A short table of numerical values is given in Table 4.2, and a graph showing $C(w)$ versus $iS(w)$, called a Cornu spiral, is shown in Figure 4.24.

The Cornu spiral is useful for graphical evaluation of the Fresnel integrals. The limit points $w_1 = v_1$ and $w_2 = v_2$ are marked on the spiral. A straight line segment drawn from v_1 to v_2, Figure 4.24(b), then gives the value of the integral $\int_{v_1}^{v_2} e^{i(1/2)\pi v^2} dv$. The length of the line segment is the magnitude of the integral. The projection of the line on the C

Table 4.2 FRESNEL INTEGRALS

w	$C(w)$	$S(w)$
0.0	0.000	0.000
0.2	0.200	0.004
0.4	0.398	0.033
0.6	0.581	0.111
0.8	0.723	0.249
1.0	0.780	0.438
1.2	0.715	0.623
1.4	0.543	0.714
1.6	0.366	0.638
1.8	0.334	0.451
2.0	0.488	0.343
2.5	0.457	0.619
3.0	0.606	0.496
3.5	0.533	0.415
4.0	0.498	0.420
∞	0.500	0.500

axis gives the real part, and the projection on the S axis gives the imaginary part.

The limiting case of an infinite aperture, that is, *no diffraction screen at all,* is obtained by setting $u_1 = v_1 = -\infty$ and $u_2 = v_2 = +\infty$. Since $C(\infty) = S(\infty) = 1/2$, and $C(-\infty) = S(-\infty) = -1/2$, we obtain the value $U_1(1 + i)^2$ for the unobstructed optical disturbance. On the Cornu spiral this would be U_1 times the length of the line from $-\infty$ to ∞, Figure 4.24(b). Setting this equal to U_o, we can express the general case in the normalized form

$$U_p = \frac{U_o}{(1 + i)^2} \left[C(u) + iS(u) \right]_{u_1}^{u_2} \left[C(v) + iS(v) \right]_{v_1}^{v_2} \tag{4.47}$$

Slit and Straightedge Fresnel diffraction by a long slit is treated as a limiting case of a rectangular aperture, namely by letting $u_1 = -\infty$ and $u_2 = +\infty$ in Equation (4.47). This yields the formula

$$U_p = \frac{U_o}{1 + i} \left[C(v) + iS(v) \right]_{v_1}^{v_2} \tag{4.48}$$

for the slit where v_1 and v_2 define the slit edges.

The straightedge is similarly taken as a limiting case of a slit: $v_1 = -\infty$. This gives

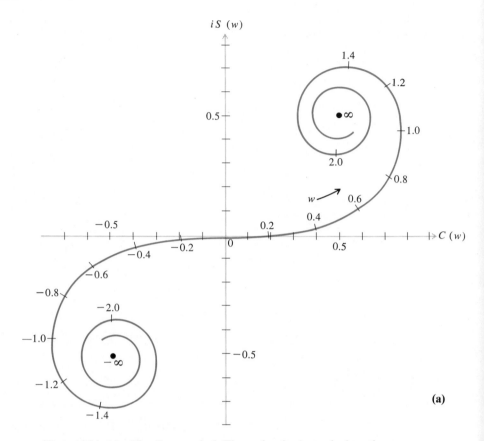

Figure 4.24. (a)   The Cornu spiral. The scale of w is marked on the curve.

$$U_p = \frac{U_o}{1+i}\left[C(v) + iS(v)\right]_{-\infty}^{v_2}$$

$$= \frac{U_o}{1+i}\left[C(v_2) + iS(v_2) + \tfrac{1}{2} + \tfrac{1}{2}i\right]$$

(4.49)

which is a function of only the one variable v_2. This variable specifies the position of the diffracting edge. If the receiving point P is exactly at the geometrical shadow edge, then $v_2 = 0$. We have then $U_p = U_o/(1+i)\,(\tfrac{1}{2} + \tfrac{1}{2}i) = \tfrac{1}{2}U_o$. Hence the amplitude at the shadow edge is one-half, and the intensity is one-fourth the unobstructed value. A plot of $I_p = |U_p|^2$ as given by Equation (4.49) is shown in Figure

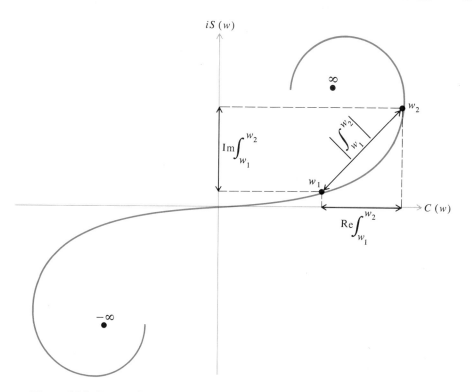

Figure 4.24. (b)   Evaluation of Fresnel integrals with the Cornu spiral.

4.25. Here I_p is plotted as a function of v_2. This is equivalent to having a fixed position for the receiving point and varying the position of the diffracting edge. The result is virtually the same as a diffraction pattern. From the graph it can be seen that the intensity falls off rapidly and monotonically in the shadow zone ($v_2 < 0$) as $v_2 \to -\infty$. On the other hand, in the illuminated zone ($v_2 > 0$) the intensity oscillates with diminishing amplitude about the unobstructed value U_o as $v_2 \to +\infty$. The highest intensity occurs just inside the illuminated region at the point $v_2 \approx 1.25$ where I_p is 1.37 times the intensity of the unobstructed wave. This is seen as a bright fringe next to the geometrical shadow.

4.6   Applications of the Fourier Transform to Diffraction

Let us return to the discussion of Fraunhoffer diffraction. We now consider the general problem of diffraction by an aperture having not only an arbitrary shape, but also an arbitrary transmission including phase retardation, which may vary over different parts of the aperture.

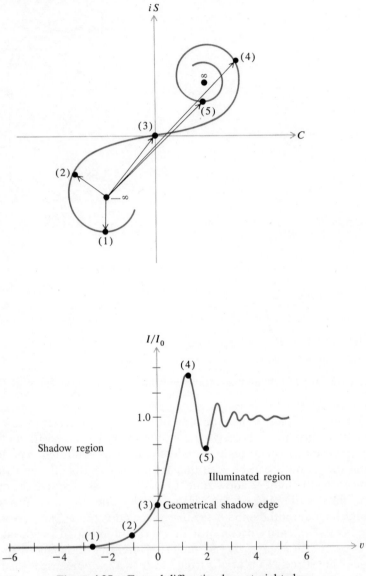

Figure 4.25. Fresnel diffraction by a straightedge.

We choose coordinates as indicated in Figure 4.26. The diffracting aperture lies in the xy plane, and the diffraction pattern appears in the XY plane, which is the focal plane of the focusing lens. According to elementary geometrical optics, all rays leaving the diffracting aperture in a given direction, specified by direction cosines α, β, and γ are

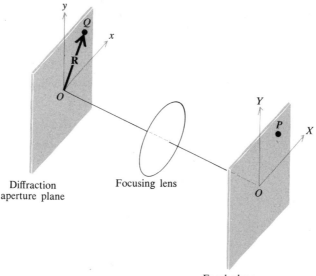

Figure 4.26. Geometry of the general diffraction problem.

brought to a common focus. This focus is located at the point $P(X, Y)$ where $X \approx L\alpha$ and $Y \approx L\beta$, L being the focal length of the lens. The assumption is here made that α and β are small so that $\alpha \approx \tan \alpha$, and $\beta \approx \tan \beta$.

Now the path difference δr, between a ray starting from the point $Q(x, y)$ and a parallel ray starting from the origin O, is given by $\mathbf{R} \cdot \hat{\mathbf{n}}$, Figure 4.27, where $\mathbf{R} = \hat{\mathbf{i}}x + \hat{\mathbf{j}}y$ and $\hat{\mathbf{n}}$ is a unit vector in the direction of the ray. Since $\hat{\mathbf{n}}$ can be expressed as $\hat{\mathbf{n}} = \hat{\mathbf{i}}\alpha + \hat{\mathbf{j}}\beta + \hat{\mathbf{k}}\gamma$, then

$$\delta r = \mathbf{R} \cdot \hat{\mathbf{n}} = x\alpha + y\beta = x\frac{X}{L} + y\frac{Y}{L} \tag{4.50}$$

It follows that the fundamental diffraction integral, Equation (4.16), giving the diffraction pattern in the XY plane is, aside from a constant multiplying factor, expressible in the form

$$U(X, Y) = \iint e^{ik\,\delta r}\,d\mathcal{A} = \iint e^{ik(xX + yY)/L}\,dx\,dy \tag{4.51}$$

This is the case for a uniform aperture. For a nonuniform aperture we introduce a function $g(x, y)$ called the *aperture function*. This function is defined such that $g(x, y)dx\,dy$ is the amplitude of the diffracted wave originating from the element of area $dx\,dy$. Thus, instead of Equation (4.51), we have

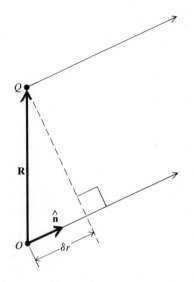

Figure 4.27. Path difference between two parallel rays of light originating from points O and Q in the xy plane.

$$U(X, Y) = \int\int g(x, y)\, e^{ik(xX + yY)/L}\, dx\, dy \qquad \text{(4.52)}$$

It is convenient at this point to introduce the quantities

$$\mu = kX/L \text{ and } \nu = kY/L \qquad \text{(4.53)}$$

μ and ν are called *spatial frequencies,* although they have the dimensions of reciprocal length, that is, wavenumber. We now write Equation (4.52) as

$$U(\mu, \nu) = \int\int g(x, y)\, e^{i(\mu x + \nu y)}\, dx\, dy \qquad \text{(4.54)}$$

We see that the functions $U(\mu, \nu)$ and $g(x, y)$ constitute a two-dimensional Fourier transform pair. The diffraction pattern, in this context, is actually a Fourier resolution of the aperture function.

Consider as an example, a grating. For simplicity we treat it as a one-dimensional problem. The aperture function $g(y)$ is then a periodic step function as shown in Figure 4.28. It is represented by a Fourier series of the form

$$g(y) = g_0 + g_1 \cos(\nu_0 y) + g_2 \cos(2\nu_0 y) + \cdots \qquad \text{(4.55)}$$

The fundamental spatial frequency ν_0 is given by the periodicity of the grating, namely

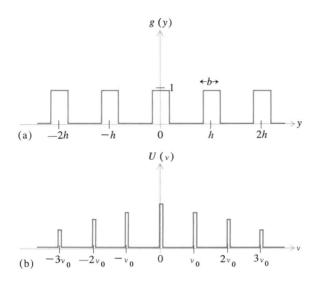

Figure 4.28. Aperture function for a grating and its Fourier transform.

$$\nu_0 = \frac{2\pi}{h} \tag{4.56}$$

where h is the grating spacing. This dominant spatial frequency appears in the diffraction pattern as the first-order maximum, the amplitude of which is proportional to g_1. Maxima of higher order correspond to higher Fourier components of the aperture function $g(y)$. Thus if the aperture function were of the form of a cosine function $g_0 + g_1 \cos(\nu_0 y)$ instead of a periodic-step function, then the diffraction pattern would consist only of the central maximum and the two first-order maxima. Second or higher diffraction orders would not appear.

Apodization   Apodization is the name given to any process by which the aperture function is altered in such a way as to produce a redistribution of energy in the diffraction pattern. Apodization is usually employed to reduce the intensity of the secondary diffraction maxima.

It is perhaps easiest to explain the theory of apodization by means of a specific example. Let the aperture consist of a single slit. The aperture function in this case is a single step function: $g(y) = 1$ for $-b/2 < y < b/2$ and $g(y) = 0$ otherwise, Figure 4.29. The corresponding diffraction pattern, expressed in terms of spatial frequencies, is

$$U(\nu) = \int_{-b/2}^{+b/2} e^{i\nu y}\, dy = b\,\frac{\sin\left(\tfrac{1}{2}\nu b\right)}{\left(\tfrac{1}{2}\nu b\right)} \tag{4.57}$$

This is equivalent to the normal case already discussed in Section 4.5.

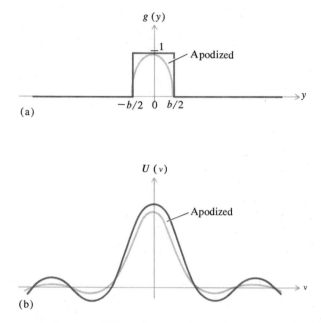

Figure 4.29. (a) Aperture functions for a slit and an apodized slit. (b) The Fourier transforms.

Suppose now that the aperture function is altered by apodizing in such a way that the resultant aperture transmission is a cosine function: $g(y) = \cos(\pi y/b)$ for $-b/2 < y < b/2$ and zero otherwise, as shown in Figure 4.28. This could be accomplished for example, by means of a suitably coated-glass plate placed over the aperture. The new diffraction pattern is given by

$$U(v) = \int_{-b/2}^{+b/2} \cos(\pi y/b)\, e^{ivy}\, dy = \cos(\tfrac{1}{2}vb) \left[\frac{1}{v + \dfrac{\pi}{b}} - \frac{1}{v - \dfrac{\pi}{b}} \right] \quad (4.58)$$

A comparison of the two diffraction patterns is shown graphically in the figure. The result of apodization in this case is a substantial reduction in the secondary maxima relative to the central maximum, in other words, apodization has suppressed the higher spatial frequencies.

In a similar way, it is possible to apodize the circular aperture of a telescope so as to greatly reduce the relative intensities of the diffraction rings that appear around the images of stars (discussed in Section 4.5). This enhances the ability of the telescope to resolve the image of a dim star near that of a bright one.

Spatial Filtering Consider the diagram shown in Figure 4.30. Here the xy plane represents the location of some *coherently* illuminated object.[1] This object is imaged by an optical system (not shown), the

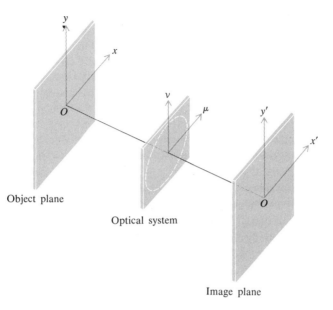

y

x

v

μ

y'

x'

O

O

Object plane

Optical system

Image plane

Figure 4.30. Geometry for the general problem of image formation by an optical system.

image appearing in the $x'y'$ plane. The diffraction pattern $U(\mu, \nu)$ of the object function $g(x, y)$ appears in the $\mu\nu$ plane. This plane is analogous to the XY plane in Figure 4.26. Hence, from Equation (4.54), $U(\mu, v)$ is the Fourier transform of $g(x, y)$. The image function $g'(x', y')$ that appears in the $x'y'$ plane is, in turn, the Fourier transform of $U(\mu, \nu)$. Now if *all* spatial frequencies in the range $\mu = \pm\infty, \nu = \pm\infty$ were transmitted equally by the optical system, then, from the properties of the Fourier transform, the image function $g'(x'\, y')$ would be *exactly* proportional to the object function $g(x, y)$. That is, the image would be a true reproduction of the object. However, the finite size of the aperture at the $\mu\nu$ plane limits the spatial frequencies that are transmitted by the optical system. Furthermore there may be lens defects, aberrations, and so forth, which result in a modification of the function $U(\mu, \nu)$. All of these effects can be incorporated into one function $T(\mu, \nu)$ called the *transfer function* of the optical system. This function is defined implicitly by the equation:

---

[1] For a discussion of the theory of spatial filtering with incoherent illumination see [10].

$$g'(x', y') = \int\limits_{-\infty}^{+\infty} \int\limits_{-\infty}^{+\infty} T(\mu, \nu)\, U(\mu, \nu)\, e^{-i(\mu x' + \nu y')}\, d\mu\, d\nu \qquad \text{(4.59)}$$

That is, the image function is the Fourier transform of the product $T(\mu, \nu) \cdot U(\mu, \nu)$. The limits of integration are $\pm\infty$ in a formal sense only. The actual limits are given by the particular form of the transfer function $T(\mu, \nu)$.

The transfer function can be modified by placing various screens and apertures in the $\mu\nu$ plane. This is known as *spatial filtering*. The situation is quite analogous to the filtering of an electrical signal by means of a passive electrical network. The object function is the input signal, and the image function is the output signal. The optical system acts like a filter that allows certain spatial frequencies to be transmitted but rejects others.

Suppose for example, that the object is a grating so that the object function is a periodic-step function. This case can be treated as a one-dimensional problem. The object function $f(y)$ and its Fourier transform $U(\nu)$ are then just those shown in Figure 4.28. Now let the aperture in the $\mu\nu$ plane be such that only those spatial frequencies that lie between $-\nu_{max}$ and $+\nu_{max}$ are transmitted. This means that we have low-pass filtering. From Equation (4.53) we have $\nu_{max} = kb/f$ where $2b$ is the physical width of the aperture in the $\mu\nu$ plane. The transfer function for this case is a step function: $T(\nu) = 1$, $-\nu_{max} < \nu < +\nu_{max}$, and zero otherwise. The image function is, accordingly,

$$g'(y') = \int\limits_{-\nu_{max}}^{+\nu_{max}} U(\nu)e^{-i\nu y'}\, d\nu \qquad \text{(4.60)}$$

Without going into the details of the calculation of $g(y')$, we show in Figure 4.31(a) a graphical plot for some arbitrary choice of ν_{max}. Instead of the sharp-step function that constitutes the object, the image is rounded at the corners and also shows small periodic variations.

A high-pass optical filter is obtained by placing in the $\mu\nu$ plane a screen that blocks off the central part of the diffraction pattern. This part of the diffraction pattern corresponds to the low frequencies. The approximate form of the resulting image function is shown in Figure 4.31(b). Only the edges of the grating steps are now visible in the image plane. *The edge detail comes from the higher spatial frequencies.*

Phase Contrast   The method of phase contrast was invented by the Dutch physicist Zernicke. It is used to render visible a transparent object whose index of refraction differs slightly from that of a surrounding

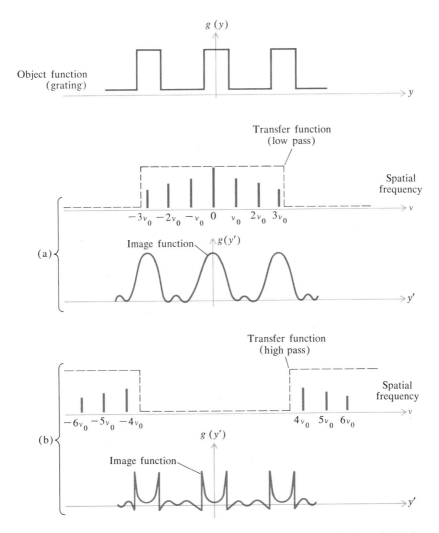

Figure 4.31. Graphs illustrating spatial filtering. (a) Low-pass filtering. (b) High-pass filtering.

transparent medium. Phase contrast is particularly useful in microscopy for examination of living organisms, and so forth. In essence, the method consists of the use of a special type of spatial filter.

To simplify the theory of phase contrast, we shall treat the case of a so-called "phase grating" consisting of alternate strips of high- and low-index material, all strips being perfectly transparent. The grating is coherently illuminated and constitutes the object. The object function is thus represented by the exponential

$$g(y) = e^{i\phi(y)} \tag{4.61}$$

where the phase factor $\phi(y)$ is a periodic-step function as shown in Figure 4.32(a). The "height" of the step is the optical phase difference between the two kinds of strips. That is, $\Delta\phi = kz\,\Delta n$ where z is the thickness and Δn is the difference between the two indices of refraction.

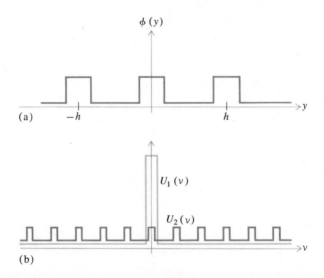

Figure 4.32. (a) The phase function of a periodic phase grating. (b) Fourier transforms of the aperture U_1 and the grating U_2.

If we assume that this phase difference is very small, then to a good approximation, we can write

$$g(y) = 1 + i\phi(y) \tag{4.62}$$

The Fourier transform of the above function is

$$U(\nu) = \int_{-\infty}^{\infty} [1 + i\phi(y)]e^{i\nu y}\,dy = \int_{-b/2}^{+b/2} e^{i\nu y}\,dy + i\int_{-b/2}^{+b/2} \phi(y)\,e^{i\nu y}\,dy$$

$$= U_1(\nu) + iU_2(\nu) \tag{4.63}$$

Here $U_1(\nu)$ represents the diffraction pattern of the whole object aperture. It is essentially zero everywhere except for $\nu \approx 0$, that is, $U_1(\nu)$ contains only very low spatial frequencies. On the other hand, $U_2(\nu)$

represents the diffraction pattern of the periodic-step function $\phi(y)$. The two functions are plotted in Figure 4.32(b).

By virtue of the factor i in the result, $U_1 + iU_2$, the two components U_1 and iU_2 are 90 degrees out of phase. The essential trick in the phase contrast method consists of inserting a spatial filter in the $\mu\nu$ plane, which has the property of shifting the phase of iU_2 by an additional 90 degrees. In practice this is accomplished by means of a device known as a *phase plate*. The physical arrangement is shown in Figure 4.33.

Figure 4.33. Physical arrangement of the optical elements for phase contrast microscopy.

The phase plate is just a transparent glass plate having a small section whose optical thickness is 1/4 wavelength greater than the remainder of the plate. This thicker section is located in the central part of the $\mu\nu$ plane, that is, in the region of low spatial frequencies. The result of inserting the phase plate is to change the function $U_1 + iU_2$ to $U_1 + U_2$. The new image function is given by the Fourier transform of the new $U(\nu)$, namely

$$g'(y') = \int U_1(\nu)e^{-i\nu y'}\,d\nu + \int U_2(\nu)e^{-i\nu y'}\,d\nu$$

$$= g_1(y') + g_2(y') \tag{4.64}$$

Now the first function g_1 is just the image function of the whole-object aperture. It represents the constant background. The second function g_2 is the image function for a regular grating of alternate transparent and opaque strips. This means that the phase grating has been rendered visible. It appears in the image plane as alternate bright and dark strips. Although the above analysis has been for a periodic grating, a similar argument can be applied to a transparent-phase object of any shape.

The method of optical-phase contrast has a close analogy in electrical communications. A phase-modulated signal is converted into an amplitude-modulated signal by introduction of a phase shift of 90 degrees to the carrier frequency. This is essentially what the phase plate does in the phase contrast method. The net result is that phase modulation in the object is converted into amplitude modulation in the image.

4.7 Reconstruction of the Wavefront by Diffraction. Holography

An unusual and interesting method of producing an image—known as the method of *wave-front reconstruction*—has recently become of importance in the field of optics. Although the basic idea was originally proposed by Gabor in 1947 [12], it attracted little attention until the highly coherent light of the laser became available.

In this method a special diffraction screen, called a *hologram,* is used to reconstruct in detail the wave field emitted by the subject. To make the hologram, the output from a laser is separated into two beams, one of which illuminates the subject. The other beam, called the *reference beam,* is reflected onto a fine-grained photographic film by means of a mirror. The film is exposed simultaneously to the reference beam and the reflected laser light from the subject, Figure 4.34(a). The resulting complicated interference pattern recorded by the film constitutes the hologram. It contains all the information needed to reproduce the wave field of the subject.

In use, the developed hologram is illuminated with a single beam from a laser as shown in Figure 4.34(b). Part of the resulting diffracted wave field is a precise, three-dimensional copy of the original wave reflected by the subject. The viewer looking at the hologram sees the image in depth and by moving his head can change his perspective of the view.

In order to simplify the discussion of the theory of holography, we shall assume that the reference beam is collimated, that is, it consists of plane waves, although this is not actually necessary in practice. Let x and y be the coordinates in the plane of the recording photographic plate, and let $U(x,y)$ denote the complex amplitude of the reflected wavefront in the xy plane. Since $U(x,y)$ is a complex number, we can write it as

$$U(x,y) = a(x,y)\, e^{i\phi(x,y)} \tag{4.65}$$

where $a(x,y)$ is real.

Similarly, let $U_0(x,y)$ denote the complex amplitude of the reference beam. Since this beam is plane, we can write

$$U_0(x,y) = a_0\, e^{i(\mu x\, +\, \nu y)} \tag{4.66}$$

where a_0 is a constant, and μ and ν are the spatial frequencies of the reference beam in the xy plane. They are given by

$$\mu = k \sin \alpha \qquad \nu = k \sin \beta \qquad \text{(4.67)}$$

in which k is the wavenumber of the laser light, and α and β specify the direction of the reference beam.

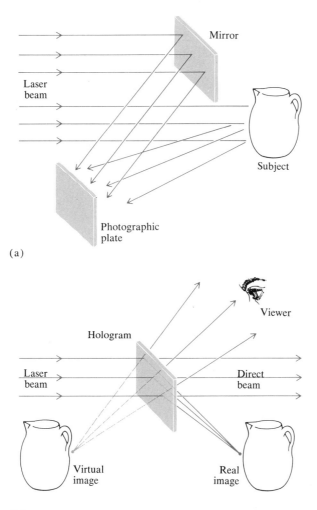

(a)

(b)

Figure 4.34. (a) Arrangement for producing a hologram. (b) Use of the hologram in producing the real and virtual images.

The intensity $I(x,y)$ that is recorded by the photographic film is thus given by the expression

$$I(x,y) = |U + U_0|^2 = a^2 + a_0{}^2 + aa_0 e^{i[\phi(x,y) - \mu x - \nu y]}$$
$$+ aa_0 e^{-i[\phi(x,y) - \mu x - \nu y]}$$
$$= a^2 + a_0{}^2 + 2aa_0 \cos[\phi(x,y) - \mu x - \nu y] \qquad \text{(4.68)}$$

This is actually an interference pattern. It contains information in the form of amplitude and phase modulations of the spatial frequencies of the reference beam. The situation is somewhat analogous to the impression of information on the carrier wave of a radio transmitter by means of amplitude or phase modulation.

When the developed hologram is illuminated with a single beam U_0 similar to the reference beam, the resulting transmitted wave U_T is proportional to U_0 times the transmittance of the hologram at the point (x,y). The transmittance will be proportional to $I(x,y)$. Hence, except for a constant proportionality factor that we ignore,

$$U_T(x,y) = U_0 I = a_0(a^2 + a_0{}^2)e^{i(\mu x + \nu y)} + a_0{}^2 a\, e^{i\phi} + a_0{}^2 a\, e^{-i(\phi - 2\mu x - 2\nu y)}$$
$$= (a^2 + a_0{}^2)U_0 + a_0{}^2 U + U^{-1}U_0{}^{-2}a^2 \qquad \text{(4.69)}$$

The hologram acts somewhat like a diffraction grating. It produces a direct beam and two first-order diffracted beams on either side of the direct beam, Figure 4.34(b). The term $(a^2 + a_0{}^2)U_0$ in Equation (4.69) comprises the direct beam. The term $a_0{}^2 U$ represents one of the diffracted beams. Since it is equal to a constant times U, this beam is the one that reproduces the reflected light from the subject and forms the virtual image. The last term represents the other diffracted beam and gives rise to a real image.

We shall not attempt to prove the above statements in detail. They can be verified by considering a very simple case, namely, that in which the subject is a single white line on a dark background. In this case the hologram turns out to be, in fact, a simple periodic grating. The zero order of the diffracted light is the direct beam, while the two first orders on either side comprise the virtual and the real images.

In holography the viewer always sees a positive image whether a positive or a negative photographic transparency is used for the hologram. The reason for this is that a negative hologram merely produces a wave field that is shifted 180 degrees in phase with respect to that of a positive hologram. Since the eye is insensitive to this phase difference, the view seen by the observer is identical in the two cases.

PROBLEMS

4.1. A point (pinhole) source is to be used in a diffraction experiment. The distance from the source to the diffracting aperture is 5 m. If the aperture is 1 mm in diameter, determine whether Fraunhofer or Fresnel diffraction applies when the screen-to-aperture distance is (a) 10 cm, (b) 50 cm, (c) 5 m. Take $\lambda = 5000$ Å.

4.2. Prove that the secondary maxima of a single-slit Fraunhofer diffraction pattern occur at the points for which $\beta = \tan \beta$. Show that the first three roots are given by $\beta = 1.43\pi, 2.46\pi$, and 3.47π, approximately. Show further that for large n, the roots approach the values $(n + \frac{1}{2})\pi$ where n is an integer.

4.3. Find the value of I/I_0 for the first diagonal maximum of the Fraunhofer diffraction pattern of a rectangular aperture. (The diagonal maxima are those that occur on the line $\alpha = \beta$.)

4.4. What are the angular diameters of the second and third dark rings of the Fraunhofer diffraction pattern of a circular aperture.

4.5. What size telescope (diameter of aperture) would be required to resolve the components of a double star whose linear separation is 100 million km and whose distance from the earth is 10 light years? (Take $\lambda = 5000$ Å.)

4.6. In the Fraunhofer diffraction pattern of a double slit, it is found that the fourth secondary maximum is missing. What is the ratio of slit width b to slit separation h?

4.7. Show that the Fraunhofer diffraction pattern of a double slit reduces to that of a single slit of width $2b$ when the slit width is equal to the separation, that is, when $h = b$.

4.8. (a) A grating is used to resolve the sodium D lines (5890 Å and 5896 Å) in the first order. How many rulings are needed?
(b) If the focal length of the focusing lens is 20 cm, and the total width of the grating is 2 cm, what is the linear separation, at the focal plane, between the two D lines?

4.9. A grating has 100 lines. What is the ratio of the intensity of a primary maximum to that of the first secondary maximum?

4.10. Show that there are $2 + 2h/b$ maxima under the central diffraction envelope of a double-slit pattern, where h is the slit separation and b is the slit width.

4.11. A grating has 1000 lines/mm of width. How wide must the grating be in order to resolve the mode structure of a laser beam of 6328 Å. The frequency difference between the modes is 450 MHz.

4.12. What is the minimum resolvable wavelength separation for a grating of 1200 lines/mm having a width of 5 cm? The wavelength is 5000 Å, and the grating is to be used in the first order.

4.13. A point source $S(\lambda = 5000$ Å$)$ is placed 1 m from an aperture consisting of a hole of 1-mm radius in which there is a circular opaque obstacle whose radius is 1/2 mm, as shown in the figure. The receiving point P is 1 m from the aperture. What is the intensity at P compared to the intensity if the aperture were removed?

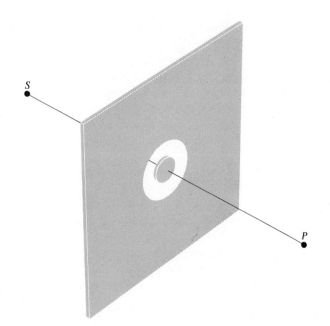

Figure 4.35. Dimensions of the diffraction aperture for Problem 4.13.

4.14. A radiotelescope is observing a distant point source at a wavelength of 20 cm. As the moon passes in front of the source, a Fresnel diffraction pattern is traced out by the telescope's recorder. What is the time interval between the first maximum and the first minimum? (Assume the edge of the moon to be effectively straight.)

4.15. Apply Equation (4.12) directly to show that the value of U_p, contributed by the first Fresnel zone alone, is twice the value with no aperture at all.

4.16. Find the intensity at the receiving point P in Problem 4.13 if the aperture is an open square 2 mm by 2 mm.

4.17. Using Cornu's spiral, make a plot of the Fresnel diffraction pattern of (a) a slit and (b) a complementary opaque strip. Note how

Babinet's principle applies here. (Take the equivalent width to be $\Delta v = 3$.) (c) If the actual width is 1 mm and the incident light is parallel, $\lambda = 5000$ Å, what is the observing position in order that $\Delta v = 3$?

4.18. An object consists of a single white strip of width b. Treating the case as a one-dimensional problem, find the spatial frequency function $U(v)$ for coherent illumination of the object.

4.19. Referring to Problem 18, if the μv aperture is limited to $\pm v_{max}$ where v_{max} lies at the second zero of the $U(v)$ function, find the resulting image function $g(y')$. Express as an integral.

4.20. A simple hologram is made in the following manner:

The object is a single narrow white strip located a distance d from the base of the recording plate. The wavelength of the laser is λ. The plate is illuminated normally by the reference beam. Show that the resulting pattern on the hologram is a one-dimensional grating with a variable spacing in the y direction. Give the numerical values of this spacing for $\lambda = 6328$ Å, $d = 10$ cm when $y = 0$, 1 cm, 5 cm, 10 cm.

4.21. Referring to Problem 4.20, show in detail how, if the hologram is illuminated with monochromatic light, there will be two diffracted beams, one producing a real image of the strip, the other producing a virtual image. One beam appears to diverge from a line 0 corresponding to the original object, the other converges to a line 0′, the real image. Find the actual angles of diffraction for various values of y given in Problem 4.20. Will there be a second order (or higher order) diffracted beam?

4.22. Calculate the diffraction pattern of an apodized slit for which the transmission function is $[\frac{1}{2} + \frac{1}{2} \cos(2\pi y/b)] = g(y)$ for $-b/2 < y < b/2$ and zero otherwise. Find the relative intensity of the first secondary maximum.

CHAPTER 5

Optics of Solids

5.1 General Remarks

The study of the propagation of light through matter, particularly solid matter, comprises one of the important and interesting branches of optics. The many and varied optical phenomena exhibited by solids include such things as selective absorption, dispersion, double refraction, polarization effects, and electro-optical and magneto-optical effects. Many of the optical properties of solids can be understood on the basis of classical electromagnetic theory. The present chapter is essentially a detailed application of the macroscopic Maxwell theory to the propagation of light through solids. The microscopic origin of the optical properties of solids will be treated classically, since the quantum-theoretical treatment is beyond the scope of this book. But the way in which the phenomena are described by the classical theory gives considerable physical insight and helps to provide a fundamental background for later study.

5.2 Macroscopic Fields and Maxwell's Equations

The electromagnetic state of matter at a given point is described by four quantities:

(1) the volume density of electric charge ρ;
(2) the volume density of electric dipoles, called the *polarization* $\mathbf{P}$;
(3) the volume density of magnetic dipoles, called the *magnetization* $\mathbf{M}$;
(4) the electric current per unit area, called the *current density* $\mathbf{J}$.

All of these quantities are considered to be macroscopically averaged in order to smooth out the microscopic variations due to the atomic makeup of all matter. They are related to the macroscopically averaged fields $\mathbf{E}$ and $\mathbf{H}$ by the following Maxwell equations:

$$\nabla \times \mathbf{E} = -\mu_0 \frac{\partial \mathbf{H}}{\partial t} - \mu_0 \frac{\partial \mathbf{M}}{\partial t} \tag{5.1}$$

$$\nabla \times \mathbf{H} = \varepsilon_0 \frac{\partial \mathbf{E}}{\partial t} + \frac{\partial \mathbf{P}}{\partial t} + \mathbf{J} \tag{5.2}$$

$$\nabla \cdot \mathbf{E} = -\frac{1}{\varepsilon_0} \nabla \cdot \mathbf{P} + \rho \tag{5.3}$$

$$\nabla \cdot \mathbf{H} = -\nabla \cdot \mathbf{M} \tag{5.4}$$

If one introduces the abbreviation $\mathscr{D}$ for the quantity $\varepsilon_0\mathbf{E} + \mathbf{P}$, known as the *electric displacement,* and the abbreviation $\mathbf{B}$ for $\mu_0(\mathbf{H} + \mathbf{M})$, called the *magnetic induction,* then Maxwell's equations assume the more compact forms:

$$\nabla \times \mathbf{E} = -\frac{\partial \mathbf{B}}{\partial t} \tag{5.5}$$

$$\nabla \times \mathbf{H} = \frac{\partial \mathscr{D}}{\partial t} + \mathbf{J} \tag{5.6}$$

$$\nabla \cdot \mathscr{D} = \rho \tag{5.7}$$

$$\nabla \cdot \mathbf{B} = 0 \tag{5.8}$$

The response of the conduction electrons to the electric field is given by the current equation (Ohm's law)

$$\mathbf{J} = \sigma\mathbf{E}$$

where σ is the conductivity. The constitutive relation

$$\mathscr{D} = \varepsilon\mathbf{E}$$

describes the aggregate response of the bound charges to the electric field. The corresponding magnetic relation is

$$\mathbf{B} = \mu\mathbf{H}$$

An alternate way to express the response of the bound charges is

$$\mathbf{P} = (\varepsilon - \varepsilon_0)\mathbf{E} = \chi\varepsilon_0\mathbf{E} \tag{5.9}$$

which gives the proportionality between the polarization and the impressed electric field. The proportionality factor

$$\chi = \frac{\varepsilon}{\varepsilon_0} - 1$$

is known as the *electric susceptibility.*

In the case of isotropic media, for example, glass, χ is a scalar quantity having the same value for any direction of the applied electric field. For nonisotropic media, such as most crystals, the magnitude of the polarization varies with the direction of the applied field, and consequently, χ must be expressed as a tensor. We shall find that the χ-tensor of a crystal summarizes most of its optical properties.

5.3   The General Wave Equation

In our study of solid-state optics, we shall be concerned only with nonmagnetic, electrically neutral media. Hence $\mathbf{M}$ and ρ are both zero. Maxwell's equations, in the form expressed by Equations (5.1) to (5.4), then reduce to the following:

$$\nabla \times \mathbf{E} = -\mu_0 \frac{\partial \mathbf{H}}{\partial t} \tag{5.10}$$

$$\nabla \times \mathbf{H} = \varepsilon_0 \frac{\partial \mathbf{E}}{\partial t} + \frac{\partial \mathbf{P}}{\partial t} + \mathbf{J} \tag{5.11}$$

$$\nabla \cdot \mathbf{E} = -\frac{1}{\varepsilon_0} \nabla \cdot \mathbf{P} \tag{5.12}$$

$$\nabla \cdot \mathbf{H} = 0 \tag{5.13}$$

The general wave equation for the $\mathbf{E}$ field is obtained by taking the curl of Equation (5.10) and the time derivative of Equation (5.11) and eliminating $\mathbf{H}$. The result is

$$\nabla \times (\nabla \times \mathbf{E}) + \frac{1}{c^2} \frac{\partial^2 \mathbf{E}}{\partial t^2} = -\mu_0 \frac{\partial^2 \mathbf{P}}{\partial t^2} - \mu_0 \frac{\partial \mathbf{J}}{\partial t} \tag{5.14}$$

The two terms on the right-hand side of the above equation are called *source terms*. They stem from the presence of polarization charges and conduction charges, respectively, within the medium. The way in which the propagation of light is affected by the sources is revealed by the solution of the wave equation when the source terms are included. In the case of nonconducting media the polarization term $-\mu_0 \partial^2 \mathbf{P}/\partial t^2$ is of importance. It turns out that this term leads to an explanation of many optical effects, including dispersion, absorption, double refraction, and optical activity to mention only a few. In the case of metals it is the conduction term $-\mu_0 \partial \mathbf{J}/\partial t$ that is important, and the resulting solutions of the wave equation explain the large opacity and high reflectance of metals. Both source terms must be taken into account in the case of semiconductors. The result is a rather complicated wave equation and the solutions are somewhat difficult to interpret. Nevertheless, a qualitative description of many of the optical properties of semiconductors is furnished by classical theory. A rigorous treatment of semiconductor optics must await the application of quantum theory.

5.4 Propagation of Light in Isotropic Dielectrics. Dispersion

In a nonconducting, isotropic medium, the electrons are permanently bound to the atoms comprising the medium and there is no preferential direction. This is what is meant by a simple dielectric. Suppose that each electron, of charge $-e$, in a dielectric is displaced a distance $\mathbf{r}$ from its equilibrium position. The resulting macroscopic polarization $\mathbf{P}$ of the medium is given by

$$\mathbf{P} = -N e \mathbf{r} \tag{5.15}$$

where N is the number of electrons per unit volume. If the displacement of the electron is the result of the application of a static electric field $\mathbf{E}$, and if the electron is elastically bound to its equilibrium position with a force constant K, then the force equation is

$$-e\mathbf{E} = K\mathbf{r} \tag{5.16}$$

The *static* polarization is therefore given by

$$\mathbf{P} = \frac{Ne^2}{K}\mathbf{E} \tag{5.17}$$

However, if the impressed field $\mathbf{E}$ varies with time, the above equation is incorrect. In order to find the true polarization in this case, we must take the actual motion of the electrons into account. To do this we consider the bound electrons as classical damped harmonic oscillators. The differential equation of motion is

$$m\frac{d^2\mathbf{r}}{dt^2} + m\gamma\frac{d\mathbf{r}}{dt} + K\mathbf{r} = -e\mathbf{E} \tag{5.18}$$

The term $m\gamma(d\mathbf{r}/dt)$ represents a frictional damping force that is proportional to the velocity of the electron, the proportionality constant being written as $m\gamma$.[1]

Now suppose that the applied electric field varies harmonically with time according to the usual factor $e^{-i\omega t}$. Assuming that the motion of the electron has the same harmonic time dependence, we find that Equation (5.18) becomes

---

[1] The magnetic force $e\mathbf{v}\times\mathbf{B}$ is neglected here. For electromagnetic waves, this force is normally much smaller than the electric force $e\mathbf{E}$.

$$(-m\omega^2 + i\omega m\gamma + K)\mathbf{r} = -e\mathbf{E} \qquad (5.19)$$

Consequently the polarization, from Equation (5.15), is given by

$$\mathbf{P} = \frac{Ne^2}{-m\omega^2 - i\omega m\gamma + K}\mathbf{E} \qquad (5.20)$$

It reduces to the static value, Equation (5.17), when $\omega = 0$. Thus, for a given amplitude of the impressed electric field, the amount of polarization varies with frequency. The phase of $\mathbf{P}$, relative to that of the electric field, also depends on the frequency. This is shown by the presence of the imaginary term in the denominator.

Now the $\mathbf{E}$ of Equation (5.20) is actually the *effective* field at the position of the electron. This effective field is equal to the sum of the macroscopic electric field and the field due to polarization of the medium. It can be shown [16] that this latter field is $\mathbf{P}/3\varepsilon_0$. Thus, instead of Equation (5.20) we should correctly write

$$\mathbf{P} = \frac{Ne^2}{-m\omega^2 - i\omega m\gamma + K}\left(\mathbf{E} + \frac{1}{3\varepsilon_0}\mathbf{P}\right) \qquad (5.21)$$

where $\mathbf{E}$ is now the macroscopic electric field. Solving for $\mathbf{P}$, we obtain

$$\mathbf{P} = \frac{Ne^2/m}{\omega_0^2 - \omega^2 - i\omega\gamma}\mathbf{E} \qquad (5.22)$$

in which we have introduced the abbreviation ω_0 given by

$$\omega_0 = \sqrt{\frac{K}{m} - \frac{Ne^2}{3\varepsilon_0 m}} \qquad (5.23)$$

This is the *effective resonance frequency* of the bound electrons.

The polarization formula (5.22) is similar to the amplitude formula for a driven harmonic oscillator, as indeed it should be, since it is the displacement of the elastically bound electrons that actually constitutes the polarization. We should, therefore, expect to find an optical resonance phenomenon of some kind to occur for light frequencies in the neighborhood of the resonance frequency ω_0. As we shall presently see, this resonance phenomenon is manifest as a large change in the index of refraction of the medium, and also by a strong absorption of light at or near the resonance frequency.

To show how the polarization affects the propagation of light, we return to the general wave equation (5.14). For a dielectric there is no conduction term. The polarization is given by Equation (5.22). Hence we have

$$\mathbf{\nabla} \times (\mathbf{\nabla} \times \mathbf{E}) + \frac{1}{c^2}\frac{\partial^2 \mathbf{E}}{\partial t^2} = \frac{-\mu_0 Ne^2}{m}\left(\frac{1}{\omega_0^2 - \omega^2 - i\gamma\omega}\right)\frac{\partial^2 \mathbf{E}}{\partial t^2} \qquad (5.24)$$

Also, from the linear relationship between $\mathbf{P}$ and $\mathbf{E}$, it follows from (5.12) that $\nabla \cdot \mathbf{E} = 0$. Consequently $\nabla \times (\nabla \times \mathbf{E}) = -\nabla^2\mathbf{E}$, and the above wave equation reduces to the somewhat simpler one

$$\nabla^2\mathbf{E} = \frac{1}{c^2}\left(1 + \frac{Ne^2}{m\varepsilon_0} \cdot \frac{1}{\omega_0^2 - \omega^2 - i\gamma\omega}\right)\frac{\partial^2\mathbf{E}}{\partial t^2} \tag{5.25}$$

after rearranging terms.

Let us seek a solution of the form

$$\mathbf{E} = \mathbf{E}_0\, e^{i(\mathscr{K}z - \omega t)} \tag{5.26}$$

This trial solution represents what are called *homogeneous* plane harmonic waves. Direct substitution shows that this is a possible solution provided that

$$\mathscr{K}^2 = \frac{\omega^2}{c^2}\left(1 + \frac{Ne^2}{m\varepsilon_0} \cdot \frac{1}{\omega_0^2 - \omega^2 - i\gamma\omega}\right) \tag{5.27}$$

The presence of the imaginary term in the denominator implies that the wavenumber $\mathscr{K}$ must be a complex number. Let us inquire as to the physical significance of this. We express $\mathscr{K}$ in terms of its real and imaginary parts as

$$\mathscr{K} = k + i\alpha \tag{5.28}$$

This amounts to the same thing as introducing a complex index of refraction $\mathscr{N} = n + i\kappa$ where

$$\mathscr{K} = \frac{\omega}{c}\mathscr{N} \tag{5.29}$$

Our solution in Equation (5.26) can then be written as

$$\mathbf{E} = \mathbf{E}_0 e^{-\alpha z}\, e^{i(kz - \omega t)} \tag{5.30}$$

The factor $e^{-\alpha z}$ indicates that the amplitude of the wave decreases exponentially with distance. This means that as the wave progresses, the energy of the wave is absorbed by the medium. The quantity α, known as the *coefficient of absorption* is the imaginary part of the propagation constant. The imaginary part κ of the complex index of refraction is called the *extinction coefficient*. The two numbers α and κ are related by the equation

$$\alpha = \frac{\omega}{c}\kappa \tag{5.31}$$

The factor $e^{i(kz - \omega t)}$ indicates that we have a harmonic wave in which the phase velocity is

$$v = \frac{\omega}{k} = \frac{c}{n} \tag{5.32}$$

OPTICS OF SOLIDS

From Equations (5.27) and (5.29) we have

$$\mathcal{N}^2 = (n + i\kappa)^2 = 1 + \frac{Ne^2}{m\varepsilon_0}\left(\frac{1}{\omega_0{}^2 - \omega^2 - i\gamma\omega}\right) \tag{5.33}$$

Equating real and imaginary parts yields the following equations:

$$n^2 - \kappa^2 = 1 + \frac{Ne^2}{m\varepsilon_0}\left(\frac{\omega_0{}^2 - \omega^2}{(\omega_0{}^2 - \omega^2)^2 + \gamma^2\omega^2}\right) \tag{5.34}$$

$$2n\kappa = \frac{Ne^2}{m\varepsilon_0}\left(\frac{\gamma\omega_0\omega}{(\omega_0{}^2 - \omega^2)^2 + \gamma^2\omega^2}\right) \tag{5.35}$$

from which the optical constants n and κ may be found.

Figure 5.1 shows the general way in which n and κ depend on frequency. The absorption is strongest at the resonance frequency ω_0.

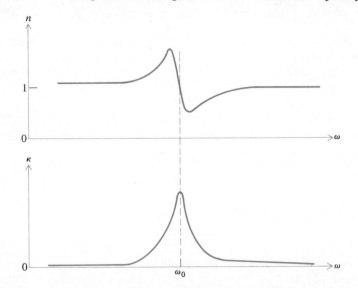

Figure 5.1. Graphs of the index of refraction and extinction coefficient versus frequency near a single resonance line.

The index of refraction is greater than unity for small frequencies and increases with frequency as the resonance frequency is approached. This is the case of "normal" dispersion, which is exhibited by most transparent substances over the visible region of the spectrum, the principal resonance frequencies being in the ultraviolet region. At or near the resonance frequency, however, the dispersion becomes "anomalous" in the sense that the index of refraction *decreases* with increasing frequency.

Anomalous dispersion can be observed experimentally if the substance is not too opaque at the resonance frequency. For instance, certain dyes have absorption bands in the visible region of the spectrum and exhibit anomalous dispersion in the region of these bands. Prisms made of these dyes produce a spectrum that is reversed; that is, the longer wavelengths are refracted more than the shorter wavelengths.

Now in the above discussion it has been tacitly assumed that all of the electrons were identically bound, and hence, all had the same resonance frequencies. In order to take into account the fact that different electrons may be bound differently, we may assume that a certain fraction f_1 have an associated resonance frequency ω_1, a fraction f_2 have the resonance frequency ω_2, and so on. The resulting formula for the square of the complex index of refraction is of the form

$$\mathcal{N}^2 = 1 + \frac{Ne^2}{m\varepsilon_o} \sum_j \left(\frac{f_j}{\omega_j{}^2 - \omega^2 - i\gamma_j\omega} \right) \tag{5.36}$$

The summation extends over all the various kinds of electrons indicated by the subscript j. The fractions f_j are known as *oscillator strengths*. The damping constants associated with the various frequencies are denoted by γ_j. Figure 5.2 shows graphically the general dependence of the real and imaginary parts of N as determined by Equation (5.36). This graph is intended to show qualitatively the case for a substance, such as glass, which is transparent in the visible region and has absorption bands in the infrared and ultraviolet regions of the spectrum. In the limit of zero frequency, the square of the index approaches the value $1 + (Ne^2/m\varepsilon_o) \sum f_j/\omega_j{}^2$. This is just the static dielectric constant of the medium.

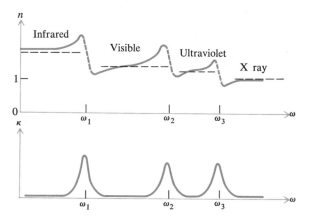

Figure 5.2. Index of refraction and extinction coefficient for a hypothetical substance with absorption bands in the infrared, visible, and ultraviolet regions of the spectrum.

In the high frequency region, the theory predicts that the index should dip below unity and then approach unity from below as ω becomes infinite. This effect is actually seen experimentally. The case of quartz is shown in Figure 5.3. Here the measured index of refraction of quartz is plotted as a function of wavelength for the appropriate region of the spectrum (x-ray region).

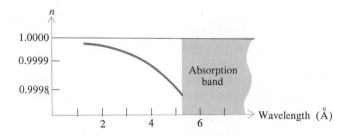

Figure 5.3.   Measured index of refraction of quartz in the x-ray region.

If the damping constants γ_j are sufficiently small so that the terms $\gamma_j\omega$ can be neglected in comparison to the quantities $\omega_j{}^2 - \omega^2$ in Equation (5.36), then the index of refraction is essentially real and its square is given by

$$n^2 = 1 + \frac{Ne^2}{m\varepsilon_o} \sum_j \left(\frac{f_j}{\omega_j{}^2 - \omega_o{}^2}\right) \tag{5.37}$$

It is possible, by an empirical curve fitting procedure, to make a formula of the above type match the experimental data quite well for many transparent substances. When expressed in terms of wavelength instead of frequency, the equation is known as Sellmeier's formula.

5.5   Propagation of Light in Conducting Media

The effects of conduction on the propagation of light through a medium can be treated in much the same manner as the effects of polarization were treated in the preceeding section. The difference is that we are now interested in the conduction term in the general wave equation, not the polarization term. Again, owing to the inertia of the conduction electrons, we cannot merely put $\mathbf{J} = \sigma\mathbf{E}$ for the current density where σ is the static conductivity. We must consider actual motion of the electrons under the action of the alternating electric field of the light wave.

Since the conduction electrons are not bound, there is no elastic restoring force as there was in the case of polarization. The differential equation of motion of the electron is therefore of the form

$$m\frac{d\mathbf{v}}{dt} + m\tau^{-1}\mathbf{v} = -e\mathbf{E} \tag{5.38}$$

where $\mathbf{v}$ is the velocity of the electron. The frictional dissipation constant is expressed in the form $m\tau^{-1}$. This constant is related to the static conductivity as we shall presently see. Since the current density is

$$\mathbf{J} = -N e \mathbf{v} \tag{5.39}$$

where N is now the number of conduction electrons per unit volume, then Equation (5.38) can be expressed in terms of $\mathbf{J}$ as follows:

$$\frac{d\mathbf{J}}{dt} + \tau^{-1}\mathbf{J} = \frac{Ne^2}{m}\mathbf{E} \tag{5.40}$$

The decay of a transient current is governed by the associated homogeneous equation

$$\frac{d\mathbf{J}}{dt} + \tau^{-1}\mathbf{J} = 0 \tag{5.41}$$

whose solution is $\mathbf{J} = \mathbf{J}_0 e^{-t/\tau}$. Thus a transient current will decay to e^{-1} of its initial value in a time τ. This is called the *relaxation time*. Now for a static electric field, Equation (5.40) becomes

$$\tau^{-1}\mathbf{J} = \frac{Ne^2}{m}\mathbf{E} \tag{5.42}$$

The static conductivity σ is, therefore, given by

$$\sigma = \frac{Ne^2}{m}\tau \tag{5.43}$$

Let us now assume a harmonic time dependence $e^{-i\omega t}$ for both electric field $\mathbf{E}$ and the resulting current $\mathbf{J}$ in our differential equation (5.40). It follows that

$$(-i\omega + \tau^{-1})\mathbf{J} = \frac{Ne^2}{m}\mathbf{E} = \tau^{-1}\sigma\mathbf{E} \tag{5.44}$$

Solving for $\mathbf{J}$, we find

$$\mathbf{J} = \frac{\sigma}{1 - i\omega\tau}\mathbf{E} \tag{5.45}$$

When $\omega = 0$, the above equation reduces to $\mathbf{J} = \sigma\mathbf{E}$, which is the correct equation for the static case.

Using the dynamic expression for $\mathbf{J}$, Equation (5.45), we find that the general wave Equation (5.14) reduces to

$$\nabla^2\mathbf{E} = \frac{1}{c^2}\frac{\partial^2\mathbf{E}}{\partial t^2} + \frac{\mu_0\sigma}{1 - i\omega\tau}\frac{\partial\mathbf{E}}{\partial t} \tag{5.46}$$

For a trial solution, we take a simple homogeneous plane-wave solution of the type

$$\mathbf{E} = \mathbf{E}_0\, e^{i(\mathcal{K}z - \omega t)} \tag{5.47}$$

where, as in Equation (5.26), $\mathcal{K}$ is assumed to be complex. It is easily found that $\mathcal{K}$ must then satisfy the relation

$$\mathcal{K}^2 = \frac{\omega^2}{c^2} + \frac{i\omega\mu_0\sigma}{1 - i\omega\tau} \tag{5.48}$$

For very low frequencies the above formula reduces to the approximate formula

$$\mathcal{K}^2 \approx i\omega\mu_0\sigma \tag{5.49}$$

so that $\mathcal{K} \approx \sqrt{i\omega\mu_0\sigma} = (1 + i)\sqrt{\omega\mu_0\sigma/2}$. In this case the real and imaginary parts of $\mathcal{K} = k + i\alpha$ are equal and are given by

$$k \approx \alpha \approx \sqrt{\frac{\omega\sigma\mu_0}{2}} \tag{5.50}$$

The corresponding values of n and κ are

$$n \approx \kappa \approx \sqrt{\frac{\sigma}{2\omega\varepsilon_0}} \tag{5.51}$$

The so-called "skin depth" δ of a metal is that distance at which the amplitude of an electromagnetic wave drops to e^{-1} of its value at the surface. Thus

$$\delta = \frac{1}{\alpha} = \sqrt{\frac{2}{\omega\sigma\mu_0}} = \sqrt{\frac{\lambda_0}{c\pi\sigma\mu_0}} \tag{5.52}$$

where λ_0 is the vacuum wavelength. This shows why good conductors are also highly opaque. A high value of the conductivity σ gives a large coefficient of absorption α and a correspondingly small skin depth. For example, the skin depth in copper ($\sigma = 5.8 \times 10^7$ mho/m) for 1-mm microwaves is about 10^{-4} mm.

Let us return to the more accurate expression for $\mathcal{K}$, Equation (5.48). The equivalent form of this equation written in terms of the complex index of refraction, as defined by Equation (5.29), is

$$\mathcal{N}^2 = 1 - \frac{\omega_p^2}{\omega^2 + i\omega\tau^{-1}} \tag{5.53}$$

Here we have introduced *plasma frequency* for the metal. It is given by

$$\omega_p = \sqrt{\frac{Ne^2}{m\varepsilon_0}} = \sqrt{\frac{\mu_0\sigma c^2}{\tau}} \qquad (5.54)$$

By equating real and imaginary parts in Equation (5.53), we find

$$n^2 - \kappa^2 = 1 - \frac{\omega_p^2}{\omega^2 + \tau^{-2}} \qquad (5.55)$$

$$2n\kappa = \frac{\omega_p^2}{\omega^2 + \tau^{-2}}\left(\frac{1}{\omega\tau}\right) \qquad (5.56)$$

from which the optical "constants" n and κ may be obtained. According to the above theory, these are determined entirely by the plasma frequency ω_p, the relaxation time τ, and the frequency ω of the light wave.

Typical relaxation times for metals, as deduced from conductivity measurements, are of the order of 10^{-13} s, which corresponds to frequencies in the infrared region of the spectrum. On the other hand, plasma frequencies of metals are typically around 10^{15} s^{-1}, corresponding to the visible and near ultraviolet regions. Figure 5.4 shows the behavior of n and κ plotted as functions of ω from Equations (5.55)

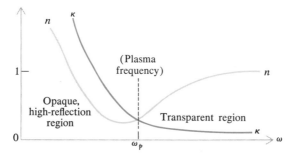

Figure 5.4. Index of refraction and extinction coefficient versus frequency for a metal.

and (5.56). As seen from the figure, the index of refraction n is less than unity for a wide range of frequencies in the region of the plasma frequency. The extinction coefficient κ is very large at low frequencies (long wavelengths). It decreases monotonically with increasing frequency becoming very small for frequencies greater than the plasma frequency. The metal thus becomes transparent at high frequencies. Qualitative agreement with these predictions of classical theory is obtained in the case of the alkali metals and some of the better conductors such as silver, gold, and copper.

For poor conductors and semiconductors, both free electrons and bound electrons can contribute to the optical properties. Classical theory would, accordingly, yield an equation of the type

$$n^2 = 1 - \frac{\omega_p{}^2}{\omega^2 + i\omega\tau^{-1}} + \frac{Ne^2}{m\varepsilon_0}\Sigma\left(\frac{f_j}{\omega_j{}^2 - \omega^2 - i\gamma_j\omega}\right) \tag{5.57}$$

for the complex index of refraction. It turns out that quantum theory gives a similar relation and, in addition, can predict the values of the various parameters f_j, γ_j, and so forth. The theoretical calculations are difficult however, as are also the experimental measurements. The optics of semiconductors is one of the most active areas of current experimental and theoretical research.

5.6 Reflection and Refraction at the Boundary of an Absorbing Medium

Let a plane wave be incident on the boundary of a medium having a complex index of refraction

$$\mathcal{N} = n + i\kappa \tag{5.58}$$

Denote the complex propagation vector of the refracted wave by

$$\mathcal{K} = \mathbf{k} + i\boldsymbol{\alpha} \tag{5.59}$$

For simplicity, we shall consider only the case in which the first medium is nonabsorbing. The following notation will be employed (deleting the amplitudes):

incident wave $\quad e^{i(\mathbf{k}_0\cdot\mathbf{r} - \omega t)}$

reflected wave $\quad e^{i(\mathbf{k}_0'\cdot\mathbf{r} - \omega t)}$

refracted wave $\quad e^{i(\mathcal{K}\cdot\mathbf{r} - \omega t)} = e^{-\boldsymbol{\alpha}\cdot\mathbf{r}}\, e^{i(\mathbf{k}\cdot\mathbf{r} - \omega t)}$

As is the case with reflection and refraction at a dielectric interface, discussed earlier in Section 2.6, the requirement that a constant ratio exists among the fields at the boundary plane leads to the equations

$$\mathbf{k}_0\cdot\mathbf{r} = \mathbf{k}_0'\cdot\mathbf{r} \quad \text{at boundary} \tag{5.60}$$

$$\mathbf{k}_0\cdot\mathbf{r} = \mathcal{K}\cdot\mathbf{r} = (\mathbf{k} + i\boldsymbol{\alpha})\cdot\mathbf{r} \quad \text{at boundary} \tag{5.61}$$

The first equation gives the usual law of reflection. The second equation, after equating real and imaginary parts, yields

$$\mathbf{k}_0\cdot\mathbf{r} = \mathbf{k}\cdot\mathbf{r} \tag{5.62}$$

$$0 = \boldsymbol{\alpha}\cdot\mathbf{r} \tag{5.63}$$

This result means that, in general, $\mathbf{k}$ and $\boldsymbol{\alpha}$ have different directions. In this case the wave is said to be *inhomogeneous*. In particular, $\boldsymbol{\alpha}\cdot\mathbf{r} = 0$ implies that $\boldsymbol{\alpha}$, which definies the direction of planes of constant amplitude, is always normal to the boundary. On the other hand, the planes of constant phase are defined by the vector $\mathbf{k}$, which may have any

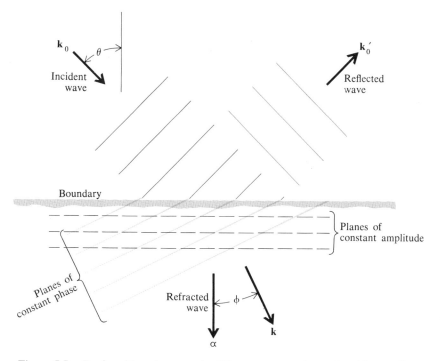

Figure 5.5. Real and imaginary parts of the wave vector in an absorbing medium for the case of oblique incidence of light at the boundary.

direction. The situation is illustrated in Figure 5.5. The waves are traveling in the direction of the vector $\mathbf{k}$, but their amplitudes diminish exponentially with the distance z where the z axis is normal to the boundary plane, as shown.

If we denote the angle of incidence by θ and the angle of refraction by ϕ, then Equation (5.62) is equivalent to

$$k_0 \sin \theta = k \sin \phi \qquad (5.64)$$

Now we cannot simply put $k = nk_0$ as we did, in effect, in the case of homogeneous waves discussed in the two preceding sections. In order to determine the relationship between the propagation vector and the complex index of refraction, we must go back to the wave equation. This can be written as

$$\nabla^2 \mathbf{E} = \frac{\mathcal{N}^2}{c^2} \frac{\partial^2 \mathbf{E}}{\partial t^2} \qquad (5.65)$$

For plane harmonic waves we have $\nabla \rightarrow i\,\mathcal{K}$, $\partial/\partial t \rightarrow -i\omega$, so that

$$\mathcal{K} \cdot \mathcal{K} = \frac{\mathcal{N}^2\omega^2}{c^2} = \mathcal{N}^2 k_0{}^2 \qquad (5.66)$$

where $k_0 = \omega/c$. Written out in terms of real and imaginary parts, we have

$$(\mathbf{k} + i\boldsymbol{\alpha}) \cdot (\mathbf{k} + i\boldsymbol{\alpha}) = (n + i\kappa)^2 k_0{}^2 \tag{5.67}$$

By equating real and imaginary parts, we obtain

$$k^2 - \alpha^2 = (n^2 - \kappa^2)k_0{}^2 \tag{5.68}$$

$$\mathbf{k} \cdot \boldsymbol{\alpha} = k\alpha \cos \phi = n\kappa \, k_0{}^2 \tag{5.69}$$

After some algebraic manipulation, the above results can be shown to lead to the following formula:

$$k \cos \phi + i\alpha = k_0 \sqrt{\mathcal{N}^2 - \sin^2 \theta} \tag{5.70}$$

This reduces to $k + i\alpha = k_0 \mathcal{N}$ for normal incidence ($\theta = 0$) which is the relation for homogeneous waves discussed earlier.

We now express the law of refraction in terms of the complex index of refraction in a purely formal way as

$$\mathcal{N} = \frac{\sin \theta}{\sin \phi} \tag{5.71}$$

Here the angle ϕ is a complex number. It has no simple physical interpretation, but can be considered as being defined by the above equation. It turns out, however, that ϕ is very useful in simplifying the equations related to reflection and refraction by an absorbing medium. From the above definition of ϕ, we have

$$\cos \phi = \sqrt{1 - \sin^2 \theta / \mathcal{N}^2} \tag{5.72}$$

This, with Equation (5.70), gives a second formula involving the complex index of refraction:

$$\mathcal{N} = \frac{k \cos \phi + i\alpha}{k_0 \cos \phi} \tag{5.73}$$

We are now ready to attack the problem of finding the amplitudes of the reflected and refracted waves. We shall use the following notation for the amplitudes of the electric and magnetic fields:

incident $\quad$ $\mathbf{E}$ $\qquad$ $\mathbf{H} = \dfrac{1}{\mu_0 \omega} \mathbf{k}_0 \times \mathbf{E}$ $\hfill$ (5.74)

reflected $\quad$ $\mathbf{E}'$ $\qquad$ $\mathbf{H}' = \dfrac{1}{\mu_0 \omega} \mathbf{k}_0{}' \times \mathbf{E}'$ $\hfill$ (5.75)

refracted $\quad$ $\mathbf{E}''$ $\qquad$ $\mathbf{H}'' = \dfrac{1}{\mu_0 \omega} \mathcal{K} \times \mathbf{E}'' = \dfrac{1}{\mu_0 \omega}(\mathbf{k} \times \mathbf{E}'' + i\boldsymbol{\alpha} \times \mathbf{E}'')$ $\hfill$ (5.76)

The equation will be derived for the transverse electric (TE) case. A similar procedure can be used for the transverse magnetic (*TM*) case. The relevant vectors are essentially the same as those shown in Figure 2.11, with an obvious difference in the k's.

The boundary conditions giving the continuity of the tangential components of the electric and magnetic fields for *TE* polarization are

$$E + E' = E'' \tag{5.77}$$

$$-H \cos \theta + H' \cos \theta = H''_{\tan g} \tag{5.78}$$

By applying Equations (5.74) to (5.76) to the second equation, we find

$$-k_0 E \cos \theta + k_0 E' \cos \theta$$

$$= -(kE'' \cos \phi + i\alpha E'') \tag{5.79}$$

$$= -\mathcal{N} k_0 E'' \cos \phi$$

The last step follows from Equation (5.73). We now eliminate E'' from Equations (5.79) and (5.77) to obtain the final result

$$(TE \text{ polarization}) \quad \frac{E'}{E} = \frac{\cos \theta - \mathcal{N} \cos \phi}{\cos \theta + \mathcal{N} \cos \phi} \tag{5.80}$$

This equation for the ratio of the reflected amplitude to the incident amplitude is of the same form as that for the dielectric case, Equation (2.54). The only difference is that $\mathcal{N}$ and ϕ are now complex. The corresponding equation for *TM* polarization turns out to be also of the same form as that of the dielectric case, namely

$$(TM \text{ polarization}) \quad \frac{E'}{E} = \frac{-\mathcal{N} \cos \theta + \cos \phi}{\mathcal{N} \cos \theta + \cos \phi} \tag{5.81}$$

The derivation is left as an exercise. Knowing the amplitudes of the reflected waves, the amplitudes of the refracted waves can be found from the boundary conditions.

The general behavior of the reflectance $R = |E'/E|^2$ as calculated from the above theory is shown graphically in Figure 5.6, in which R is plotted as a function of θ for the case of a typical metal. The reflectance for *TE* polarization increases monotonically from its value at normal incidence, to unity for grazing incidence. On the other hand, for *TM* polarization, the reflectance goes through a shallow minimum for some angle θ_1 whose value depends on the optical constants. This angle is called the *principal angle of incidence* and corresponds to the Brewster angle for dielectrics.

Normal Incidence   In the case of normal incidence, both Equations (5.80) and (5.81) for E'/E give the same result, namely

$$\frac{E'}{E} = \frac{1 - \mathcal{N}}{1 + \mathcal{N}} = \frac{1 - n - i\kappa}{1 + n + i\kappa} \tag{5.82}$$

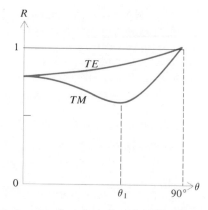

Figure 5.6.   Reflectance as a function of angle of incidence for a typical metal.

The following expression for the normal reflectance is then obtained:

$$R = \left| \frac{1 - \mathcal{N}}{1 + \mathcal{N}} \right|^2 = \frac{(1 - n)^2 + \kappa^2}{(1 + n)^2 + \kappa^2} \tag{5.83}$$

This reduces to the previously found value for dielectrics (Section 2.7) as κ approaches zero and the index of refraction becomes real. On the other hand, for metals the extinction coefficient κ is large. This results in a high value of the reflectance R, which approaches unity as κ becomes infinite.

In the previous section we showed that for metals, both n and κ in fact become very large and approach the value $\sqrt{\sigma/2\omega\varepsilon_o}$ in the limit of low frequencies, Equation (5.51). It is easy to show from Equation (5.83) that the reflectance in this case is given by the approximate formula

$$R \approx 1 - \frac{2}{n} \approx 1 - \sqrt{\frac{8\omega\varepsilon_o}{\sigma}} \tag{5.84}$$

This is known as the Hagen-Rubens formula. It has been verified experimentally for a number of metals in the far infrared.

5.7   Propagation of Light in Crystals

The distinguishing basic feature of the crystalline state, as far as optical properties are concerned, is the fact that crystals are generally electrically anisotropic. This means that the polarization produced in the crystal by a given electric field is not just a simple scalar constant times the field, but varies in a manner that depends on the direction of the applied field in relation to the crystal lattice. One of the consequences is that the speed of propagation of a light wave in a crystal is a function of the direction of propagation and the polarization of the light.

It turns out that there are generally *two* possible values of the phase velocity for a given direction of propagation. These two values are associated with mutually orthogonal polarizations of the light waves. Crystals are said to be *doubly refracting* or *birefringent*. Actually, not all crystals exhibit double refraction. Whether they do or do not depends on their symmetry. Crystals of the cubic class of symmetry, such as sodium chloride, never exhibit double refraction, but are optically isotropic. All crystals, other than cubic crystals, do show double refraction, however.

A model to illustrate the anisotropic polarizability of a crystal is shown in Figure 5.7. A bound electron is here pictured as attached to

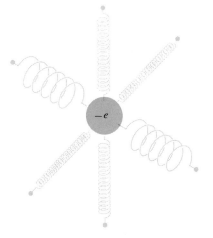

Figure 5.7. Model to show anisotropic binding of an electron in a crystal.

a set of fictitious elastic springs. The springs have different stiffnesses for different directions of the electron's displacement from its equilibrium position within the crystal lattice. Consequently, the displacement of the electron under the action of an external field **E** depends on the direction of the field as well as its magnitude. This is also true of the resulting polarization **P**.

The dependence of **P** on **E** is expressible as a tensor relation in the form

$$
\begin{bmatrix} P_x \\ P_y \\ P_z \end{bmatrix} = \varepsilon_0 \begin{bmatrix} \chi_{11} & \chi_{12} & \chi_{13} \\ \chi_{21} & \chi_{22} & \chi_{23} \\ \chi_{31} & \chi_{32} & \chi_{33} \end{bmatrix} \begin{bmatrix} E_x \\ E_y \\ E_z \end{bmatrix} \tag{5.85}
$$

This is customarily abbreviated as

$$\mathbf{P} = \varepsilon_0 \chi \mathbf{E} \tag{5.86}$$

where χ is the susceptibility tensor:

$$\chi = \begin{bmatrix} \chi_{11} & \chi_{12} & \chi_{13} \\ \chi_{21} & \chi_{22} & \chi_{23} \\ \chi_{31} & \chi_{32} & \chi_{33} \end{bmatrix} \tag{5.87}$$

The corresponding displacement vector $\mathscr{D}$ is given by $\mathscr{D} = \varepsilon_0(1 + \chi)\mathbf{E}$

$= \varepsilon \mathbf{E}$ where $\mathbf{1}$ is the unit matrix $\begin{bmatrix} 1 & 0 & 0 \\ 0 & 1 & 0 \\ 0 & 0 & 1 \end{bmatrix}$, and

$$\varepsilon = \varepsilon_0(1 + \chi) \tag{5.88}$$

which is known as the dielectric tensor.

Now it can be shown [5] that for ordinary nonabsorbing crystals, there always exists a set of coordinate axes, called *principal axes*, such that the χ-tensor assumes the diagonal form

$$\chi = \begin{bmatrix} \chi_{11} & 0 & 0 \\ 0 & \chi_{22} & 0 \\ 0 & 0 & \chi_{33} \end{bmatrix} \tag{5.89}$$

The three χ's are known as the *principal susceptibilities*. Corresponding to these, the quantities $\varepsilon_{11} = 1 + \chi_{11} \cdots$, and so forth, are called the *principal dielectric constants*.

In view of Equation (5.86), the general wave equation (5.14) can be written in the following form:

$$\nabla \times (\nabla \times \mathbf{E}) + \frac{1}{c^2} \frac{\partial^2 \mathbf{E}}{\partial t^2} = -\frac{1}{c^2} \chi \frac{\partial^2 \mathbf{E}}{\partial t^2} \tag{5.90}$$

It then follows that the crystal can sustain monochromatic plane waves of the usual form $e^{i(\mathbf{k} \cdot \mathbf{r} - \omega t)}$ provided the propagation vector $\mathbf{k}$ satisfies the equation

$$\mathbf{k} \times (\mathbf{k} \times \mathbf{E}) + \frac{\omega^2}{c^2} \mathbf{E} = -\frac{\omega^2}{c^2} \chi \mathbf{E} \tag{5.91}$$

Written out in terms of components, the above equation is equivalent to the following three equations:

$$\left(-k_y{}^2 - k_z{}^2 + \frac{\omega^2}{c^2}\right)E_x + k_x k_y\, E_y + k_x k_z\, E_z = -\frac{\omega^2}{c^2} \chi_{11}\, E_x$$

$$-k_y k_x \, E_x + \left(-k_x{}^2 - k_y{}^2 + \frac{\omega^2}{c^2}\right)E_y + k_y k_z \, E_z = -\frac{\omega^2}{c^2} \chi_{22} \, E_y \quad \text{(5.92)}$$

$$k_z k_x \, E_x + k_z k_y \, E_y + \left(-k_x{}^2 - k_y{}^2 + \frac{\omega^2}{c^2}\right)E_z = -\frac{\omega^2}{c^2} \chi_{33} \, E_z$$

In order to interpret the physical meaning of these equations, suppose we have a particular case of a wave propagating in the direction of one of the principal axes, say the x axis. In this case $k_x = k$, $k_y = k_z = 0$, and the three equations reduce to

$$\frac{\omega^2}{c^2} \, E_x = -\frac{\omega^2}{c^2} \chi_{11} \, E_x$$

$$\left(-k^2 + \frac{\omega^2}{c^2}\right)E_y = -\frac{\omega^2}{c^2} \chi_{22} \, E_y \quad \text{(5.93)}$$

$$\left(-k^2 + \frac{\omega^2}{c^2}\right)E_z = -\frac{\omega^2}{c^2} \chi_{33} \, E_z$$

The first equation implies that $E_x = 0$, because neither ω nor χ_{11} is zero. This means that the **E** field is transverse to the x axis, which is the direction of propagation. Consider next the second equation. If $E_y \neq 0$, then

$$k = \frac{\omega}{c}\sqrt{1 + \chi_{22}} = \frac{\omega}{c}\sqrt{\varepsilon_{22}} \quad \text{(5.94)}$$

The third equation, likewise, implies that if $E_z \neq 0$, then

$$k = \frac{\omega}{c}\sqrt{1 + \chi_{33}} = \frac{\omega}{c}\sqrt{\varepsilon_{33}} \quad \text{(5.95)}$$

Now ω/k is the phase velocity of the wave. Thus we have two possible phase velocities, namely $c/\sqrt{\varepsilon_{22}}$ if the **E** vector points in the y direction, and $c/\sqrt{\varepsilon_{33}}$ if the **E** vector is in the z direction.

More generally, we can show that for any direction of the propagation vector **k** there are two possible values of the magnitude k and hence two possible values of the phase velocity. To do this, let us introduce the three *principal indices of refraction* n_1, n_2, and n_3, defined by

$$n_1 = \sqrt{1 + \chi_{11}} = \sqrt{\varepsilon_{11}}$$

$$n_2 = \sqrt{1 + \chi_{22}} = \sqrt{\varepsilon_{22}} \quad \text{(5.96)}$$

$$n_3 = \sqrt{1 + \chi_{33}} = \sqrt{\varepsilon_{33}}$$

Now in Equation (5.92), in order for a nontrivial solution for E_x, E_y, and E_z to exist, the determinant of the coefficients must vanish, namely,

$$\begin{vmatrix} (n_1\omega/c)^2 - k_y^2 - k_z^2 & k_xk_y & k_xk_z \\ k_yk_x & (n_2\omega/c)^2 - k_x^2 - k_z^2 & k_yk_z \\ k_zk_x & k_zk_y & (n_3\omega/c)^2 - k_x^2 - k_y^2 \end{vmatrix} = 0 \qquad (5.97)$$

where we have used Equation (5.96). The above equation can be represented by a three-dimensional surface in **k** space. The form of this **k** surface, or wave-vector surface, is shown in Figure 5.8. To see how the

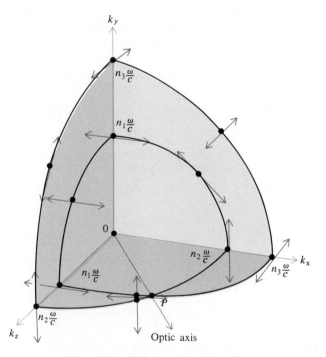

Figure 5.8. The wave-vector surface.

surface is constructed, consider any one of the coordinate planes, say the xy plane. In this plane $k_z = 0$, and the determinant reduces to the product of the two factors

$$\left[\left(\frac{n_3\omega}{c}\right)^2 - k_x^2 - k_y^2\right]\left\{\left[\left(\frac{n_1\omega}{c}\right)^2 - k_y^2\right]\left[\left(\frac{n_2\omega}{c}\right)^2 - k_x^2\right] - k_x^2k_y^2\right\} = 0 \qquad (5.98)$$

Since the product must vanish, either or both of the factors must be equal to zero. Setting the first factor equal to zero gives the equation of a circle

$$k_x{}^2 + k_y{}^2 = (n_3\omega/c)^2 \qquad (5.99)$$

The second factor gives the equation of an ellipse

$$\frac{k_x{}^2}{(n_2\omega/c^2)} + \frac{k_y{}^2}{(n_1\omega/c)^2} = 1 \qquad (5.100)$$

Similar equations are obtained for the xz and the yz planes. The intercept of the **k** surface with each coordinate plane therefore consists of one circle and one ellipse as shown. The complete **k** surface is double; that is, it consists of an inner sheet and an outer sheet. This implies that for any given direction of the wave vector **k**, there are two possible values for the wavenumber k. It follows that there are also two values of the phase velocity. Now we just showed that for a wave propagating in the x direction, the two phase velocities correspond to two mutually orthogonal directions of polarization. It can be shown [5] that the same is true for any direction of propagation; that is, the two phase velocities always correspond to two mutually orthogonal polarizations.

The nature of the **k** surface is such that the inner and outer sheets touch at a certain point P as shown in Figure 5.9. This point defines a direction for which the two values of k are equal. The direction so defined is called an *optic axis* of the crystal. There is only one value of k and, consequently, only one phase velocity for any wave propagating in the direction of an optic axis.

The general case is shown in Figures 5.8 and 5.9(a). Here the three principal indices n_1, n_2, and n_3 are all different. It is easy to see from the intercepts that there are *two* optic axes. In this case the crystal is said to be *biaxial*. In many crystals it happens that two of the principal indices are equal, in which case there is only *one* optic axis and the crystal is called *uniaxial*. The **k** surface for a uniaxial crystal consists of a sphere and an ellipsoid of revolution, the axis of which is the optic axis of the crystal, Figure 5.9(b) and (c). If all three indices are equal, then the **k** surface degenerates to a single sphere, and the crystal is not doubly refracting at all but is optically isotropic.

In view of the fact that the principal indices are related to the components of the χ tensor by Equation (5.96), we can conveniently classify crystals according to the χ tensor as follows:

Isotropic cubic	$\chi = \begin{bmatrix} a & 0 & 0 \\ 0 & a & 0 \\ 0 & 0 & a \end{bmatrix}$	$\chi_{11} = \chi_{22} = \chi_{33} = a$ $n = \sqrt{1 + a}$
Uniaxial trigonal tetragonal hexagonal	$\chi = \begin{bmatrix} a & 0 & 0 \\ 0 & a & 0 \\ 0 & 0 & b \end{bmatrix}$	$\chi_{11} = \chi_{22} = a, \chi_{33} = b$ $n_o = \sqrt{1 + a}$ $n_e = \sqrt{1 + b}$

Biaxial	$\chi = \begin{bmatrix} a & 0 & 0 \\ 0 & b & 0 \\ 0 & 0 & c \end{bmatrix}$	$\chi_{11} = a$	$\chi_{22} = b$	$\chi_{33} = c$
triclinic			$n_1 = \sqrt{1 + a}$	
monoclinic			$n_2 = \sqrt{1 + b}$	
orthorhombic			$n_3 = \sqrt{1 + c}$	

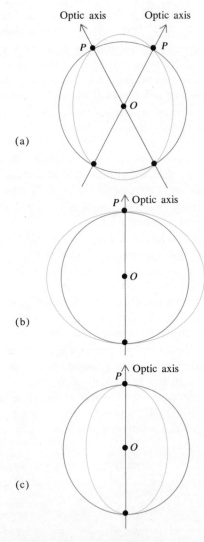

Figure 5.9.   Intercepts of the wave-vector surfaces in the xz plane for (a) biaxial crystals; (b) uniaxial positive crystals; (c) uniaxial negative crystals.

In a uniaxial crystal the index of refraction that corresponds to the two equal elements, $\chi_{11} = \chi_{22}$, is called the *ordinary* index n_o, and the other index, corresponding to χ_{33}, is called the *extraordinary* index n_e. If $n_o < n_e$, the crystal is said to be *positive*, whereas if $n_o > n_e$, it is called a *negative* crystal. Table 5.1 lists some examples of crystals with their indices of refraction.

Table 5.1. SOME COMMON CRYSTALS

OPTICALLY ISOTROPIC (CUBIC) CRYSTALS		
	n	
Sodium Chloride	1.544	
Diamond	2.417	
Fluorite	1.392	

UNIAXIAL POSITIVE CRYSTALS		
	n_o	n_e
Ice	1.309	1.310
Quartz	1.544	1.553
Zircon	1.923	1.968
Rutile	2.616	2.903

UNIAXIAL NEGATIVE CRYSTALS		
	n_o	n_e
Beryl	1.598	1.590
Sodium Nitrate	1.587	1.336
Calcite	1.658	1.486
Tourmaline	1.669	1.638

BIAXIAL CRYSTALS		
	n_1	n_2	n_3
Gypsum	1.520	1.523	1.530
Feldspar	1.522	1.526	1.530
Mica	1.552	1.582	1.588
Topaz	1.619	1.620	1.627

Phase-Velocity Surface   Knowing that the wavenumber k is related to the magnitude v of the phase velocity by $k = \omega/v$, we can write the relation vectorially as

$$\mathbf{k} = \mathbf{v}\,\frac{\omega}{v^2} \qquad (5.101)$$

In terms of components, the above vector equation is equivalent to the three scalar equations

$$k_x = v_x \frac{\omega}{v^2} \qquad k_y = v_y \frac{\omega}{v^2} \qquad k_z = v_z \frac{\omega}{v^2} \qquad \text{(5.102)}$$

Let us substitute the above values into the equation of the **k** surface in Equation (5.97). The result is

$$\begin{vmatrix} n_1{}^2 v^4/c^2 - v_y{}^2 - v_z{}^2 & v_x v_y & v_x v_z \\ v_y v_x & n_2{}^2 v^4/c^2 - v_x{}^2 - v_z{}^2 & v_y v_z \\ v_z v_x & v_z v_y & n_3{}^2 v^4/c^2 - v_x{}^2 - v_y{}^2 \end{vmatrix} = 0 \qquad \text{(5.103)}$$

after cancellation of ω^2 and division by v^4. This equation defines a three-dimensional surface that can be considered as the *reciprocal surface* to the **k** surface. It is called the *phase velocity surface*. It is a double-sheeted surface and gives directly the two possible values of the phase velocity for a given direction of a plane wave propagating in the crystal. The general form of the phase velocity surface is shown in Figure 5.10. The intercepts with the coordinate planes consists of circles and *fourth-degree ovals*. Thus, for the xy plane, the two equations for the intercepts are:

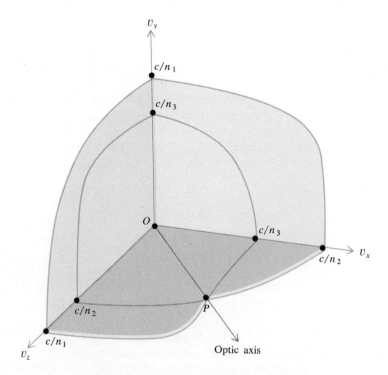

Figure 5.10. The phase-velocity surface.

$$v_x^2 + v_y^2 = c^2/n_3^2 \tag{5.104}$$

$$\frac{v_x^2}{n_2^2} + \frac{v_y^2}{n_1^2} = \frac{v^4}{c^2} \tag{5.105}$$

Similar relations hold for the other coordinate planes.

The Poynting Vector and the Ray Velocity   Although the propagation vector **k** defines the direction of the planes of constant phase for light waves in a crystal, the actual direction of the energy flow **E** × **H** is not in the same direction, generally, as that of **k**. This stems from the fact that in anisotropic media **E** and **k** are not, in general, mutually perpendicular, as can be seen by inspection of Equation (5.91). On the other hand, the magnetic field **H** is perpendicular to both **E** and **k** because of the relation **k** × **E** = $\mu_o\omega$**H**, which comes from the first Maxwell equation. The situation is shown graphically in Figure 5.11. The three

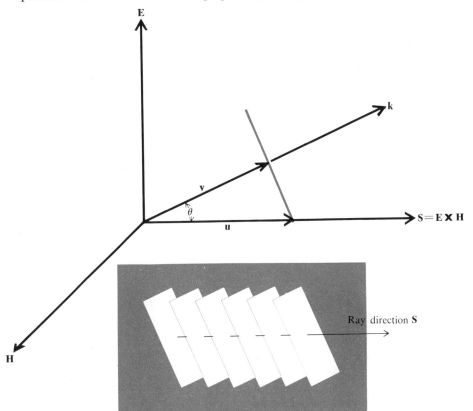

Figure 5.11.   Relationships among the electric and magnetic fields, the Poynting vector, the wave vector, the ray-velocity vector, and the phase-velocity vector for plane waves in a crystal.

vectors $\mathbf{E}$, $\mathbf{k}$, and $\mathbf{S} = \mathbf{E} \times \mathbf{H}$ are all perpendicular to $\mathbf{H}$, and further, $\mathbf{E}$ is perpendicular to $\mathbf{S}$.

Consider a narrow beam or ray of light in a crystal. The planes of constant phase are perpendicular to $\mathbf{k}$, but they move along the direction of the ray $\mathbf{S}$. Thus the planes of constant phase are inclined to their direction of motion as shown in the figure. Let θ denote the angle between $\mathbf{k}$ and $\mathbf{S}$. Then the surfaces of constant phase move with a velocity u—called the *ray velocity*—along the ray direction. The magnitude of u is given by

$$u = v/\cos \theta \qquad (5.106)$$

where v is the phase velocity (in the direction of $\mathbf{k}$). Evidently the ray velocity is greater than the phase velocity except, of course, when $\theta = 0$. In the latter case the phase and ray velocities are equal. This occurs when the direction of propagation is along one of the principal axes of the crystal. In this case $\mathbf{S}$ and $\mathbf{k}$ also have the same direction.

The Ray-Velocity Surface   This surface gives the magnitude of the ray velocity for any given direction of the ray. It is shown in Appendix I that the equation of the ray-velocity surface is

$$\begin{vmatrix} c^2/n_1^2 - u_y^2 - u_z^2 & u_x u_y & u_x u_z \\ u_y u_x & c^2/n_2^2 - u_x^2 - u_z^2 & u_y u_z \\ u_z u_x & u_z u_y & c^2/n_3^2 - u_x^2 - u_y^2 \end{vmatrix} = 0 \qquad (5.107)$$

In particular, the equations of the intercepts in the xy plane are obtained by setting $u_z = 0$. The result gives a circle

$$u_x^2 + u_y^2 = \frac{c^2}{n_3^2} \qquad (5.108)$$

and an ellipse

$$n_2^2 u_x^2 + n_1^2 u_y^2 = c^2 \qquad (5.109)$$

Corresponding equations can be obtained for the other coordinate planes by cyclic permutation, and in each case the intercepts consist of an ellipse and a circle. It is easily verified that the intercepts of the ray-velocity surface along the coordinate axes are the same as those of the phase-velocity surface. Figure 5.12 shows the form of the ray-velocity surface. As with the phase-velocity surface, the ray-velocity surface consists of two sheets, an inner one and an outer one corresponding to the two possible values of u for a given ray direction. The two sheets touch at a point Q that defines a direction for which the two ray velocities are equal. This direction is called the *ray axis* of the crystal.

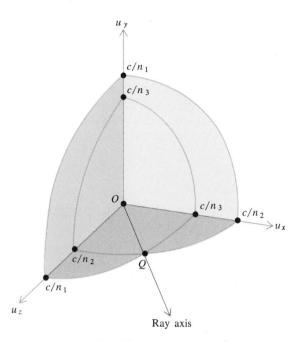

Figure 5.12. The ray-velocity surface.

In biaxial crystals there are two ray axes, and these ray axes are distinct from the optic axes of the crystal. On the other hand, in the case of a uniaxial crystal, the two sheets of the ray-velocity surface consist of a sphere and an ellipsoid of revolution (spheroid). The two surfaces are tangent at the ends of a particular diameter of the sphere. This diameter defines the ray axis that, for uniaxial crystals, also coincides with the optic axis of the crystal.

5.8   Double Refraction at a Boundary

Consider a plane wave incident on the surface of a crystal. Denote the propagation vector of the incident wave by $\mathbf{k}_0$ and that of the refracted wave by $\mathbf{k}$, and call θ and ϕ the angles of incidence and refraction. According to the arguments in Section 2.6, where we treated refraction at a dielectric boundary, the law of refraction was seen to be contained in the equation

$$\mathbf{k}_0 \cdot \mathbf{r} = \mathbf{k} \cdot \mathbf{r} \quad \text{(at boundary)} \tag{5.110}$$

This same relation is also true for refraction at a boundary of a crystal since it merely expresses the fact that some unspecified boundary condition can exist at all. The equation implies that the projections of the propagation vectors along the boundary plane must be equal for both the incident and refracted waves. Now we know that for a given direction of propagation in the crystal, there are two possible propagation vectors. Owing to the double nature of the $\mathbf{k}$ surface, it is also true that for a prescribed value of the *projection* of the propagation vector in any given direction, there are again two possible propagation vectors. This results in double refraction of a wave incident on the surface of a crystal as shown in Figure 5.13. From Equation (5.110), we can write

$$k_0 \sin \theta = k_1 \sin \phi_1 \qquad k_0 \sin \theta = k_2 \sin \phi_2 \qquad \textbf{(5.111)}$$

for the two refracted waves.

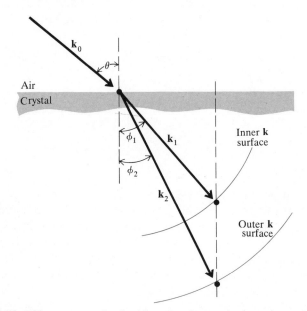

Figure 5.13.   Wave vectors for double refraction at the boundary of a crystal.

At first sight it may appear that the above equations constitute a statement of Snell's law for double refraction. However, this is not the case. The trouble is that k_1 and k_2 are not constant in general, rather, they vary with the directions of the vectors $\mathbf{k}_1$ and $\mathbf{k}_2$. This means that the ratio $\sin \theta / \sin \phi$ is not always constant as it is in the case of refraction at the boundary of an isotropic medium. The problem of determining ϕ, given the value of θ, is thus not a simple one. One way is to solve for ϕ graphically as suggested by Figure 5.13.

In the case of uniaxial crystals, as we have seen, one of the parts of the $\mathbf{k}$ surface is a sphere. The corresponding wavenumber k is constant for all directions of the wave in the crystal, and Snell's law is obeyed. This wave is known as the *ordinary wave,* and we have

$$\frac{\sin \theta}{\sin \phi} = n_0 \qquad (5.112)$$

where n_0 is the ordinary index of refraction. The **k** surface for the other wave however, is a spheroid, and Snell's law is not valid. This wave is called the *extraordinary wave.* Since the extraordinary index n_e is greater than n_0 for positive uniaxial crystals, and less than n_0 for negative crystals, we conclude that $\phi_e \leq \phi_o$ for positive crystals and $\phi_e \geq \phi_o$ for negative crystals. Some examples of double refraction are illustrated in Figure 5.14. In all cases, the polarizations of the two waves are mutually orthogonal.

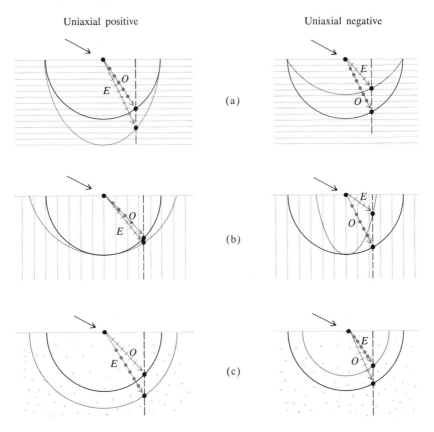

Figure 5.14.   Wave vectors for double refraction in uniaxial crystals. (a) The optic axis parallel to the boundary and parallel to the plane of incidence. (b) The optic axis perpendicular to the boundary and parallel to the plane of incidence. (c) The optic axis parallel to the boundary and perpendicular to the plane of incidence.

It can be shown that the *ray direction* is given by the normal to the **k** surface at the end points of the **k** vector. The directions of the wave vectors are indicated in the figures.

Polarizing Prisms   Let a wave be incident on a plane boundary from the *inside* of a uniaxial crystal. Consider the special case in which the optic axis is perpendicular to the plane of incidence as shown in Figure 5.14(c). Then the cross section of the **k** surface consists of two circles, as shown, and therefore Snell's law holds for both the ordinary wave and the extraordinary wave. For simplicity, let the external medium be air ($n = 1$). Then we can write

$$n_o \sin \phi_o = \sin \theta \tag{5.113}$$

$$n_e \sin \phi_e = \sin \theta \tag{5.114}$$

where θ is the internal angle of incidence, and ϕ_o and ϕ_e are the angles of refraction of the ordinary wave and the extraordinary wave, respectively. The **E** vector of the ordinary wave is perpendicular to the direction of the optic axis, and the **E** vector of the extraordinary wave is parallel to the optic axis.

Suppose now that we have a negative uniaxial crystal, such as calcite, and that the internal angle of incidence θ is such that

$$n_e < \frac{1}{\sin \theta} < n_0 \tag{5.115}$$

In this case we have total internal reflection for the ordinary wave but *not* for the extraordinary wave. The refracted wave is thus totally polarized as shown in Figure 5.15(a). This is the basic principle for producing polarized light by means of double refraction.

One of the most commonly used polarizing prisms is the Glan prism shown in Figure 5.15(b). It consists of two identical prisms of calcite cut so that the optic axes are parallel to the corner edges, and mounted so that the long faces are parallel as shown. The space between the two prisms may be air or any suitable transparent material. If an air gap is used, the apex angle must be about 38.5 degrees.

An older type of polarizing prism is the Nicol prism. It is made in the form of a rhomb having approximately the same shape as a natural crystal of calcite, Figure 5.15(c). The Nicol prism is inferior to the Glan prism in most respects and is largely of historical interest.

Another type of polarizing device makes use of double refraction to separate an incident beam of light into two diverging beams having mutually orthogonal directions of polarization. Three ways of doing this are illustrated in Figure 5.16. The figures are self-explanatory.

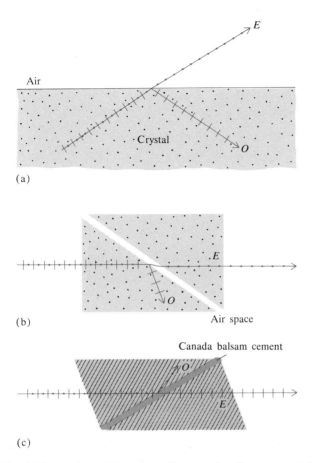

(a)

(b)

Air space

Canada balsam cement

(c)

Figure 5.15.   (a) Separation of the extraordinary and ordinary rays at the boundary of a crystal in the case of internal refraction. (b) Construction of the Glan polarizing prism. (c) The Nicol prism.

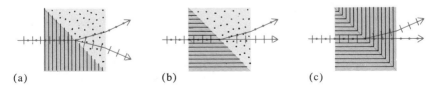

(a)   (b)   (c)

Figure 5.16.   Three types of prisms for separating unpolarized light into two divergent orthogonally polarized beams. (a) The Wollaston prism. (b) The Rochon prism. (c) The Senarmont prism. All prisms shown are made with uniaxial positive material (quartz).

5.9   Optical Activity

Certain substances are found to possess the ability to rotate the plane of polarization of light passing through them. This phenomenon is known as *optical activity*. When a beam of linearly polarized light is passed through an optically active medium, Figure 5.17, the light

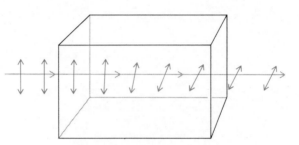

Figure 5.17.   Rotation of the plane of polarization by an optically active medium.

emerges with its plane of polarization turned through an angle that is proportional to the length of the path of the light through the medium. The amount of rotation per unit length of travel is called the *specific rotatory power*. If the sense of rotation of the plane of polarization is to the right, as a right-handed screw pointing in the direction of propagation, the substance is called *dextrorotatory* or right-handed. If the rotation is to the left, the substance is called *levorotatory* or left-handed. Sodium chloride, cinnabar, and certain kinds of sugar are examples of optically active substances. Fused quartz is optically isotropic, but crystallized quartz is optically active as well as double refracting.

Quartz occurs in two crystalline forms, right-handed and left-handed. These crystals are found to be dextrorotatory and levorotatory, respectively. The specific rotatory power of either of the two kinds of quartz for light propagating along the direction of the optic axis is tabulated for different wavelengths in Table 5.2. It is seen that the amount of optical activity of quartz varies with wavelength. This variation with wavelength is called *rotatory dispersion*.

Optical activity can be explained on the basis of the simple assumption that the speed of propagation for right circularly polarized light in the medium is different from that of left circularly polarized light. To show this, it will be convenient to use the Jones vector notation of Section 2.5. Let n_R and n_L denote respectively, the indices of refraction of the medium for right and left circularly polarized light. The corresponding wavenumbers are $k_R = n_R\omega/c$ and $k_L = n_L\omega/c$, and the expressions

$$\begin{bmatrix} 1 \\ -i \end{bmatrix} e^{i(k_R z - \omega t)} \qquad \begin{bmatrix} 1 \\ i \end{bmatrix} e^{i(k_L z - \omega t)}$$

represent the two kinds of wave in the medium.

Table 5.2. OPTICAL ACTIVITY OF QUARTZ

Wavelength in angstroms	Specific Rotatory Power in degrees per millimeter
4000	49
4500	37
5000	31
5500	26
6000	22
6500	17

Now suppose that a beam of linearly polarized light travels a distance l through the medium. Let the initial polarization be in the horizontal direction. The initial Jones vector, separated into right and left circular components, is

$$\begin{bmatrix} 1 \\ 0 \end{bmatrix} = \tfrac{1}{2} \begin{bmatrix} 1 \\ -i \end{bmatrix} + \tfrac{1}{2} \begin{bmatrix} 1 \\ i \end{bmatrix}$$

The complex amplitude of the light wave, after traveling a distance l through the medium, is

$$\tfrac{1}{2} \begin{bmatrix} 1 \\ -i \end{bmatrix} e^{ik_R l} + \tfrac{1}{2} \begin{bmatrix} 1 \\ i \end{bmatrix} e^{ik_L l}$$

$$= e^{i(\frac{1}{2}k_R l + \frac{1}{2}k_L l)} \left\{ \tfrac{1}{2} \begin{bmatrix} 1 \\ -i \end{bmatrix} e^{i(\frac{1}{2}k_R l - \frac{1}{2}k_L l)} + \tfrac{1}{2} \begin{bmatrix} 1 \\ i \end{bmatrix} e^{-i(\frac{1}{2}k_R l - \frac{1}{2}k_L l)} \right\} \tag{5.116}$$

Upon introducing the quantities ψ and θ where

$$\psi = \tfrac{1}{2}(k_R + k_L)l \tag{5.117}$$

$$\theta = \tfrac{1}{2}(k_R - k_L)l \tag{5.118}$$

we can express the complex amplitude as

$$e^{i\psi}\left\{\;\tfrac{1}{2}\begin{bmatrix}1\\-i\end{bmatrix}e^{i\theta}+\tfrac{1}{2}\begin{bmatrix}1\\i\end{bmatrix}e^{-i\theta}\right\}$$

$$=e^{i\psi}\begin{bmatrix}\tfrac{1}{2}(e^{i\theta}+e^{-i\theta})\\\tfrac{1}{2}i(e^{i\theta}-e^{-i\theta})\end{bmatrix} \qquad (5.119)$$

$$=e^{i\psi}\begin{bmatrix}\cos\theta\\\sin\theta\end{bmatrix}$$

This represents a linearly polarized wave in which the direction of polarization is turned through an angle θ with respect to the original direction of polarization. From Equation (5.118) we have

$$\theta=(n_R-n_L)\frac{\omega l}{2c}=(n_R-n_L)\frac{\pi l}{\lambda} \qquad (5.120)$$

where λ is the wavelength in vacuum. It follows that the specific rotatory power δ, as a function of wavelength, is given by

$$\delta=(n_R-n_L)\frac{\pi}{\lambda} \qquad (5.121)$$

The indices n_R and n_L are also of course, functions of wavelength.

As a numerical example, the indices for propagation along the optic axis in quartz are as follows:

λ	n_R	n_L	n_R-n_L
3960 Å	1.55810	1.55821	0.00011
5890 Å	1.54420	1.54427	0.00007
7600 Å	1.53914	1.53920	0.00006

These are for right-handed quartz. For left-handed quartz the values are just reversed.

A method of separating unpolarized light into two beams of oppositely rotating circularly polarized light was devised by Fresnel. Two prisms made of right-handed and left-handed quartz are arranged as shown in Figure 5.18. The relative index of refraction at the diagonal

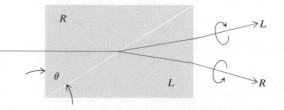

Figure 5.18. The Fresnel prism for separating unpolarized light into two divergent beams of opposite circular polarizations.

boundary is greater than unity for right polarized light and less than unity for left polarized light. Hence the beam is separated into two beams at the boundary as shown. The light emerges from the prism in two divergent beams. This prism can also be used to determine the sense of rotation of circularly polarized light.

Susceptibility Tensor of an Optically Active Medium   It is a simple matter to show that if the susceptibility tensor has conjugate imaginary off-diagonal elements, namely,

$$\chi = \begin{bmatrix} \chi_{11} & i\chi_{12} & 0 \\ -i\chi_{12} & \chi_{11} & 0 \\ 0 & 0 & \chi_{33} \end{bmatrix} \tag{5.122}$$

where χ_{12} is real, then the medium is optically active. To prove this, we write the components of the wave equation (5.91) for the above susceptibility tensor. For simplicity, we consider the case of a wave propagating in the z direction. Then we have

$$-k^2 E_x + \frac{\omega^2}{c^2} E_x = -\frac{\omega^2}{c^2}(\chi_{11}E_x + i\chi_{12}E_y) \tag{5.123}$$

$$-k^2 E_y + \frac{\omega^2}{c^2} E_y = -\frac{\omega^2}{c^2}(-i\chi_{12}E_x + \chi_{11}E_y) \tag{5.124}$$

$$\frac{\omega^2}{c^2} E_z = -\frac{\omega^2}{c^2}\chi_{33}E_z \tag{5.125}$$

The last equation merely gives $E_z = 0$, so the wave is transverse. The determinant of the coefficients of the first two equations must vanish for a nontrivial solution, namely,

$$\begin{vmatrix} -k^2 + (\omega^2/c^2)(1 + \chi_{11}) & i(\omega^2/c^2)\chi_{12} \\ -i(\omega^2/c^2)\chi_{12} & -k^2 + (\omega^2/c^2)(1 + \chi_{11}) \end{vmatrix} = 0 \tag{5.126}$$

Solving for k, we find

$$k = \frac{\omega}{c}\sqrt{1 + \chi_{11} \pm \chi_{12}} \tag{5.127}$$

Now if we substitute the above expression for k back into either of Equations (5.123) or (5.124), we obtain

$$E_x = \pm iE_y \tag{5.128}$$

where the upper sign corresponds to the upper sign in Equation (5.127) and similarly for the lower sign. The above result means that the two values of k given by Equation (5.127) correspond to right and left circularly polarized light. The indices of refraction are, accordingly

$$n_R = \sqrt{1 + \chi_{11} + \chi_{12}} \qquad (5.129)$$

$$n_L = \sqrt{1 + \chi_{11} - \chi_{12}} \qquad (5.130)$$

for right and left circularly polarized light, respectively. It follows that the difference between n_R and n_L is given approximately by

$$n_R - n_L \approx \frac{\chi_{12}}{\sqrt{1 + \chi_{11}}} = \frac{\chi_{12}}{n_0} \qquad (5.131)$$

where n_0 is the ordinary *index of refraction*. The specific rotatory power from Equation (5.121), is then

$$\delta = \frac{\chi_{12}\pi}{n_0\lambda} \qquad (5.132)$$

Our result shows that the specific rotatory power is directly proportional to the imaginary component χ_{12} of the susceptibility tensor.

The **k** *Surface for Quartz.* Crystalline quartz is optically active as well as doubly refracting. Thus the susceptibility tensor for quartz is of the form given by Equation (5.122) rather than that of a simple uniaxial crystal. The correct equation of the **k** surface for quartz is thus of the form

$$\begin{vmatrix} (n_1\omega/c)^2 - k_y^2 - k_z^2 & k_xk_y + i\chi_{12}(\omega/c)^2 & k_xk_z \\ k_yk_x - i\chi_{12}(\omega/c)^2 & (n_1/c)^2 - k_x^2 - k_z^2 & k_yk_z \\ k_zk_x & k_zk_y & (n_3\omega/c)^2 - k_x^2 - k_y^2 \end{vmatrix} = 0 \quad (5.133)$$

A plot of the surface is shown in Figure 5.19. The two sheets of the k surface no longer refer to orthogonal linear polarizations, but rather to orthogonal *elliptical* polarizations. The type of polarization is indicated on the figure for various directions of propagation. Along the direction of the optic axis, the inner and outer surfaces do not touch (as they do in the case of an ordinary uniaxial crystal) but are separated by a certain amount. The separation depends on the value of χ_{12} and is therefore a measure of the optical rotatory power.

5.10   Faraday Rotation in Solids

If an isotropic dielectric is placed in a magnetic field and a beam of linearly polarized light is sent through the dielectric in the direction of the field, a rotation of the plane of polarization of the emerging light is found to occur. In other words, the presence of the field causes the dielectric to become optically active. This phenomenon was discovered in 1845 by Michael Faraday. The amount of rotation θ of the plane of polarization of the light is proportional to the magnetic induction B

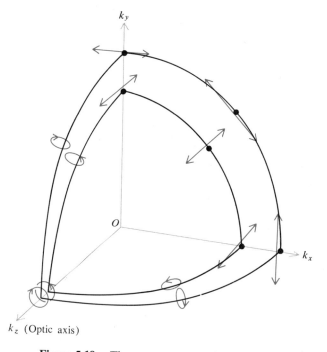

Figure 5.19.   The wave-vector surface of quartz.

and to the length *l* of travel in the medium. Thus we may write

$$\theta = VBl \qquad (5.134)$$

where V is a constant of proportionality. This constant is called the *Verdet constant*. Some examples are tabulated in Table 5.3 below. The figures given are for yellow light, 5890 Å.

In order to explain the Faraday effect, we must consider the equation of motion of the bound electrons in the presence of the static

Table 5.3.   VALUES OF THE VERDET CONSTANT FOR SOME SELECTED SUBSTANCES

Substance	V in minutes of angle per Oersted per centimeter
Fluorite	0.0009
Diamond	0.012
Glass	
Crown	0.015–0.025
Flint	0.030–0.050
Sodium Chloride	0.036

magnetic field $\mathbf{B}$ and the oscillating electric field $\mathbf{E}$ of the light wave. The differential equation of motion is

$$m\frac{d^2\mathbf{r}}{dt^2} + K\mathbf{r} = -e\mathbf{E} - e\left(\frac{d\mathbf{r}}{dt}\right) \times \mathbf{B} \tag{5.135}$$

where, as in the treatment of the theory of dispersion in dielectric media, Section 5.4, $\mathbf{r}$ is the displacement of the electron from its equilibrium position, and K is the elastic-force constant. For reasons of simplicity we neglect the force due to the magnetic field of the optical wave as well as the damping effect. These small effects are not particularly germane to the understanding of the basic theory of the Faraday effect.

We assume that the optical field $\mathbf{E}$ has the usual harmonic time dependence $e^{-i\omega t}$. The particular solution that we are interested in, is the steady state condition for which the displacement $\mathbf{r}$ has the same harmonic time dependence as the light wave. Hence we can write

$$-m\omega^2\mathbf{r} + K\mathbf{r} = -e\mathbf{E} + i\omega e\mathbf{r} \times \mathbf{B} \tag{5.136}$$

But the polarization $\mathbf{P}$ of the medium is just a constant times $\mathbf{r}$, namely $-N e\mathbf{r}$, hence the above equation implies that

$$(-m\omega^2 + K)\mathbf{P} = Ne^2\mathbf{E} + i\omega e\mathbf{P} \times \mathbf{B} \tag{5.137}$$

Now this equation can be solved for $\mathbf{P}$ by writing the equation in component form and solving for the components of $\mathbf{P}$. The result is expressible in the normal way:

$$\mathbf{P} = \varepsilon_0 \chi \mathbf{E} \tag{5.138}$$

where χ is the "effective" susceptibility tensor. Its form is precisely that of an optically active medium, namely

$$\chi = \begin{bmatrix} \chi_{11} & +i\chi_{12} & 0 \\ -i\chi_{12} & \chi_{11} & 0 \\ 0 & 0 & \chi_{33} \end{bmatrix} \tag{5.139}$$

where

$$\chi_{11} = \frac{Ne^2}{m\varepsilon_0}\left[\frac{\omega_0^2 - \omega^2}{(\omega_0^2 - \omega^2)^2 - \omega^2\omega_c^2}\right] \tag{5.140}$$

$$\chi_{33} = \frac{Ne^2}{m\varepsilon_0}\left[\frac{1}{\omega_0^2 - \omega^2}\right] \tag{5.141}$$

$$\chi_{12} = \frac{Ne^2}{m\varepsilon_0}\left[\frac{\omega\omega_c}{(\omega_0^2 - \omega^2)^2 - \omega^2\omega_c^2}\right] \tag{5.142}$$

In deriving the above result it has been assumed that the magnetic field **B** is in the z direction. The following abbreviations are used:

(resonance frequency) $\omega_o = \sqrt{\dfrac{K}{m}}$ (5.143)

(cyclotron frequency) $\omega_c = \dfrac{eB}{m}$ (5.144)

Finally, referring to Equation (5.132), we see that the specific rotatory power induced by a magnetic field, is given by the approximate equation

$$\delta \approx \frac{\pi N e^2}{\lambda m \varepsilon_0}\left[\frac{\omega \omega_c}{(\omega_o{}^2 - \omega^2)^2}\right] = \frac{\pi N e^3}{\lambda m^2 \varepsilon_0}\left[\frac{\omega B}{(\omega_o{}^2 - \omega^2)^2}\right]$$ (5.145)

in which it is assumed that $\omega \omega_c \ll \left|\omega_o{}^2 - \omega^2\right|.$

5.11   Other Magneto-optic and Electro-optic Effects

According to the theory developed in the previous section, a substance becomes doubly refracting as well as optically active in the presence of a static magnetic field. This is because of the fact that χ_{11} and χ_{33} are different. However, this double refraction is very small except when the frequency of the light is near the resonance frequency. Magnetically induced double refraction is observed in atomic vapors at optical frequencies close to the resonance frequencies of the atoms comprising the vapor. This phenomenon is called the *Voigt effect.*

Kerr Electro-optic Effect   When an optically isotropic substance is placed in a strong electric field, it becomes doubly refracting. The effect was discovered in 1875 by J. Kerr and is called the *Kerr electro-optic effect*. It is observed in both solids (glass) and liquids. The Kerr electro-optic effect is attributed to the alignment of the molecules in presence of the electric field. The substance then behaves optically as if it were a uniaxial crystal in which the electric field defines the optic axis. The magnitude of the effect is found to be proportional to the *square of the electric field strength*. The Kerr constant K is defined by the equation

$$n_{\parallel} - n_{\perp} = KE^2\lambda$$ (5.146)

where $n_{\parallel}$ is the index of refraction in the direction of the applied field **E**, and $n_{\perp}$ is the index at right angles to **E**. The vacuum wavelength is λ. Table 5.4 lists the Kerr constants of several liquids.

Table 5.4.   VALUES OF THE KERR CONSTANT

Substance	K in cm $\times$ volts^{-2}
Benzene	0.7×10^{-12}
Carbon Disulfide	3.5×10^{-12}
Nitrotoluene	2.0×10^{-10}
Nitrobenzene	4.4×10^{-10}

The Kerr electro-optic effect is utilized to produce a high-speed light modulator known as a "Kerr cell." This device, shown in Figure 5.20, consists of two parallel conductors immersed in a suitable liquid. (Nitrobenzene is generally used because of its high Kerr constant.) If the polarizer and analyzer are crossed and are oriented at $\pm$ 45 degrees with respect to the electric axis of the Kerr cell, then no light is transmitted except when the electric field is turned on. The transmission as a function of applied voltage is shown in Figure 5.22.

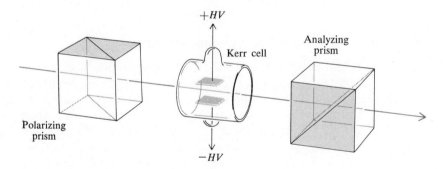

Figure 5.20.   Arrangement for using a Kerr cell light modulator.

The Cotton-Mouton Effect   This effect is the magnetic analogue of the Kerr electro-optic effect. It is observed in liquids and is attributed to the "lining up" of the molecules by the magnetic field. Like the Kerr effect, the Cotton-Mouton effect is also found to be proportional to the square of the impressed field.

The Pockels Effect   When certain kinds of birefringent crystals are placed in an electric field, their indices of refraction are altered by the presence of the field. This effect is known as the Pockels effect. It is found to be directly proportional to an applied field strength. The effect is utilized to produce light shutters and modulators. Pockels cells are commonly made with ADP (ammonium dihydrogen phosphate) or KDP (potassium dihydrogen phosphate). The crystal is placed between electrodes arranged so that light passes in the same direction as the electric field, Figure 5.21. The voltage versus transmission curve is shown in Figure 5.22.

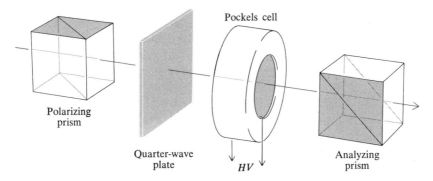

Figure 5.21.   Setup for using a Pockels cell light modulator.

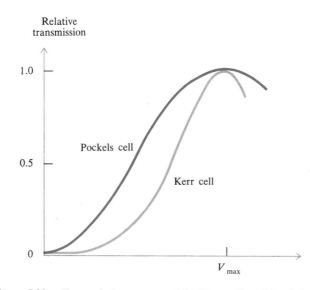

Figure 5.22.   Transmission curves of the Kerr cell and Pockels cell.

5.12   Nonlinear Optics

When a light wave propagates through an optical medium, the oscillating electromagnetic field exerts a polarizing force on all of the electrons comprising the medium. Since the inner electrons of the atoms are tightly bound to the nuclei, the major polarizing effect is exerted on the outer or valence electrons. With ordinary light sources the radiation fields are much smaller than the fields that bind the electrons to the atoms. Hence the radiation acts as a small perturbation. This produces a polarization that is proportional to the electric field of the light wave. However, if the radiation field is comparable with the atomic fields, ($\sim 10^8$ v/cm) then the relation between the polarization and the radiation field is no longer a linear one, Figure 5.23.

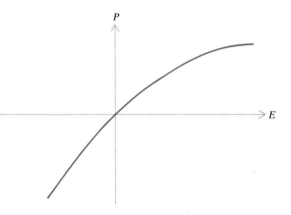

Figure 5.23.   Curve showing polarization versus electric field for a nonlinear dielectric.

The requisite light fields needed to exhibit this nonlinearity are obtainable with laser sources. Nonlinear optical effects that have been observed include optical harmonic generation, production of combination frequencies, optical rectification, and many others [3].

In an isotropic medium the general relation between the polarization **P** and the electric field **E** is expressible as a simple series expansion involving only the magnitudes since the direction of the polarization coincides with that of the field, namely,

$$P = \varepsilon_0(\chi E + \chi^{(2)}E^2 + \chi^{(3)}E^3 + \cdots) \tag{5.147}$$

In this expansion χ is the normal or linear susceptibility. It is generally much larger than the nonlinear coefficients $\chi^{(2)}$, $\chi^{(3)}$, and so forth. If the applied field has the form $E_0 e^{-i\omega t}$, then the induced polarization is

$$P = \varepsilon_0(\chi E_0 e^{-i\omega t} + \chi^{(2)}E_0^2 e^{-i2\omega t} + \chi^{(3)}E_0^3 e^{-i3\omega t} \cdots) \tag{5.148}$$

The part of the polarization associated with the second and higher terms gives rise to the generation of optical harmonics, Figure 5.24. These usually decrease rapidly in intensity with increasing order. If the general relation between **P** and **E** is such that a reversal of the direction of **E** merely results in the reversal of the direction of **P**, that is if

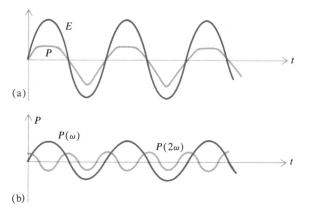

Figure 5.24. (a) Graphs of electric field and polarization as functions of time for the nonlinear case. (b) Resolution of the polarization into the fundamental and the second harmonic.

$P(E)$ is an odd function, then the even terms are all zero and there are no even harmonics. This is, in fact, the case with isotropic media.

In the case of crystalline media, $\mathbf{P}$ and $\mathbf{E}$ are not necessarily parallel. The polarization must then be expressed as an expansion of the type

$$\mathbf{P} = \varepsilon_0(\chi\mathbf{E} + \chi^{(2)}\mathbf{EE} + \chi^{(3)}\mathbf{EEE} + \cdots) \tag{5.149}$$

where χ is the ordinary susceptibility tensor. The coefficients $\chi^{(2)}$, $\chi^{(3)}$, and so forth, are higher-order tensors. The expansion is often written as the sum of two terms

$$\mathbf{P} = \mathbf{P}^{\mathrm{L}} + \mathbf{P}^{\mathrm{NL}} \tag{5.150}$$

where the linear polarization is

$$\mathbf{P}^{\mathrm{L}} = \varepsilon_0\chi\mathbf{E} \tag{5.151}$$

The remainder is the nonlinear polarization and is given by

$$\mathbf{P}^{\mathrm{NL}} = \varepsilon_0\chi^{(2)}\mathbf{EE} + \varepsilon_0\chi^{(3)}\mathbf{EEE} + \cdots \tag{5.152}$$

If the impressed field $\mathbf{E}$ is a light wave of angular frequency ω, then the second harmonic polarization $\mathbf{P}(2\omega)$ arises from the term $\varepsilon_0\chi^{(2)}\mathbf{EE}$. Its components can be written

$$P_i(2\omega) = \sum_j\sum_k \chi_{ijk}^{(2)}\, E_j E_k \tag{5.153}$$

The amount of second harmonic light that is produced depends critically on the form of the $\chi^{(2)}$ tensor. It can be shown that in order for the $\chi^{(2)}$ tensor not to vanish, the crystal must not possess inversion symmetry. This is also one of the requirements for a crystal to be piezoelectric. Thus piezoelectric crystals, such as quartz and KDP, are also useful for second harmonic generation of light.

Consider a plane wave of angular frequency ω propagating through a crystal that has the necessary type of symmetry to produce the second harmonic 2ω. The electromagnetic field of the fundamental wave has a space-time variation $e^{i(k_1 z - \omega t)}$, whereas that of the second harmonic is $e^{i(k_2 z - 2\omega t)}$.

Suppose that the crystal is in the form of a slab of thickness l. Then the amplitude of the second harmonic at the exit face of the crystal is obtained by adding the contributions from each element of thickness dz within the crystal, namely,

$$E(2\omega,l) \propto \int_0^l E^2(\omega,z)dz$$

$$\propto \int_0^l e^{2i[k_1 z - \omega(t - \tau)]}dz$$

(5.154)

Here τ is the time for the optical disturbance of frequency 2ω to travel from z to l. It is given by

$$\tau = \frac{k_2(l - z)}{2\omega}$$

(5.155)

Upon performing the integration and taking the square of the absolute value, one finds the intensity of the second harmonic to be

$$|E(2\omega)|^2 \propto \left[\frac{\sin(k_1 - \frac{1}{2}k_2)l}{k_1 - \frac{1}{2}k_2}\right]^2$$

(5.156)

The above result shows that if $k_1 = \frac{1}{2}k_2$, the intensity of second harmonic light is proportional to the square of the slab thickness. Otherwise the maximum intensity is that which can be obtained with a crystal of thickness

$$l_c = \frac{\pi}{2k_1 - k_2}$$

(5.157)

This is known as the "interaction length." Due to dispersion, the interaction length is only $10\lambda_0$ to $20\lambda_0$ for typical crystals. However, it is possible to greatly increase it by the method of *velocity matching*. In this method one makes use of the double nature of the **k** surface or the velocity surfaces of doubly refracting crystals. Actually, since the energy travels along the ray, it is the ray-velocity surface that is important in this application. Consider a uniaxial crystal. By a suitable choice of the ray direction, it is possible to have the ray velocity of the fundamental (corresponding to an ordinary ray) equal that of the second harmonic (corresponding to the extraordinary ray). This is illustrated in Figures 5.25 and 5.26. With velocity matching, the efficiency for second har-

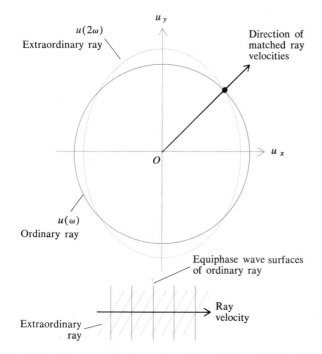

Figure 5.25. Use of the ray-velocity surfaces for velocity matching in the generation of optical harmonics.

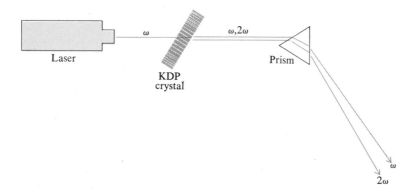

Figure 5.26. Simplified diagram showing the arrangement for optical frequency doubling. The KDP crystal is oriented at the velocity-matched angle.

monic generation of light in crystals can be improved by several orders of magnitude.

PROBLEMS

5.1. Show that the phase change that takes place on reflection at normal incidence is equal to

$$\tan^{-1}\left[\frac{-2\kappa}{-n^2 - \kappa^2 + 1}\right]$$

where n and κ are the real and imaginary parts of the index of refraction. Show that as $\kappa \to 0$, the phase change is π for $n > 1$ and 0 for $n < 1$.

5.2. A hypothetical metal has a static conductivity of 4×10^7 mho/m. Assuming that true charge carriers are free electrons of which there are $2 \times 10^{28}/m^3$, find the following quantities: (a) the relaxation time, (b) the plasma frequency, (c) the real, and (d) the imaginary parts of the index of refraction. (e) The reflectance at $\omega = 2\omega_p$.

5.3. Show that if $\kappa \ll n$, then

$$\text{(a) } n \approx 1 + \frac{Ne^2}{2m\varepsilon_o}\left(\frac{1}{\omega_o^2 - \omega^2}\right)$$

$$\text{(b) } \kappa \approx \frac{Ne^2}{2m\varepsilon_o}\left(\frac{\gamma\omega\omega_o}{\omega_o^2 - \omega^2}\right)$$

5.4. Derive Sellmeier's equation for the index of refraction as a function of wavelength:

$$n = B_0 + \frac{B_1\lambda^2}{\lambda^2 - \lambda_1^2} + \frac{B_2\lambda^2}{\lambda^2 - \lambda_2^2} + \cdots$$

5.5. Fill in steps leading to Equation (5.70) and (5.73).

5.6. Compute the reflectance of copper for $\lambda = 1$ mm, and 1 μm at normal incidence.

5.7. Derive Equation (5.81).

5.8. The reflectance, at normal incidence, of a metal is 80 percent. The coefficient of absorption is 50 cm^{-1}. Determine the real and imaginary parts of the index of refraction.

5.9. For aluminum at $\lambda = 5500$ Å, $n = 1.15$, and $\kappa = 3.2$. Find the reflectance, the absorption coefficient, and the phase change on reflection at normal incidence.

5.10. Show that if one introduces an *effective* index of refraction

$$n_{eff} = \frac{\sin \theta}{\sin \phi}$$

then, for an absorbing medium whose complex index of refraction is $\mathcal{N} = n + i\kappa$, the following equation holds for oblique incidence:

$$(n_{eff}^2 - n^2 + \kappa^2)(n_{eff}^2 - \sin^2 \theta) = n^2 \kappa^2$$

5.11. A uniaxial crystal, of indices n_o and n_e, is cut so that the optic axis is perpendicular to the surface. Show that for a light ray incident from the outside at an angle of incidence θ, the angle of refraction ϕ_e of the extraordinary ray is given by:

$$\tan \phi_e = \frac{n_o}{n_e} \frac{\sin \theta}{\sqrt{n_e^2 - \sin^2 \theta}}$$

5.12. Derive Fresnel's equation for the phase-velocity surface:

$$\frac{v_x^2}{v^2 - \dfrac{c^2}{n_1^2}} + \frac{v_y^2}{v^2 - \dfrac{c^2}{n_2^2}} + \frac{v_z^2}{v^2 - \dfrac{c^2}{n_3^2}} = 0$$

5.13. A polarizing prism of the Glan-type is to be made of quartz. Determine the angle at which the diagonal face should be cut.

5.14. A 30-degree prism is made of quartz. The optic axis is parallel to the apex edge of the prism. A beam of light ($\lambda_{vac} = 5890\text{Å}$) is incident so that the deviation is approximately minimum. Determine the angle between the E ray and the O ray.

5.15. A Fresnel prism is made of quartz as shown in Figure 5.18. The angle θ is 70 degrees. Determine the angle between the emerging right and left polarized rays for sodium light.

5.16. Referring to Equation (5.133), determine the relationship between the value of χ_{12}' and the specific rotatory power of quartz.

5.17. A beam of linearly polarized light is sent through a piece of solid glass tubing 25 cm long and 1 cm in diameter. The tubing is wound with a single layer of 250 turns of enameled copper wire along its entire length. If the Verdet constant of the glass is 0.05 min/s/cm, what is the amount of rotation of the plane of polarization of the light when a current of 5 amperes (A) is flowing through the wire?

CHAPTER 6

Thermal Radiation and Light Quanta

6.1 Thermal Radiation

The electromagnetic energy that is emitted from the surface of a heated body is called *thermal radiation*. This radiation consists of a continuous spectrum of frequencies extending over a wide range. The spectral distribution and the amount of energy radiated depend chiefly on the temperature of the emitting surface.

Regarding the spectral distribution, careful measurements show that at a given temperature, there is a definite frequency (or wavelength) at which the radiated power is maximum, although this maximum is very broad. Furthermore, the frequency of the maximum is found to vary in direct proportion to the absolute temperature. This rule is known as *Wien's law*. At room temperature, for example, the maximum occurs in the far-infrared region of the spectrum, and there is no perceptible visible radiation emitted. But at higher temperatures, the maximum shifts to correspondingly higher frequencies. Thus at about 500°C and above, a body glows visibly.

The rate at which energy is radiated by a heated body is also found to have a definite-temperature dependence. Measurements indicate that the total power increases as the *fourth power* of the absolute temperature. This is known as the *Stefan-Boltzmann law*. Both the Stefan-Boltzmann law and Wien's law may be regarded as empirical statements about thermal radiation. It is the purpose of the present chapter to derive these laws from basic theory and, in so doing, to deduce other quantitative relationships that apply to radiation emitted by heated bodies.

6.2 Kirchhoff's Law. Blackbody Radiation

Consider a hypothetical situation in which a hollow cavity contains inside it a single body thermally insulated from the cavity walls, say by a nonconducting thread, Figure 6.1. Let the cavity walls be main-

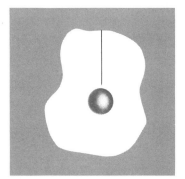

Figure 6.1. A body inside a cavity. The body exchanges heat with the cavity by thermal radiation and comes to equilibrium when the temperature of the body is the same as the temperature of the cavity walls.

tained at a constant temperature. Thermal radiation then fills the cavity and some of it is absorbed by the body. The body also emits thermal radiation, and equilibrium is attained when the body emits at the same rate that it absorbs. The temperature of the body is then equal to the temperature of the cavity walls.

Let I denote the intensity of the thermal radiation within the cavity, that is, I is the total power per unit area incident on the body. Let b be the fraction of incident power that the body absorbs, and call H the power per unit area that it emits. Then, for equilibrium

$$H = bI \qquad (6.1)$$

Now suppose that instead of just one body, there are several bodies of different b's inside the cavity. Distinguishing these by subscripts $1, 2, \cdots$, then, for thermal equilibrium of each body, we have $H_1 = b_1 I_1$, $H_2 = b_2 I_2, \cdots$, and so forth. It follows that

$$I = \frac{H_1}{b_1} = \frac{H_2}{b_2} = \cdots \qquad (6.2)$$

Thus at a given temperature the ratio of the emitted power to the fraction of power absorbed is the same for all bodies, and is equal to the intensity of radiation within a hollow cavity. This rule is known as *Kirchhoff's law*. According to it, good absorbers are also good emitters and conversely. This fact is easily demonstrated by placing a small spot of lampblack on a glass rod. If the rod is heated to incandescence, the blackened spot appears much brighter than the rest of the rod.

A perfect absorber is called a *blackbody*. For such a body $b = 1$, and the corresponding value of H is the maximum possible, namely

$$H_{\max} = I \qquad\qquad (6.3)$$

Thus a blackbody is the most efficient emitter of thermal radiation, and the emitted power per unit area is equal to the intensity within a hollow cavity. For this reason, blackbody radiation is also known as cavity or *hohlraumstralung*. A practical blackbody radiator can be produced by merely piercing a small hole in an otherwise closed cavity. If the walls of the cavity are maintained at a given temperature, the thermal radiation streaming through the hole is essentially identical with that of a perfect blackbody.

We now proceed to calculate the rate at which radiation is emitted through a hole in a cavity. Let us call u the energy density of the thermal radiation inside the cavity. This radiation streams about with speed c in all directions. Thus the fraction $d\Omega/4\pi$ of the radiation can be considered to be going in any one direction specified to within an element of solid angle $d\Omega$. Consider a hole of unit area. In one second, an amount of energy $uc \cos \theta \, d\Omega/4\pi$ streams through the hole, where θ is the angle between the direction of the radiation and the normal to the plane of the hole, Figure 6.2.

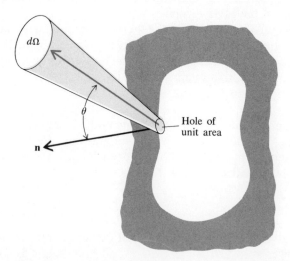

Figure 6.2.   Radiation streaming through a hole in a cavity. The unit vector **n** is normal to the hole and the radiation is spread over a solid angle $d\Omega$.

In order to find the total amount of energy passing through the hole in all possible directions, we integrate over the solid angle

$$d\Omega = \sin \theta \, d\theta \, d\phi$$

where the limits of integration are $\phi = 0$ to $\phi = 2\pi$, and $\theta = 0$ to $\theta = \pi/2$. Thus

$$\int_0^{2\pi}\int_0^{\pi/2} u\,c\,\cos\theta\,\sin\theta\,\frac{d\theta\,d\phi}{4\pi} = \frac{1}{4}u\,c \tag{6.4}$$

is the total amount of thermal radiation emitted per second per unit area. Hence, from Equation (6.3), the intensity of blackbody radiation is given by

$$I = \frac{1}{4}uc \tag{6.5}$$

The *spectral density* u_f is defined as the energy density per unit frequency interval centered at a given frequency f. In terms of spectral density, we have

$$u = \int_0^\infty u_f\,df \tag{6.6}$$

Corresponding to the spectral density, the *spectral intensity* I_f of thermal radiation is given by

$$I_f = \frac{1}{4}u_f c \tag{6.7}$$

This is the power radiated per unit area per unit frequency interval centered at the frequency f. The *spectral radiance* $\mathscr{I}_f$ is the power radiated per unit area per unit frequency interval per unit solid angle. For radiation in a direction normal to the surface, $\mathscr{I}_f = I_f/\pi$.

6.3   Modes of Electromagnetic Radiation in a Cavity

In order to find the density of radiation inside a cavity we must first investigate the standing wave patterns or *modes* of electromagnetic radiation that can exist in it. We shall find that the number of such modes in a given frequency range is of central importance to the theory of radiation. For simplicity we consider a cavity of rectangular shape. Standing waves in the cavity can then be represented by suitable linear combinations of wave functions based on the fundamental wave function

$$e^{i(\mathbf{k}\cdot\mathbf{r} - \omega t)} = e^{ik_x x}\,e^{ik_y y}\,e^{ik_z z}\,e^{-i\omega t} \tag{6.8}$$

where k_x, k_y, and k_z are the components of $\mathbf{k}$. Let A, B, and C be the linear dimensions of the cavity in the x, y, and z directions, respectively. Then a stationary pattern or *mode* will exist if the wave function is periodic in a manner expressed by the following equations:

$$k_x A = \pi n_x \qquad k_y B = \pi n_y \qquad k_z C = \pi n_z \tag{6.9}$$

where n_x, n_y, and n_z are integers. Each set (n_x, n_y, n_z) corresponds to a possible mode of the radiation in the cavity, Figure 6.3. Since $k^2 = k_x^2 + k_y^2 + k_z^2$, then

$$k^2 = \frac{\omega^2}{c^2} = \pi^2 \left(\frac{n_x^2}{A^2} + \frac{n_y^2}{B^2} + \frac{n_z^2}{C^2} \right) \tag{6.10}$$

or, equivalently,

$$\frac{4f^2}{c^2} = \frac{n_x^2}{A^2} + \frac{n_y^2}{B^2} + \frac{n_z^2}{C^2} \tag{6.11}$$

The above result shows that for a given frequency f, only certain values of n_x, n_y, and n_z are allowed.

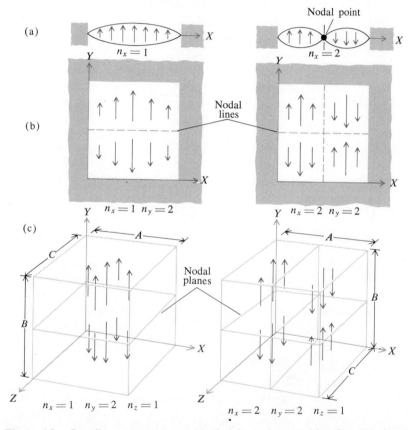

Figure 6.3. Standing wave patterns (modes) in various cavities. Part (a) shows the two lowest modes ($n = 1$ and $n = 2$) of a one-dimensional cavity. In (b) are shown the (1,2) and (2,2) modes of a two-dimensional cavity. Finally, in (c) the (1,2,1) and (2,2,1) modes of a three-dimensional cavity are illustrated.

Let us examine Figure 6.4 in which Equation (6.11) is plotted graphically in terms of coordinates n_x, n_y, and n_z. The various modes are here represented by points at the corners of unit cubes, some of which

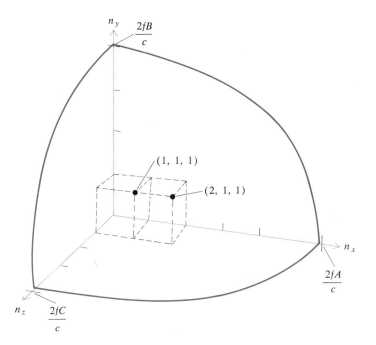

Figure 6.4. Unit cubes and associated points representing modes of a cavity. One octant of the limiting ellipsoid is shown.

are indicated in the figure. Now Equation (6.11) is the equation of an ellipsoid whose semiaxes are given by $2fA/c$, $2fB/c$, and $2fC/c$. The volume of one octant of this ellipsoid is therefore

$$\frac{1}{8} \times \frac{4\pi}{3} \times \frac{2fA}{c} \times \frac{2fB}{c} \times \frac{2fC}{c} = \frac{\pi f^3 ABC}{c^3} = \frac{4\pi}{3}\frac{f^3}{c^3}V \qquad \textbf{(6.12)}$$

where $V = ABC$ is the volume of the cavity. Since each unit cube is associated with one mode, the above expression is equal to the number of modes for *all frequencies equal to or less* than f. Only one octant of the ellipsoid is needed to count the modes, because both positive and negative values of the n's correspond to the same mode. It is necessary, however, to double the above value to obtain the total number of modes, since for a given direction of propagation, there are two orthogonal polarizations of the electromagnetic radiation inside the cavity. The final value for the number of modes g per unit volume, for all frequencies equal to or less than f, is

$$g = \frac{8\pi}{3c^3}f^3 \tag{6.13}$$

We can now find, by differentiation, the number of modes per unit volume for frequencies lying between f and $f + df$. The result is

$$dg = \frac{8\pi}{c^3}f^2\, df \tag{6.14}$$

A convenient way of interpreting the above result is to say that the number of modes per unit volume per unit frequency interval is

$$g_f = \frac{8\pi f^2}{c^3} \tag{6.15}$$

Although the above formula has been derived for a rectangular cavity, it can be shown that the result is independent of the shape of the cavity provided the cavity dimensions are large compared to the wavelength of the radiation.

6.4 Classical Theory of Blackbody Radiation. The Rayleigh-Jeans Formula

According to classical kinetic theory, the temperature of a gas is a measure of the mean thermal energy of the molecules that comprise the gas. The average energy associated with each degree of freedom of a molecule is $\frac{1}{2}kT$, where k is Boltzmann's constant and T is the absolute temperature. This well-known rule is called the *principle of equipartition of energy*. It applies, of course, only to systems in thermodynamic equilibrium.

Lord Rayleigh and Sir James Jeans suggested that the equipartition principle might also apply to the electromagnetic radiation in a cavity. If the radiation is in thermal equilibrium with the cavity walls, then one might reasonably expect an equipartition of energy among the cavity modes. Rayleigh and Jeans assumed that the mean energy per mode is kT. In effect, this assumption amounts to saying that, in a given mode, the electric field and the magnetic field each represent one degree of freedom. If there are g_f modes per unit frequency interval per unit volume, then the spectral density of the radiation would be $g_f kT$. Hence, from Equation (6.15), we have

$$u_f = g_f kT = \frac{8\pi f^2 kT}{c^3} \tag{6.16}$$

This yields, in view of Equation (6.7), the following formula for the spectral intensity, that is, the power radiated per unit area per unit frequency interval:

$$I_f = \frac{2\pi f^2 kT}{c^2} \qquad (6.17)$$

This is the famous Rayleigh-Jeans formula. It predicts a frequency-squared dependence for the spectral distribution of blackbody radiation, Figure 6.5. For sufficiently low frequencies, the formula is found to agree quite well with experimental data. However, at higher and higher frequencies, the formula predicts that a blackbody will emit more and more radiation. This, of course, is in contradiction with observation. It is the so-called "ultraviolet catastrophe" of the classical radiation theory. The ultraviolet catastrophe clearly shows that there is a fundamental error in the classical approach.

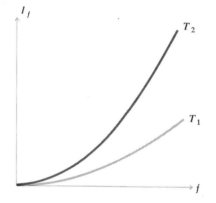

Figure 6.5.   The Rayleigh-Jeans law. The curves of I_f versus f are parabolas.

6.5   Quantization of Cavity Radiation

The way to avert the ultraviolet catastrophe was discovered by Planck in 1901. By introducing a radical concept, namely the *quantization* of electromagnetic radiation, Planck was able to derive an equation for blackbody emission that was in complete accord with experimental observations. This marked the beginning of quantum theory.

Planck did not accept the principle of equipartition for cavity radiation. He assumed that the energy associated with each mode was quantized, that is to say, the energy could exist only in integral multiples of some lowest amount or *quantum*. He postulated that the energy of the quantum was proportional to the frequency of the radiation. The name given to the quantum of electromagnetic radiation is the *photon*.

If we call the constant of proportionality h, then hf is the energy of a photon of frequency f. According to Planck's hypothesis, the modes of a cavity are occupied by integral numbers of photons and, accordingly, the energy of a given mode of frequency f can have any of the values

$$0, hf, 2hf, 3hf, \cdots$$

Let us denote the *average* number of photons per mode by $\langle n_f \rangle$. This number is known as the *occupation index*. In terms of it, the mean energy per mode is $hf \langle n_f \rangle$. In view of Equation (6.15), which gives the mode density, it follows that the spectral density of cavity radiation is given by

$$u_f = g_f hf \langle n_f \rangle = \frac{8\pi h f^3}{c^3} \langle n_f \rangle \tag{6.18}$$

The corresponding spectral intensity function for blackbody radiation is therefore

$$I_f = \frac{1}{4} c g_f hf \langle n_f \rangle = \frac{2\pi h f^3}{c^2} \langle n_f \rangle \tag{6.19}$$

Our next task is to determine how the occupation index $\langle n_f \rangle$ varies as a function of frequency.

6.6   Photon Statistics. Planck's Formula

The problem of finding the particular way that photons are distributed among the available modes of a cavity is an exercise in statistics. We address ourselves to the following question: Given a certain amount of energy in the form of photons in a cavity, is there a particular distribution that is more likely to occur than any other distribution, and if so, what is this most probable distribution? The answer is found by using a well-known method of statistical mechanics used to calculate distribution functions for systems containing large numbers of particles. In this method, one calculates the total number of ways W in which the particles, in this case photons, can be arranged in any arbitrary distribution that satisfies certain general conditions. One then proceeds to find that particular distribution for which W is a maximum. Owing to the fact that the total number of particles is extremely large for the cases of interest, the distribution having the largest value of W turns out to be overwhelmingly more probable than any other, and thus represents the actual distribution with virtually absolute certainty.

To apply the statistical method to cavity radiation, we shall divide the frequency spectrum up into an infinite number of intervals. The size of the intervals is arbitrary. For convenience we choose them to be unit intervals. The number of available quantum states (modes) in each interval is g_f. Let N_f be the number of photons in an interval, that is, N_f is the number of photons per unit frequency range. The occupation index is then that value of N_f/g_f which maximizes W, namely,

$$\langle n_f \rangle = \left(\frac{N_f}{g_f} \right)_{\max} \tag{6.20}$$

Now to find the number of arrangements of the N_f photons among the g_f different modes of the interval in question, we can think of the photons as identical objects placed in a linear array of g_f compartments, Figure 6.6. The photons are represented as dots, and the partitions

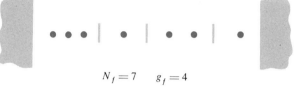

$$N_f = 7 \qquad g_f = 4$$

Figure 6.6. One possible arrangement of 7 identical objects (photons) in 4 compartments (modes).

between the compartments are represented as vertical lines of which there are $g_f - 1$. The total number of ways of arranging the dots in the compartments is just the total number of permutations of all of these $N_f + g_f - 1$ objects. This is $(N_f + g_f - 1)!$. But the dots are identical objects, so we must divide by the number of permutations of the dots: $N_f!$. Similarly, the partitions are identical, so we must also divide by the number of permutations of the partitions: $(g_f - 1)!$. The result is

$$W_f = \frac{(N_f + g_f - 1)!}{N_f! \, (g_f - 1)!} \tag{6.21}$$

This is the number of different ways of placing N_f identical objects in g_f compartments, that is, the number of different arrangements of the N_f photons in a unit frequency interval containing g_f modes. Finally, the total number of ways W of arranging the photons in all of the intervals is given by taking the product of all the W_f, namely,

$$W = \Pi_f W_f = \Pi_f \frac{(N_f + g_f - 1)!}{N_f! \, (g_f - 1)!} \tag{6.22}$$

The factorial function is awkward to handle, so we shall use Stirling's approximation:

$$\ln x! \cong x \ln x - x \tag{6.23}$$

This is not very accurate for small x, but it becomes increasingly accurate the larger x becomes.[1] In our application, x is very large. Thus

---

[1]An asymptotic expansion of $\ln x!$ is the following:

$$\ln x! = x \ln x - x + \ln \sqrt{2\pi x} + \ln \left(1 + \frac{1}{12x} + \frac{1}{288x^2} - \frac{139}{51840x^3} + \cdots \right)$$

Since $x \gg 1$, the first two terms are the only ones of importance for our purposes.

$$\ln W = \Sigma_f[(N_f + g_f - 1)\ln(N_f + g_f - 1)$$
$$- N_f \ln N_f - (g_f - 1)\ln(g_f - 1)] \tag{6.24}$$

If the distribution is such that W is maximum, then $\ln W$ is also maximum, and the first variation $\delta(\ln W)$ is zero. (Actually this is the condition for an extreme value of W. It can be shown, however, that our final result is, in fact, a maximum.) Thus for a maximum we must have

$$\delta(\ln W) = \sum_f [\ln(N_f + g_f) - \ln N_f] \, \delta N_f = 0 \tag{6.25}$$

Here we have neglected unity in comparison to $N_f + g_f$, which is presumably much greater than unity. Now if the N_f's were all independent quantities, then each separate bracket in the above summation would necessarily have to vanish in order that the equation be valid. However, the N_f's are not actually independent. This stems from the fact that the total photon energy $E = \Sigma \, hfN_f$ remains constant. Thus

$$\delta E = \sum_f hf \delta N_f = 0 \tag{6.26}$$

To find N_f as a function of f such that both Equations (6.25) and (6.26) are simultaneously satisfied, we use Lagrange's method of undetermined multipliers. This method is essentially a way of combining the two equations to obtain a single equation in which the N_f's are effectively independent. Multiply the conditional Equation (6.26) by the undetermined multiplier, a constant which we shall call $-\beta$. Add this to the first equation. The result is

$$\sum_f [\ln(N_f + g_f) - \ln N_f - \beta hf] \, \delta N_f = 0 \tag{6.27}$$

We now choose β such that each bracket vanishes in the above summation, namely,

$$\ln(N_f + g_f) - \ln N_f - \beta hf = 0 \tag{6.28}$$

Upon solving for N_f/g_f we find the following result for the occupation index

$$\langle n_f \rangle = \left(\frac{N_f}{g_f}\right)_{\max} = \frac{1}{e^{\beta hf} - 1} \tag{6.29}$$

This is the particular distribution that maximizes W subject to the condition that E is constant. It is known as the *Bose-Einstein distribution law for photons*. Other particles besides photons obey a similar law. These particles are collectively known as *bosons*. Examples are alpha particles, pi mesons, and so forth. (A different kind of statistical behavior is exhibited by a second class of particles. The distribution law for this class is called *Fermi-Dirac stastics*, and the particles are known as *fermions*. Electrons, protons, and mu mesons are examples of fermions.) For a full discussion of this subject the reader should consult any standard text on quantum statistics.

Equation (6.29) gives the average number of photons per mode as a function of frequency and the, as yet, unknown constant β. A graphical plot is shown in Figure 6.7.

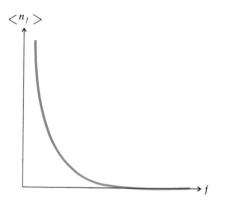

Figure 6.7.   Number of photons per unit frequency interval (occupation number) as a function of frequency for one temperature.

Substituting the above expression in Equation (6.19) we find

$$I_f = \frac{2\pi h f^3}{c^2} \frac{1}{e^{\beta h f} - 1} \tag{6.30}$$

giving intensity distribution of blackbody radiation as a function of frequency.

For small frequencies ($\beta h_f \ll 1$) the above formula reduces to

$$I_f = \frac{2\pi f^2}{c^2} \frac{1}{\beta} \tag{6.31}$$

This is identical with the Rayleigh-Jeans formula, *provided* that we identify the undetermined multiplier β with the quantity $1/kT$. This we shall do on the basis of the physical fact that the Rayleigh-Jeans formula is in agreement with the experimentally observed intensity distribution for low frequencies.

Our final formula for the spectral intensity of blackbody radiation is then

$$I_f = \frac{2\pi h f^3}{c^2} \frac{1}{e^{h f/kT} - 1} \tag{6.32}$$

which is the famous equation first derived by Planck. The equation is in complete agreement with experimental measurements. Figure 6.8(a) shows some curves of I_f plotted as a function of frequency for various temperatures. The same data is shown in Figure 6.8(b) except that the quantity I_f/T is plotted as a function of frequency in order to bring out more closely the comparison between the quantum formula (6.32) and the classical Rayleigh-Jeans formula (6.17).

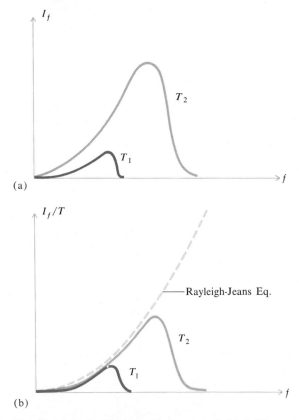

Figure 6.8.   The Planck radiation law. (a) I_f versus f. (b) I_f/T versus f with the Rayleigh-Jeans law (dotted) for comparison.

Both Wien's law and the Stefan-Boltzmann law are readily deduced from the Planck radiation formula. Let

$$x = \frac{hf}{kT} \tag{6.33}$$

Then Planck's formula may be written

$$I_f = \frac{2\pi k^3 T^3}{c^2 h^2} \frac{x^3}{e^x - 1} \tag{6.34}$$

By differentiating with respect to x and setting the result equal to zero, it is found that I_f is maximum for $x \approx 2.82$. This means that the frequency f_{max} at which the spectral intensity is maximum is given by

$$f_{max} = \frac{2.82 \, kT}{h} \tag{6.35}$$

This is one form of Wien's law. (Another way of stating Wien's law is in terms of wavelength. See Problem 5 at the end of the chapter.)

To find the total radiated power, we have

$$I = \int_0^\infty I_f \, df = \frac{2\pi k^4 T^4}{c^2 h^3} \int_0^\infty \frac{x^3 \, dx}{e^x - 1} \tag{6.36}$$

The value of the definite integral is $\pi^4/15$. Thus we obtain the Stefan-Boltzmann law

$$I = \sigma T^4 \tag{6.37}$$

where the Stefan-Boltzmann constant σ is given by

$$\sigma = \frac{2\pi^5 k^4}{15 c^2 h^3} \approx \frac{5.67 \times 10^{-8} W}{m^2 ({}^0 K)^4} \tag{6.38}$$

6.7 The Photoelectric Effect and the Detection of Individual Photons

When a metal surface is exposed to a beam of light, electrons are emitted from the surface of the metal. This well-known phenomenon, the photoelectric effect, is used in many ways for the measurement and control of light, and so forth.

The photoelectrons are emitted with a wide range of kinetic energies. Careful measurements show that if the light is monochromatic, then the photoelectrons, although having a certain energy spread, never have energies greater than a certain amount E_{max}. The value of E_{max} is found to depend linearly on the frequency f of the incident light according to the following equation:

$$E_{max} = hf - e\varphi \tag{6.39}$$

where h is Planck's constant and e is the electronic charge. The value of the constant φ depends on the particular metal used and is known as the *work function* of the metal. It is of the order of a few volts for most metals. The quantity $e\varphi$ represents essentially the work required to separate the electron from the metal surface.

According to the above equation, the energy of the emitted electron does not depend at all on the intensity of the incident light but only on the frequency. However, the photocurrent is found to vary directly with the intensity of the light. In other words, the number of photo-electrons emitted per second is directly proportional to the number of photons per second striking the metal surface. Now the intensity of the light can be made so low that individual photoelectrons may be counted. Since the energy of each photoelectron is still represented by Equation (6.39), we must conclude that energy is transferred to an electron by a single photon. The photoelectric effect thus makes possible the detection of individual photons.

6.8   Momentum of a Photon. Light Pressure

According to a well-known derivation based on classical electromagnetic theory [16], [34], the pressure exerted by a beam of light of intensity I normally on a black surface, is I/c. This was demonstrated experimentally many years ago [28]. The magnitude of the effect is very small, however, and requires a very sensitive pressure-measuring device to detect it.

In terms of the quantum description of light, the existence of light pressure implies that photons must carry momentum as well as energy. The linear momentum of a photon can be calculated very easily if it is assumed that Einstein's mass-energy relation holds, that is,

$$hf = mc^2 \tag{6.40}$$

where f is the frequency and m is the mass of the photon.[2] Since the speed of the photon is c, the linear momentum p is given by

$$p = mc = \frac{hf}{c} \tag{6.41}$$

An alternative way of expressing the momentum of a photon is in terms of its wavelength λ. This expression is

$$p = \frac{h}{\lambda} \tag{6.42}$$

which follows immediately from the fact that $f\lambda = c$.

Suppose that a stream of photons falls normally on a perfectly absorbing surface. Assuming that momentum is conserved, a given photon transfers its entire momentum hf/c to the surface upon being absorbed. If there are N photons per unit area that hit the surface every second, then the pressure P, being equal to the time rate of transfer of linear

---

[2] The rest mass m_0 of a photon must be zero. Otherwise, by the mass-velocity formula

$$m = m_0 \frac{1}{\sqrt{1 - v^2/c^2}}$$

m would be infinite, since $v = c$.

momentum per unit area is given by

$$P = \frac{Nhf}{c} \tag{6.43}$$

Now the intensity I of the beam is the power per unit area. Since each photon carries an energy hf, it follows that

$$I = Nhf \tag{6.44}$$

Consequently,

$$P = \frac{I}{c} \tag{6.45}$$

which is the same as the classical expression for the pressure.

If the surface is perfectly reflecting, then the pressure is just *twice* the above value, namely $2I/c$. This is because a photon, upon being reflected back, undergoes a change of momentum of $p - (-p) = 2p$. Each photon, therefore, transfers twice as much momentum to the surface as it would if it had been absorbed.

6.9 Angular Momentum of a Photon

If a beam of circularly polarized light is incident on an absorbing surface, classical electromagnetic theory predicts that the surface must experience a torque [34]. The calculation gives the magnitude $\mathcal{T}$ of the torque per unit area as

$$\mathcal{T} = \frac{I}{2\pi f} = \frac{I}{\omega} \tag{6.46}$$

where I is the intensity of the beam, as before. The above result, in view of (6.44), can be written in the alternative form

$$\mathcal{T} = \frac{Nh}{2\pi} \tag{6.47}$$

This implies that photons must carry angular momentum as well as linear momentum. This intrinsic angular momentum is called *spin*. From the above equation we see the magnitude of the spin of a single photon is $h/2\pi$. For left circularly polarized light, the direction of the spin of the photon is parallel to the direction of propagation, while for right circularly polarized light, it is antiparallel to the direction of propagation. Both linearly polarized light and unpolarized light can be considered to be equal mixtures of right and left circular polarizations, so that the average angular momentum is zero. *In the case of linearly polarized light, the mixture is coherent, whereas for unpolarized light, it is incoherent.*

6.10 Wavelength of a Material Particle. de Broglie's Hypothesis

In 1924 the French physicist Louis de Broglie proposed that just as light exhibits both wavelike and particlelike properties, so material particles might also exhibit a wavelike behavior. In analogy with the expression for a photon's momentum, $p = h/\lambda$, de Broglie suggested that the same relation might apply to *any* particle. Thus a moving particle of momentum $p = mv$ would have an associated wavelength λ given by

$$\lambda = \frac{h}{p} = \frac{h}{mv} \tag{6.48}$$

where h is Planck's constant.

The validity of de Broglie's bold hypothesis was verified by a famous experiment performed by Davisson and Germer in 1927. They demonstrated that a beam of electrons impinging on a crystal is reflected from the crystal in just the same way that a beam of light is reflected by a diffraction grating. The electrons were preferentially reflected at certain angles. The value of these angles of strong reflection were found to obey the optical grating formula

$$n\lambda = d \sin \theta \tag{6.49}$$

where n is an integer and d is the grating spacing. For a crystal, d is the spacing between adjacent rows of atoms of the crystal. In Davisson and Germer's experiment, the wavelength found for the electrons agreed precisely with the de Broglie equation.

Since Davisson and Germer's experiment, many others have been performed verifying de Broglie's formula, not only for electrons, but for other particles as well, including protons, neutrons, simple atoms, and molecules. Light and matter both have dual natures. Each exhibits both particlelike and wavelike properties depending on the experimental situation. This schizophrenic behavior of matter and radiation shows that neither the particle model nor the wave model is strictly correct. They are not mutually exclusive, however, but rather, are *complementary* descriptions. Each model emphasizes a certain aspect, and each has its own limitations.

6.11 Heisenberg's Uncertainty Principle

One of the most basic and far reaching concepts of modern physical theory was formulated in 1927 by Werner Heisenberg and is known as the *uncertainty principle*. This principle is concerned with the limit to the precision of our knowledge about physical systems. Specifically, the principle may be stated as follows: If P and Q are two conjugate variables in the sense of classical mechanics, then the simultaneous values of these variables can never be known to a precision greater than that given by

$$\Delta P \, \Delta Q \approx h \tag{6.50}$$

where h is Planck's constant. Examples of conjugate quantities are energy and time, position and momentum, angle and angular momentum, and so forth.

To illustrate how the uncertainty principle applies to light quanta, suppose one were given the task of determining the precise energy of a photon, or equivalently, the frequency. Suppose further that this measurement had to be made within a definite time interval Δt, say by letting a light shutter be open for this amount of time and then closing it. Now even if the source of light were strictly monochromatic, the fact that the light pulse lasts for a finite time means that there is a resulting frequency spread in the Fourier resolution of the pulse given by

$$\Delta f \Delta t \approx 1 \tag{6.51}$$

This can be written

$$\Delta(hf)\Delta t \approx h \tag{6.52}$$

that is,

$$\Delta E \Delta t \approx h \tag{6.53}$$

Here the quantity ΔE means the uncertainty in the energy of the photon, corresponding to the uncertainty Δf of its frequency. Thus the energy of the photon cannot be measured with absolute precision unless the time interval is infinite. Conversely, the knowledge of the time t at which the photon left the shutter cannot be known with certainty unless we are willing to give up all knowledge concerning its frequency or, equivalently, its energy. In any case, the product of the two uncertainties ΔE and Δt can never be less than h.

A second application concerns the position of a photon. As in the previous example, let the shutter be open for a time Δt and suppose the released photons are traveling in the x direction. Then

$$\Delta x = c\Delta t \approx \frac{c}{\Delta f} \tag{6.54}$$

But from Equation (6.41),

$$\Delta p = \frac{h\Delta f}{c} \tag{6.55}$$

Hence

$$\Delta x \Delta p \approx h \qquad (6.56)$$

This means that we cannot know the instantaneous values of both the position and momentum of a photon to an arbitrary degree of accuracy. If we know its momentum with absolute accuracy, we know nothing about its location, and conversely, if we know its position accurately, we have no knowledge at all concerning its momentum.

The uncertainty principle brings out the inadequacy of describing a photon as a particle. If we push the description too far by specifying the photon's exact location in space and time, the description loses meaning, because the momentum and the energy of the photon become completely undetermined.

PROBLEMS

6.1. Compute the number of available modes in a cubical box 10 cm on a side, for the following intervals:
   (a) A frequency interval of 10^3 Hz centered at a wavelength of 5000 Å.
   (b) A wavelength interval of 1 Å centered at 5000 Å.

6.2. Determine the number of photons in the box of the above problem for the two intervals given when the temperature of the walls is (a) room temperature $300°$K and (b) the sun's temperature $6000°$K.

6.3. A 100-W tungsten lamp operates at a temperature of $1800°$K. How many photons does it emit per second in the interval 5000 Å to 5001 Å? (Assume the filament emits as a blackbody.)

6.4. Determine the number of photons per mode in a cavity whose temperature is $300°$K and $6000°$K for the following wavelengths:
   (a) 5000 Å, (b) 50 μm, and (c) 5 mm.

6.5. Calculate the total number of photons of *all* frequencies in a cavity of volume V at a temperature T.

6.6. Calculate the total number of photons per unit area per unit time emitted by a blackbody at temperature T.

6.7. Give the Planck radiation law in terms of power per unit area per unit *wavelength* interval. Express it in terms of wavelength.

6.8. Find the wavelength of maximum radiation per unit wavelength interval. The result will be different from the equivalent wavelength of Equation (6.35). Why?

6.9. The linewidth of a He-Ne laser is 10^3 Hz. The operating wavelength is 6328 Å and the power is 1 milliwatt (mW). (a) How many photons are emitted per second? (b) If the output beam is 1 mm in diameter, at what temperature would a blackbody have to be in order to emit the same number of photons from an equal area and over the same frequency interval as the laser?

6.10. Derive an equation giving the pressure exerted on the walls of a cubical cavity at temperature T due to the photons inside. (Assume that one-third of the photons are effective in any one direction, say the x direction.)

6.11. From the result of Problem 10, find the temperature at which the pressure is equal to 10^{-3} atmosphere.

6.12. A laser beam is focused to a diffraction-limited spot of 1 μm diameter. If the total power of the laser is 10 W, what is the pressure at the focal point?

CHAPTER 7
Optical Spectra

7.1 General Remarks

A *spectrum* may be defined as an ordering of electromagnetic radiation according to frequency, or what amounts to the same thing, an ordering by wavelength. The complete spectrum of a given source comprises all the frequencies that the source emits. Since no single universal frequency-resolving instrument exists, the various regions of the electromagnetic spectrum must be investigated by different methods. The main regions have already been mentioned in Section 1.4.

The so-called optical region extends over a wide range from the far infrared on the one end, to the far ultraviolet on the other. It includes the visible region as a relatively small portion, Figure 7.1. Basically, the optical region is distinguished by

(1) the fact that the radiation is focused, directed, and controlled by mirrors and lenses, and

(2) the use of prisms and gratings for dispersing the radiation into a spectrum.

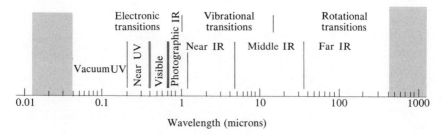

Figure 7.1. The optical region of the electromagnetic spectrum.

Unlike the continuous spectrum of thermal radiation given off by solid bodies, the radiation emitted by excited atoms or molecules is found to consist of various discrete frequencies. These frequencies are characteristic of the particular kinds of atoms or molecules involved. The term "line" spectrum is commonly used when referring to such radiation. This terminology originates from the fact that a *slit* is generally the type of entrance aperture for spectroscopic instruments used in the optical region, so a separate *line* image of the slit is formed at the focal plane for each different wavelength comprising the radiation. Sources of line spectra include such things as arcs, sparks, and electrical discharges through gases.

The optical spectra of most atoms are quite complex, and the line patterns are seemingly random in appearance. A few elements, notably hydrogen and the alkali metals, exhibit relatively simple spectra that are characterized by easily recognized *series* of lines converging towards a limit.

The optical spectra of many molecules, particularly diatomic molecules, appear as more or less regularly spaced "bands" when examined with a spectroscopic instrument of low resolving power. However, under high resolution, these bands are found to be sequences of closely spaced lines.

When white light is sent through an unexcited gas or vapor, it is generally found that the atoms or molecules comprising the vapor absorb just those same frequencies that they would emit if excited. The result is that those particular frequencies are either weakened or are entirely missing from the light that is transmitted through the vapor. This effect is present in ordinary sunlight, the spectrum of which appears as numerous dark lines on a bright continuous background.

The dark lines are called Fraunhoffer lines after J. Fraunhoffer who made early quantitative measurements. These lines reveal the presence of a relatively cool layer of gas in the sun's upper atmosphere. The atoms in this layer absorb their own characteristic wavelengths from the light coming from the hot, dense surface of the sun below, which emits thermal radiation corresponding to a temperature of about $5500°K$.

Selective absorption is also exhibited by solids. Virtually all transparent solids show broad absorption bands in the infrared and ultraviolet. In most colored substances these absorption bands extend into the visible region. However, relatively sharp absorption bands may occur in certain cases such as crystals and glasses that contain rare earth atoms as impurities.

7.2   Elementary Theory of Atomic Spectra

The mathematical theory of atomic spectra had its beginning in 1913 when Niels Bohr, a Danish physicist, announced his now famous work. He was concerned mainly with a theoretical explanation of the spectrum of hydrogen, although his basic ideas are applicable to other systems as well.

In order to explain the fact that atoms emit only certain characteristic frequencies, Bohr introduced two fundamental assumptions. These are:

(1) *The electrons of an atom can occupy only certain discrete quantized states or orbits. These states have different energies, and the one of lowest energy is the normal state of the atom, also known as the ground state.*

(2) *When an electron undergoes a transition from one state to another, it can do so by emitting or absorbing radiation. The frequency f of this radiation is given by*

$$f = \frac{\Delta E}{h} \tag{7.1}$$

where ΔE is the energy difference between the two states involved, and h is Planck's constant.

These assumptions represent a radical departure from the classical or Newtonian concept of the atom. The first is suggestive of the quantization of cavity radiation introduced earlier by Planck. The second idea amounts to saying that an atom emits, or absorbs, a single photon upon changing from one quantized state to another, the energy of the photon being equal to the energy difference between the two states, Figure 7.2.

The frequency spectrum of an atom or molecule is given by taking the various possible energy differences $|E_1 - E_2|$ and dividing by h. In order to calculate the actual spectrum of a given atom, one must first know the energies of the various quantum states of the atom in question. Conversely, the energies of the quantum states can be inferred from the measured frequencies of the various spectrum lines.

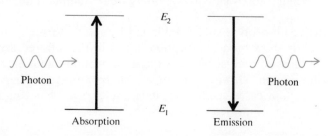

Figure 7.2.   Diagram showing the processes of absorption and emission.

The Bohr Atom and the Hydrogen Spectrum   In his study of the hydrogen atom, Bohr was able to obtain the correct formula for the energy levels by introducing a fundamental postulate concerning angular momentum. According to this postulate, *the angular momentum of an electron is always an integral multiple of the quantity $h/2\pi$, where h is Planck's constant.*

An electron of mass m traveling with speed v in a circular orbit of radius r has angular momentum mvr. Hence the relation

$$mvr = \frac{nh}{2\pi} \qquad (n = 1, 2, 3, \cdots) \qquad (7.2)$$

expresses the quantization of the orbital angular momentum of the electron. The integer n is known as the principal quantum number.

The classical force equation for an electron of charge $-e$ revolving in a circular orbit or radius r, centered on a proton of charge $+e$, is

$$\frac{e^2}{4\pi\varepsilon_0 r^2} = \frac{mv^2}{r} \qquad (7.3)$$

By elimination of v between the two equations, one obtains the following formula for the radii of the quantized orbits:

$$r = \frac{\varepsilon_0 h^2}{\pi m e^2} n^2 \qquad (7.4)$$

The radius of the smallest orbit ($n = 1$) is called the *first Bohr radius* and is denoted by a_H. Its numerical value is

$$a_H = \frac{\varepsilon_0 h^2}{\pi m e^2} = 0.529 \text{ Å} \qquad (7.5)$$

The various orbits are then given by the sequence a_H, $4a_H$, $9a_H$, $\cdots$, and so forth.

The total energy of a given orbit is given by the sum of the kinetic and the potential energies, namely,

$$E = \frac{1}{2}mv^2 - \frac{e^2}{4\pi\varepsilon_0 r} \qquad (7.6)$$

Eliminating v, by means of Equation (7.3), one finds

$$E = -\frac{e^2}{8\pi\varepsilon_0 r} \qquad (7.7)$$

This is the classical value for the energy of a bound electron. If all values of r were allowed, then any (negative) value of energy would be possible. But the orbits are quantized according to Equation (7.5). The resultant quantized energies are given by

$$E_n = -\frac{me^4}{8\varepsilon_0 h^2}\left(\frac{1}{n^2}\right)(n = 1, 2, 3, \cdots) \qquad (7.8)$$

The formula for the hydrogen spectrum follows immediately by combining the above equation with the Bohr frequency condition,

Equation (7.1). Calling E_1 and E_2 the energies of the orbits n_1 and n_2, respectively, we have

$$f = \frac{\Delta E}{h} = \frac{E_2 - E_1}{h} = R \left(\frac{1}{n_1{}^2} - \frac{1}{n_2{}^2} \right) \tag{7.9}$$

where R, the Rydberg constant, is given by

$$R = \frac{me^4}{8\varepsilon_0{}^2 h^3} \tag{7.10}$$

Its value in frequency units is 3.29×10^{15} Hz.

A transition diagram of the hydrogen atom is shown in Figure 7.3. The energies of the various allowed orbits are plotted as horizontal

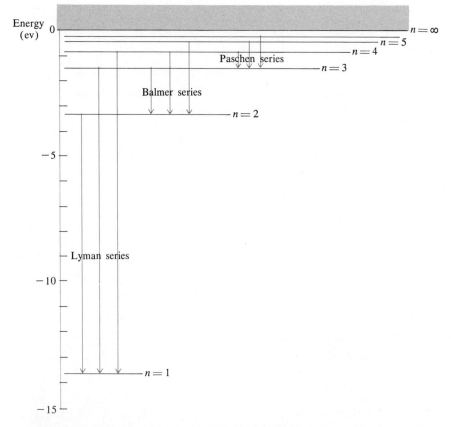

Figure 7.3. Energy levels of atomic hydrogen. Transitions for the first three series are indicated.

lines, and the transitions, corresponding to the various spectral lines, are shown as vertical arrows. Various combinations of the integers n_1 and n_2 give the observed spectral series. These are as follows:

$n_1 = 1$ $n_2 = 2, 3, 4, \cdots$ Lyman Series (far ultraviolet)

$n_1 = 2$ $n_2 = 3, 4, 5, \cdots$ Balmer Series (visible and near ultraviolet)

$n_1 = 3$ $n_2 = 4, 5, 6, \cdots$ Paschen Series (near infrared)

$n_1 = 4$ $n_2 = 5, 6, 7, \cdots$ Brackett Series (infrared)

$n_1 = 5$ $n_2 = 6, 7, 8, \cdots$ Pfund Series (infrared)

$\vdots$ $\vdots$

Some of the series are shown in Figure 7.4 on a logarithmic wavelength scale.

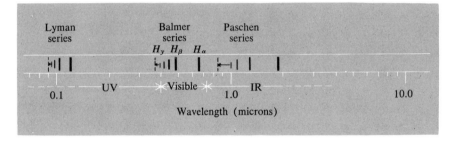

Figure 7.4.   The first three series of atomic hydrogen on a logarithmic wavelength scale.

The first three lines of the Balmer series, namely H_α at a wavelength of 6563 Å, H_β at 4861 Å, and H_γ at 4340 Å, are easily seen by viewing a simple hydrogen discharge tube through a small spectroscope. The members of the series up to $n_2 = 22$ have been recorded by photography. The intensities of the lines of a given series diminish with increasing values of n_2. Furthermore, the intensities of the various series decrease markedly as n_1 increases. Observations using ordinary laboratory sources have extended as far as the line at 12.3 μm in the infrared, corresponding to $n_1 = 6$, $n_2 = 7$.

The hydrogen spectrum is of particular astronomical importance. Since hydrogen is the most abundant element in the universe, the spectra of most stars show the Balmer series as prominent absorption lines. The series also appears as bright emission lines in the spectra of many luminous nebulae. Recent radiotelescope observations [26] have revealed interstellar hydrogen emission lines corresponding to very large quantum numbers. For instance, the line $n_1 = 158$, $n_2 = 159$ at a frequency of 1651 MHz has been received.

Effect of a Finite Nuclear Mass   The value of the Rydberg constant given by Equation (7.10) is for a nucleus of infinite mass. Since the nucleus actually has a finite mass, the electron does not revolve about the nucleus as a center, rather, both particles revolve about their common center of mass. This requires that m, the mass of the electron, be replaced by the reduced mass in order to obtain the correct value for the Rydberg constant. Thus the Rydberg constant for hydrogen is more accurately given by the formula

$$R_H = \frac{\mu e^4}{8\varepsilon_0{}^2 h^3} \tag{7.11}$$

where

$$\mu = \frac{mM}{m + M} \tag{7.12}$$

is the reduced mass, M is the mass of the atomic nucleus, and m is the mass of the electron.

In the case of ordinary hydrogen the nucleus is a single proton and the mass ratio M/m is equal to 1836. For the heavy isotope of hydrogen, deuterium, the mass ratio is about twice as much. The Rydberg constant for deuterium is, therefore, slightly different from that for hydrogen. The result is that a small difference exists between the frequencies of corresponding spectrum lines of the two isotopes. This effect, called *isotope shift*, can be seen as a "doubling" of the lines from a discharge tube containing a mixture of hydrogen and deuterium.

The Bohr model of the hydrogen atom, although giving essentially correct numerical results, is unable to account for the fact that the electron does not radiate while traveling in its circular orbit in the ground state, as required by classical electromagnetic theory. Further, the theory is difficult to apply to more complicated atoms and is completely inapplicable to molecules. Early attempts were made by various theorists to modify Bohr's theory in order to account for such things as the fine structure of spectrum lines, and so forth on (Section 7.7 below). These attempts met with varying degrees of success. However, the Bohr theory has now been superseded by the modern quantum theory of the atom, which will be discussed in the following sections.

Spectra of the Alkali Metals   An empirical formula similar to that for hydrogen gives fairly accurate results for the spectra of the alkali metals lithium, sodium, and so forth. This formula is

$$f = R \left[\frac{1}{(n_1 - \delta_1)^2} - \frac{1}{(n_2 - \delta_2)^2} \right] \qquad (7.13)$$

The Rydberg constant R is approximately the same as R_H. It has a slightly different value for each element. The quantum numbers n_1 and n_2 are integers, and the associated quantities δ_1 and δ_2 are known as *quantum defects*.

In a given spectral series, specified by a fixed value of n_1 and a sequence of increasing values of n_2, the quantum defects are very nearly constant. The most prominent series for the alkalis are designated as *sharp, principal, diffuse,* and *fundamental,* respectively. As a typical example, the quantum numbers and quantum defects for the series in sodium are listed in Table 7.1.

Table 7.1. SERIES IN SODIUM

SERIES	n_1	n_2	δ_1	δ_2
Sharp	3	4, 5, 6, · · ·	0.87	1.35
Principal	3	3, 4, 5, · · ·	1.35	0.87
Diffuse	3	3, 4, 5, · · ·	0.87	0.01
Fundamental	3	4, 5, 6, · · ·	0.01	0.00

The sharp and the diffuse series are so-named because of the appearance of the spectral lines.

The principal series is the most intense in emission and is also the one giving the strongest absorption lines when white light is passed through the vapor of the metal.

In the case of the fundamental series, the quantum defects are very small. As a consequence, the frequencies of the lines of this series are very nearly the same as those of the corresponding series in hydrogen. This is the reason for the name fundamental.

7.3 Quantum Mechanics

Modern quantum theory was pioneered by Schrödinger, Heisenberg, Born, and others in the 1920s. Originally there were two apparently different quantum theories called *wave mechanics* and *matrix mechanics*. These two formulations of quantum theory were later shown to be completely equivalent. Quantum mechanics, as it is known today, includes both. We shall not attempt a rigorous development of quantum mechanics here, but we shall merely state some of the essential results that apply to atomic theory.

The quantum mechanical description of an atom or atomic system is made in terms of a *wave function* or *state function*. The commonly used symbol for this function is Ψ. Ordinarily Ψ is a complex number and is considered to be a function of all of the configurational coordinates of the system in question including the time.

According to the basic postulates of quantum mechanics, the state function Ψ has the property that the square of its absolute value, $|\Psi|^2$ or $\Psi^*\Psi$, is a measure of the *probability* that the system in question is located at the configuration corresponding to particular values of the coordinates. $\Psi^*\Psi$ is sometimes referred to as the *probability distribution function* or the *probability density*.

If the system is a single electron, for example, with coordinates x, y, and z, then the probability that the electron is located between x and $x + \Delta x$, y and $y + \Delta y$, z and $z + \Delta z$ is given by the expression

$$\Psi^*(x,y,z,t)\Psi(x,y,z,t)\Delta x\Delta y\Delta z \tag{7.14}$$

It is evident from the above interpretation of the state function that one can never be certain that the electron is located at any given place. Only the chance of its being there within certain limits can be known. This is entirely consistent with the Heisenberg uncertainty principle discussed earlier in Section 6.11.

Now the total probability that the electron is located *somewhere* in space is necessarily unity. It follows that the integral, over all space, of the probability density is finite and has, in fact, the value 1, namely,

$$\int_{-\infty}^{\infty} \int_{-\infty}^{\infty} \int_{-\infty}^{\infty} \Psi^*\Psi\, dx\, dy\, dz = 1 \tag{7.15}$$

Functions satisfying the above equation are said to be *quadratically integrable, normalized* functions.

Stationary States   A *characteristic state* or *eigenstate* is one that corresponds to a perfectly defined energy. A given system may have many eigenstates, each possessing, in general, a different energy. If E_n denotes the particular energy of a system when it is in one of its characteristic states, then the time dependence of the state function is given by the complex exponential factor $\exp(-iE_n\, t/\hbar)$ where

$$\hbar = \frac{h}{2\pi}$$

Consequently the complete state function is expressible as

$$\Psi_n(x,y,z,t) = \psi_n(x,y,z)\, e^{-iE_n\, t/\hbar} \tag{7.16}$$

Here ψ_n is a function of the configurational coordinates only. It does not involve the time.

Consider the probability density of a system in one of its characteristic states. We have

$$\Psi_n{}^*\,\Psi_n = \psi_n{}^*\,e^{iE_n\,t/\hbar}\,\psi_n\,e^{-iE_n\,t/\hbar} = \psi_n{}^*\psi_n \tag{7.17}$$

We see that the exponential factors cancel out. This means that the probability distribution is constant in time, or stationary. Thus characteristic states are also called *stationary states*. A system that is in a stationary state is a static system in the sense that no changes at all are taking place with respect to the external surroundings.

In the particular case in which the quantum mechanical system is an atom, consisting of a nucleus with surrounding electrons, the probability distribution function is actually a measure of the mean electron density at a given point in space. One sometimes refers to this as a *charge cloud*. When an atom is in a stationary state, the electron density is constant in time. The surrounding electromagnetic field is static, and the atom does not radiate.

Coherent States Consider a system that is in the process of changing from one eigenstate Ψ_1 to another Ψ_2. During the transition the state function is given by a linear combination of the two state functions involved, namely

$$\Psi = c_1\psi_1\,e^{-iE_1\,t/\hbar} + c_2\psi_2\,e^{-iE_2\,t/\hbar} \tag{7.18}$$

Here c_1 and c_2 are parameters whose variation with time is slow in comparison with that of the exponential factors. A state of the above type is known as a *coherent state*. One essential difference between a coherent state and a stationary state is that the energy of a coherent state is not well defined, whereas that of a stationary state is.

The probability distribution of the coherent state represented by Equation (7.18) is given by the following expression:

$$\begin{aligned}\Psi^*\Psi &= c_1{}^*c_1\psi_1{}^*\psi_1 + c_2{}^*c_2\psi_2{}^*\psi_2 \\ &+ c_1{}^*c_2\psi_1{}^*\psi_2\,e^{i\omega t} + c_2{}^*c_1\psi_2{}^*\psi_1\,e^{-i\omega t}\end{aligned} \tag{7.19}$$

where

$$\omega = \frac{E_1 - E_2}{\hbar} \tag{7.20}$$

or, equivalently

$$f = \frac{E_1 - E_2}{h}$$

The above result shows that *the probability density of a coherent state undergoes a sinusoidal oscillation with time. The frequency of this oscillation is precisely that given by the Bohr frequency condition.*

The quantum-mechanical description of a radiating atom may be stated as follows. During the change from one quantum state to another, the probability distribution of the electron becomes coherent and oscillates sinusoidally. This sinusoidal oscillation is accompanied by an oscillating electromagnetic field that constitutes the radiation.

7.4   The Schrödinger Equation

Thus far we have not discussed the question of just how one goes about finding the state functions of a particular physical system. This is one of the basic tasks of quantum theory, and the performance of this task involves the solution of a differential equation known as the Schrödinger equation. A simple derivation of this important equation for the case of a single particle proceeds as follows.

Consider any wave function Ψ whose time dependence has the usual sinusoidal variation. Let λ be the wavelength. Then we know that the spatial part ψ of the wave function must obey the standard time-independent wave equation

$$\nabla^2\psi + \left(\frac{2\pi}{\lambda}\right)^2\psi = 0$$

Now according to de Broglie's hypothesis, Section 6.10, a particle having momentum p has an associated wavelength h/p. Thus a particle would be expected to obey a wave equation of the form

$$\nabla^2\psi + \left(\frac{2\pi p}{h}\right)^2\psi = 0$$

But a particle of mass m has energy E given by $E = (\frac{1}{2})mv^2 + V$ in which V is the potential energy and v is the speed. Since the linear momentum $p = mv$, then

$$p^2 = 2m(E - V)$$

The wave equation of the particle can, therefore, be written as

$$\nabla^2\psi + \frac{8\pi^2 m}{h^2}(E - V)\psi = 0 \tag{7.21}$$

This is the famous equation first announced by Erwin Schrödinger in 1926. It is a linear partial differential equation of the second order. The physics involved in the application of the equation essentially amounts to the selection of a potential function $V(x,y,z)$ appropriate to the particular physical system in question. Given the potential function $V(x,y,z)$, the mathematical problem is that of finding the function (or functions) ψ, which satisfy the equation.

Not all mathematical solutions of the Schrödinger equation are physically meaningful. In order to represent a real system, the function ψ must tend to zero for infinite values of the coordinates in such a way as to be quadratically integrable. This has already been implied by Equation (7.15).

The details of solving partial differential equations of the Schrödinger type are often very involved and complicated, but the results are easily understood. It turns out that the requirement that the solutions be quadratically integrable leads to the result that acceptable solutions can exist only if the energy E has certain definite values. These allowed values of E, called *eigenvalues*, are, in fact, just the characteristic energy levels of the system. The corresponding solutions are called *eigenfunctions*. They are the state functions of the system.

The Schrödinger equation thus leads to the determination of the energy states of the system as well as the associated state functions. In the next section it is shown how the Schrödinger equation is applied to the problem of calculating the energy levels and state functions of the hydrogen atom.

7.5 Quantum Mechanics of the Hydrogen Atom

The quantum theory of a single electron moving in a central field, briefly outlined here, forms the basis of modern atomic theory. In the mathematical treatment of the one-electron atom it is convenient to employ polar coordinates r, θ, and ϕ, owing to spherical symmetry of the field in which the electron moves. The Laplace operator in these coordinates is

$$\nabla^2 = \frac{1}{r^2}\left[\frac{\partial}{\partial r}\left(r^2\frac{\partial}{\partial r}\right) + \frac{1}{\sin\theta}\frac{\partial}{\partial\theta}\left(\sin\theta\frac{\partial}{\partial\theta}\right) + \frac{1}{\sin^2\theta}\frac{\partial^2}{\partial\phi^2}\right] \tag{7.22}$$

The corresponding Schrödinger equation is

$$\frac{1}{r^2}\left[\frac{\partial}{\partial r}\left(r^2\frac{\partial}{\partial r}\right) + \frac{1}{\sin\theta}\frac{\partial}{\partial\theta}\left(\sin\theta\frac{\partial}{\partial\theta}\right) + \frac{1}{\sin^2\theta}\frac{\partial^2}{\partial\phi^2}\right]\psi$$
$$+ \frac{8\pi^2\mu}{h^2}(E - V)\psi = 0 \tag{7.23}$$

Here μ is the reduced mass of the electron. In the case of the hydrogen atom, the potential V is given by

$$V = -\frac{e^2}{4\pi\varepsilon_0 r} \tag{7.24}$$

Ground State of the H Atom   We shall first obtain a simple solution of the Schrödinger equation by the trial method. Substituting a simple exponential trial solution of the form

$$\psi = e^{-\alpha r} \tag{7.25}$$

where α is an undetermined constant, we find that the Schrödinger equation reduces to

$$\left(\alpha^2 + \frac{8\pi^2 \mu E}{h^2}\right)e^{-\alpha r} + \left(\frac{2\pi \mu e^2}{\varepsilon_0 h^2} - 2\alpha\right)\frac{e^{-\alpha r}}{r} = 0 \tag{7.26}$$

This equation can hold for all values of r only if each expression enclosed by parentheses vanishes, namely,

$$\alpha^2 + \frac{8\pi^2 \mu E}{h^2} = 0 \qquad \frac{2\pi \mu e^2}{\varepsilon_0 h^2} - 2\alpha = 0 \tag{7.27}$$

The second equation gives the value of α. We find that it turns out to be just the reciprocal of the first Bohr radius:

$$\alpha = \frac{\pi \mu e^2}{\varepsilon_0 h^2} = \frac{1}{a_H} \tag{7.28}$$

Substituting this value of α into the first equation and solving for E, we obtain

$$E = -\frac{\mu e^4}{8\varepsilon_0 h^2} \tag{7.29}$$

This is identical with the value of the energy of the first Bohr orbit, obtained in Section 7.3. It is the energy of the ground state of the hydrogen atom.

Now the solution given by Equation (7.25), in which α is given by Equation (7.28), does not yet represent a completely acceptable state function, for it is not normalized. But one can always multiply any solution by an arbitrary constant and still have a solution of the differential equation. Thus, by introducing a normalizing constant C, we can write

$$\psi = Ce^{-\alpha r} \tag{7.30}$$

This does not affect the value of the energy E. The normalizing condition Equation (7.23), reduces to

$$\int_0^\infty C^2 e^{-2\alpha r}\, 4\pi r^2 dr = 1 \tag{7.31}$$

from which C may be found. If one is interested only in the spatial variation of the state function, it is not necessary to include the normalizing constant.

According to the above results, the ground state of the hydrogen atom is such that the probability density of the electron is spherically symmetric and decreases exponentially with the radial distance r. The density is greatest at the center and diminishes by the factor e^{-2} in a distance of one Bohr radius. A plot of the density function is shown in Figure 7.5.

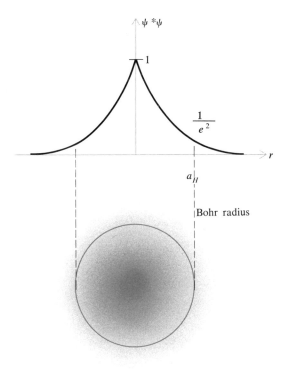

Figure 7.5.   Probability density of the ground state (1s) of the hydrogen atom.

Excited States   In order to find the state functions and the energies of the excited states of the hydrogen atom, it is necessary to solve the Schrödinger equation completely. To do this, the method of separation of variables is used.

The state function ψ is expressed as a product of three functions, a radial function and two angular functions, namely

$$\psi(r,\theta,\varphi) = R(r) \cdot \Theta(\theta) \cdot \Phi(\varphi) \tag{7.32}$$

The Schrödinger equation (7.23) can then be written as

$$\frac{1}{\Phi}\frac{d^2\Phi}{d\varphi^2} + \frac{\sin\theta}{\Theta}\frac{d}{d\theta}\left(\sin\theta\frac{d\Theta}{d\theta}\right) + \frac{\sin^2\theta}{R}\frac{d}{dr}\left(r^2\frac{dR}{dr}\right)$$

$$+ \sin^2\theta\,\frac{8\pi^2\mu r^2}{h^2}\,(E - V) = 0 \qquad (7.33)$$

Now in order that our assumed solution satisfy the differential equation for all values of the independent variables r, θ, and ϕ, the first term $(1/\Phi)\,(d^2\Phi/d\phi^2)$ must necessarily be equal to a constant. Otherwise r and θ would be dependent on ϕ. We denote this constant by $-m^2$. The remaining equation can then be split into two parts, a radial part and a part dependent only on θ. Setting each part equal to a second constant, denoted by $l(l + 1)$, one obtains the following separated differential equations:

$$\frac{1}{\Phi}\frac{d^2\Phi}{d\phi^2} = -m^2 \qquad (7.34)$$

$$\frac{m^2}{\sin^2\theta} - \frac{1}{\Theta\sin\theta}\frac{d}{d\theta}\left(\sin\theta\frac{d\Theta}{d\theta}\right) = l(l + 1) \qquad (7.35)$$

$$\frac{1}{R}\frac{d}{dr}\left(r^2\frac{dR}{dr}\right) + \frac{8\pi^2\mu r^2}{h^2}(E - V) = l(l + 1) \qquad (7.36)$$

where, in the case of the hydrogen atom,

$$V = -\frac{e^2}{4\pi\varepsilon_0 r}$$

A solution of the differential equation (7.34) involving ϕ is clearly

$$\Phi = e^{im\phi} \qquad (7.37)$$

In order for this to be a physically acceptable solution, it is necessary that Φ assumes the same value for ϕ, $\phi + 2\pi$, $\phi + 4\pi$, and so forth; otherwise, the state function would not be uniquely defined at a given point in space. This requirement restricts the allowed values of m to integers, namely

$$m = 0, \pm 1, \pm 2, \pm 3, \cdots \qquad (7.38)$$

The number m is called the *magnetic quantum number*.

The θ-dependent equation (7.35) and the radial equation (7.36) are more difficult to solve. We shall not go into the details of their solution here, but shall merely give the results as given in any standard text on quantum mechanics. It happens that both differential equations were well known long before the time of Schrödinger. Their solutions had been worked out in connection with other problems in mathematical physics.

The equation in θ, Equation (7.35) is one form of an equation known as Legendre's differential equation. This equation yields acceptable (single-valued) solutions only if l is a positive integer whose value is equal to or greater than $|m|$. The integer l is called the *azimuthal quantum number*. The resulting solutions are known as *associated Legendre polynomials*, denoted by $P_l^{|m|} (\cos \theta)$. They may be found by means of a generating formula

$$P_l^{|m|}(x) = \frac{(1 - x^2)^{(\frac{1}{2})|m|}}{2^l l!} \left(\frac{d}{dx}\right)^{|m| + l} (x^2 - 1)^l \tag{7.39}$$

A few of these are:

$$P_0^0(x) = 1 \qquad P_2^1(x) = 3x(1 - x^2)^{1/2} \qquad P_2^0(x) = (\tfrac{1}{2})(3x^2 - 1)$$

$$P_1^0(x) = x \qquad P_1^1(x) = (1 - x^2)^{1/2} \qquad P_2^2(x) = 3(1 - x^2)$$

The radial equation, (7.36), is called Laguerre's differential equation. Acceptable solutions (ones leading to quadratically integrable functions) are given by the formula

$$R(\rho) = \rho^l \, e^{-(\frac{1}{2})\rho} \, L_{n + l}^{2l + 1} (\rho) \tag{7.40}$$

The variable ρ is defined as a certain constant times r, namely

$$\rho = \frac{2r}{n a_H}$$

The quantity n is the *principal quantum number*. It is an integer whose value is equal to or greater than $l + 1$. The functions $L_{n + l}^{2l + 1} (\rho)$ are called *associated Laguerre polynomials*. A formula for generating them is

$$L_{n + l}^{2l + 1} (\rho) = \left(\frac{d}{d\rho}\right)^{2l + 1} \left[e^\rho \left(\frac{d}{d\rho}\right)^{n + l} (\rho^{n + l} \, e^{-\rho}) \right] \tag{7.41}$$

Some of these are as follows:

$$L_0^0(\rho) = 1$$

$$L_1^0(\rho) = 1 - \rho \qquad L_1^1(\rho) = -1$$

$$L_2^0(\rho) = \rho^2 - 4\rho + 2 \qquad L_2^1(\rho) = 2\rho - 4 \qquad L_2^2(\rho) = 2$$

In the process of solving the radial differential equation, it is found that the eigenvalues of the energy E are determined solely by the principal quantum number n. The eigenvalues are given by the formula

$$E_n = -\frac{\mu e^4}{8\varepsilon_0 n^2}\left(\frac{1}{n^2}\right) \tag{7.42}$$

This is exactly the same formula as that given by the simple Bohr theory.

For each value of the principal quantum number n, with energy E_n given by the above equation, there are n different possible values of the azimuthal quantum number l, namely $0, 1, 2, \cdots n - 2, n - 1$. Each value of l represents a different kind of eigenstate. States in which $l = 0, 1, 2, 3$, are traditionally called s, p, d, and f states, respectively.

For each value of l, there are $2l + 1$ possible values of the magnetic quantum number m. These are $-l, -(l-1), \cdots, -1, 0, +1, \cdots, +(l-1), +l$. As a result, there are n^2 different eigenfunctions or states for each value of n. The following diagram summarizes the situation:

n	1		2			3				
l	0	0	1	0	1	2				
	(s)	(s)	(p)	(s)	(p)	(d)				
m	0	0	-1 $\quad$ 0 $\quad$ $+1$	0	-1 $\quad$ 0 $\quad$ $+1$	-2 $\quad$ -1 $\quad$ 0 $\quad$ $+1$ $\quad$ $+2$				

The complete state function, corresponding to prescribed values of n, l, and m, is given by the formula

$$\psi_{n,l,m} = C\rho^l\, e^{-\rho/2}\, L_{n+l}^{2l+1}(\rho)\, P_l^{|m|}(\cos\theta)\, e^{im\phi} \tag{7.43}$$

where $\rho = 2r/na_H$, and C is a normalizing constant. Table 7.2 shows a few of the simpler state functions of the hydrogen atom. Some of these are illustrated in Figure 7.6.

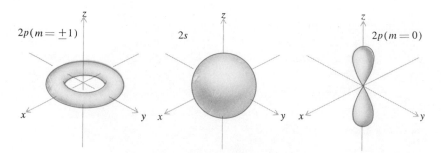

Figure 7.6. Probability density for the first excited state ($n = 2$) of the hydrogen atom.

Angular Momentum　The angular momentum of an electron moving in a central force field can be obtained by standard quantum-mechanical methods. It develops that the angular momentum is quantized, as in the Bohr theory, and that the magnitude is determined by the quantum numbers designating the various quantum states.

The *total orbital angular momentum* is given by an expression involving only the azimuthal quantum number l, namely

$$\sqrt{l(l+1)}h/2\pi = \sqrt{l(l+1)}\,\hbar$$

This is different from the value $nh/2\pi$ of the Bohr theory. In particular, for s states ($l = 0$), the angular momentum is zero. Physically, this means that the electron cloud for s states does not possess a net rotation. It does not preclude any motion of the electron.

Table 7.2. EIGENFUNCTIONS OF THE HYDROGEN ATOM (NORMALIZING CONSTANTS ARE OMITTED.)

STATE	n	l	m		
1s	1	0	0	$e^{-(1/2)\rho}$	
2s	2	0	0	$e^{-(1/2)\rho}(1-\rho)$	
2p	2	1	-1 0 $+1$	$e^{-(1/2)\rho}\rho$	$\begin{cases} \sin\theta\,e^{-i\phi} \\ \cos\theta \\ \sin\theta\,e^{+i\phi} \end{cases}$
3s	3	0	0	$e^{-(1/2)\rho}(\rho^2 - 4\rho + 2)$	
3p	3	1	-1 0 $+1$	$e^{-(1/2)\rho}(\rho^2 - 2\rho)$	$\begin{cases} \sin\theta\,e^{-i\phi} \\ \cos\theta \\ \sin\theta\,e^{+i\phi} \end{cases}$
3d	3	2	-2 -1 0 $+1$ $+2$	$e^{-(1/2)\rho}\rho^2$	$\begin{cases} \sin^2\theta\,e^{-i2\phi} \\ \sin\theta\cos\theta\,e^{-i\phi} \\ (1 - 3\cos^2\theta) \\ \sin\theta\cos\theta\,e^{+i\phi} \\ \sin^2\theta\,e^{+i2\phi} \end{cases}$

Theory also shows that the *z component of the angular momentum is quantized*. This component has the value

$$mh/2\pi = m\hbar$$

where m is the magnetic quantum number. As we have seen, m is the quantum number associated with the angle of rotation ϕ about the z axis. Since m can assume any of the values $0, \pm 1, \pm 2, \cdots \pm l$, it follows that there are $2l + 1$ different possible values of the z component of the angular momentum for a given value of l. This is illustrated in Figure 7.7.

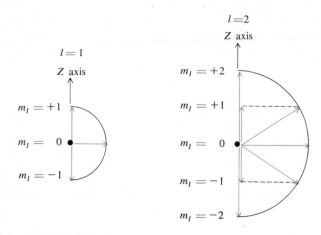

Figure 7.7. Space quantization of angular momentum for the cases $l = 1$ and $l = 2$.

7.6 Radiative Transitions and Selection Rules

As already mentioned in Section 7.6, when an atom is in the process of changing from one eigenstate to another, the probability density of the electronic charge becomes coherent and oscillates sinusoidally with a frequency given by the Bohr frequency condition. The way in which the charge cloud oscillates depends on the particular eigenstates involved. In the case of a so-called *dipole transition*, the centroid of the negative charge of the electron cloud oscillates about the positively charged nucleus. The atom thereby becomes an *oscillating electric dipole*.

Figure 7.8 is a diagram showing the time variation of the charge distribution for the hydrogen atom when it is in the coherent state represented by the combination $1s + 2p(m = 0)$. It is seen that the centroid of the charge moves back and forth along the z axis. The

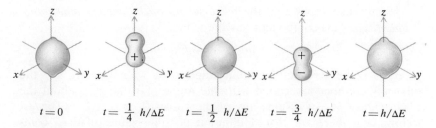

Figure 7.8. Charge distribution in the coherent state $1s + 2p_0$ as a function of time. The atom is an oscillating dipole.

associated electromagnetic field has a directional distribution that is the same as that of a simple dipole antenna lying along the z axis. Thus, the radiation is maximum in the xy plane and zero along the z axis. The radiation field, in this case, is linearly polarized with its plane of polarization parallel to the dipole axis.

A different case is shown in Figure 7.9. Here the coherent state is

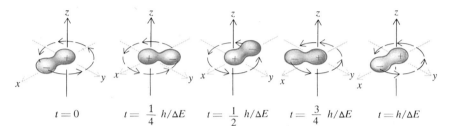

$t = 0$ $t = \dfrac{1}{4}\, h/\Delta E$ $t = \dfrac{1}{2}\, h/\Delta E$ $t = \dfrac{3}{4}\, h/\Delta E$ $t = h/\Delta E$

Figure 7.9. Charge distribution in the coherent state $1s + 2p_1$ as a function of time. The atom is a rotating dipole.

the combination $1s + 2p(m = +1)$. The centroid of the electronic charge now moves in a circular path around the z axis. The angular frequency of the motion is also that given by the Bohr frequency formula $\omega = \Delta E/\hbar$.

Instead of an oscillating dipole, the atom is now a *rotating dipole*. The associated radiation field is such that the polarization is circular for radiation traveling in the direction of the z axis and linear for radiation traveling in a direction perpendicular to the z axis. For intermediate directions, the polarization is elliptical. The cases are illustrated in Figure 7.10. The coherent state $1s + 2p(m = -1)$ is just the same as the state $1s + 2p(m = +1)$ except that the direction of rotation of the electronic charge is reversed. Consequently, the sense of rotation of the associated circularly polarized radiation is also reversed.

In an ordinary spectral-light source, the radiating atoms are randomly oriented in space and their vibrations are mutually incoherent. The total radiation is thus an incoherent mixture of all types of polarization. In other words, the radiation is unpolarized. However, if the source is placed in a magnetic field, the field provides a preferred direction in space—the z axis in the above discussions, Figure 7.11(a). In addition, the interaction between the radiating electron and the magnetic field causes each energy level to become split into several sublevels—one for each value of the magnetic quantum number m. As a result, each spectrum line is split into several components. This splitting is known as the *Zeeman effect*. By means of the Zeeman effect, it is

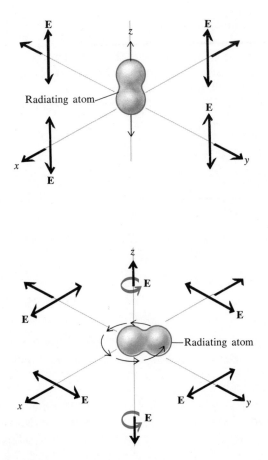

Figure 7.10. Polarization of the associated electromagnetic radiation (**E** vector) for (a) an oscillating dipole and (b) a rotating dipole.

possible to observe the polarization effects mentioned above. This is illustrated in Figure 7.11(b).

The general theory of atomic emission and absorption involves the calculation of certain integrals known as *matrix elements*. The matrix element involved in electric dipole radiation is the quantity $\mathbf{M}_{AB}$ defined as

$$\mathbf{M}_{AB} = \int \int \int \psi_A{}^* \, e \, \mathbf{r} \, \psi_B \, dx \, dy \, dz \qquad (7.44)$$

where $\mathbf{r} = \hat{\mathbf{i}}x + \hat{\mathbf{j}}y + \hat{\mathbf{k}}z$, and e is the electric charge. The dipole matrix element is a measure of the amplitude of the oscillating dipole moment of the coherent state formed by the two stationary states ψ_A and ψ_B.

In the case of hydrogen, it turns out that $\mathbf{M}_{AB}$ is zero for all pairs

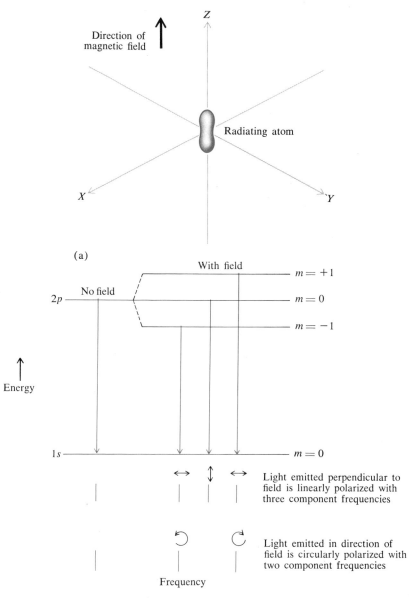

Figure 7.11. The Zeeman effect. (a) Direction of the external magnetic field. (b) Transition diagram. For light that is emitted in a direction perpendicular to the magnetic field, there are three components which are linearly polarized as shown. There are only two components for the light emitted parallel to the field, and these are circularly polarized as indicated. The fundamental Zeeman splitting is $\Delta f = eH/4\pi\mu_0 m$ where H is the magnetic field, e is the electronic charge, and m is the mass of the electron [39].

245

of states except those for which the azimuthal quantum numbers l_A and l_B differ by exactly one. In other words, electric dipole transitions are "allowed" if

$$\Delta l = \pm 1 \tag{7.45}$$

This is known as the *l-selection rule*. It implies that the angular momentum of the atom changes by an amount $\hbar$ during a dipole transition. This angular momentum is taken up by the photon involved in the transition.

There is also an *m*-selection rule, which is

$$\Delta m = 0 \text{ or } \pm 1 \tag{7.46}$$

Transitions for which $\Delta m = 0$ are of the simple linear-dipole type, whereas those for which $\Delta m = \pm 1$ are associated with a rotating dipole. The two types of transition are, in fact, those just discussed for hydrogen and illustrated in Figure 7.11.

Transition Rates and Lifetimes of States   The classical expression for the total power P emitted by an oscillating electric dipole, of moment $M = M_0 \cos \omega t$, is

$$P = \frac{1}{3} \frac{\omega^4 M_0^2}{\pi \varepsilon_0 c^3} \tag{7.47}$$

The same formula applies to atomic emission, provided $|M_{AB}|$ is used for M_0. We must, however, interpret the formula somewhat differently in this case. Since for each transition, an atom emits a quantum of energy hf, the number N of quanta per second per atom is equal to P/hf. Thus

$$N = \frac{2}{3} \frac{\omega^3 |M_{AB}|^2}{h \varepsilon_0 c^3} \tag{7.48}$$

is the number of transitions per second for each atom. This is known as the *transition probability*. The reciprocal, $1/N$, of the transition probability has the dimension of time. It is known as the *lifetime* and is a measure of the time an excited atom takes to emit a light quantum. Typically, atomic lifetimes are of the order of 10^{-8} s.

Higher-Order Transitions   Although electric dipole transitions generally give rise to the strongest spectral lines, such transitions are not the only ones that occur. It is possible for an atom to radiate or absorb electromagnetic radiation when it has an oscillating electric quadrupole moment, but no dipole moment. Such transitions are called *electric* *quadrupole transitions.* The selection rule for quadrupole transition is

$$\Delta l = \pm 2$$

It is easily shown that the charge distribution for a coherent state such as 1s + 3d($m = 0$) consists of an oscillating electric quadrupole. Transition probabilities for quadrupole radiation are usually several orders of magnitude smaller than those for electric dipole radiation. Lifetimes against quadrupole radiation are typically of the order of 1 s. Higher-order transitions such as octupole transitions, $\Delta l \pm 3$, and so forth, can also occur. Such transitions are seldom observed in connection with optical spectra, but they frequently occur in processes involving the atomic nucleus.

7.7   Fine Structure of Spectrum Lines. Electron Spin

If the spectrum of hydrogen is examined with an instrument of high resolving power, it is found that the lines are not single, but consist of several closely spaced components. The line Hα, for example, appears as two lines having a separation of about 0.14 Å. (This is not the same as the hydrogen-deuterium splitting discussed earlier.) This splitting of spectrum lines into several is known as *fine structure.* The lines of other elements besides hydrogen also possess a fine structure. These are designated as singlets, doublets, triplets, and so forth, depending on the number of components.

The theoretical explanation of fine structure was first made by Pauli who postulated that the electron, in addition to its orbital angular moment, possesses an *intrinsic angular momentum.* This angular momentum is known as *spin.* All electrons have the same amount of spin, regardless of their motion, binding to atoms, and so forth. Theory shows that the component of this spin, in a given direction, must always be one or the other of the two values:

$$+(\tfrac{1}{2})\hbar \text{ or } -(\tfrac{1}{2})\hbar$$

The total angular momentum of an electron in an atom then consists of the vector sum of its orbital angular momentum $\mathbf{l}$ and its spin $\mathbf{s}$. The total angular momentum of a single electron, denoted by the symbol $\mathbf{j}$, is then given by

$$\mathbf{j} = \mathbf{l} + \mathbf{s} \tag{7.49}$$

It is customary to express the various angular momenta in units of $\hbar$. The angular momenta in these units are then essentially quantum numbers. For a given value of the azimuthal quantum number l, there are two values of the quantum number for the total angular momentum of a single electron, namely,

$$j = l + 1/2 \text{ and } j = l - 1/2 \qquad (7.50)$$

Thus, for $l = 1$, $j = 3/2$ or $1/2$, for $l = 2$, $j = 5/2$ or $3/2$, and so forth. For the case $l = 0$ there is only one value because the two states $j = +1/2$ and $j = -1/2$ are actually the same.

Now it was stated earlier that those states of hydrogen with a given value of the principal quantum number n, all have the same energy. This is not strictly true, since the electron spin was not taken into account. Actually, as the electron undergoes its orbital motion around the positively charged nucleus, it experiences a magnetic field arising from this motion. The magnetic moment associated with the spin interacts with the magnetic field. This is called *spin-orbit* interaction.[1] The result of the spin-orbit interaction is that the two states $j = l + s$ and $j = l - s$ have slightly different energies. This, in turn, produces a splitting of the spectrum lines. A simplified diagram illustrating the splitting for the case of a $p \rightarrow s$ transition is shown in Figure 7.12.

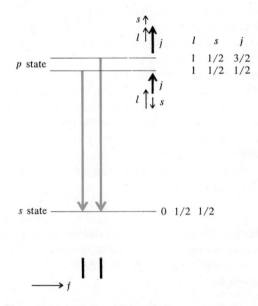

Figure 7.12. Fine structure (spin splitting) of a spectrum line for a $p \rightarrow s$ transition.

---

[1] In hydrogen, in addition to the spin-orbit splitting, there is a splitting of the energy levels due to relativistic effects. This relativity splitting is also very small, and causes the energies of states with the same n but different l to be slightly different [24].

7.8 Multiplicity in the Spectra of Many-Electron Atoms. Spectroscopic Notation

For atoms containing more than one electron, the total angular momentum $\mathbf{J}$ is given by the vector sum of all the individual orbital momenta $\mathbf{l}_1, \mathbf{l}_2, \cdots$, and spins $\mathbf{s}_1, \mathbf{s}_2, \cdots$, and so forth.

In the usual case, the orbital angular momenta couple together to produce a resultant orbital angular momentum $\mathbf{L} = \mathbf{l}_1 + \mathbf{l}_2 + \cdots$. Similarly the spins couple to form an overall resultant spin $\mathbf{S} = \mathbf{s}_1 + \mathbf{s}_2 + \cdots$. The total angular momentum is then given by the coupling of $\mathbf{L}$ and $\mathbf{S}$,

$$\mathbf{J} = \mathbf{L} + \mathbf{S} \tag{7.51}$$

This type of coupling is known as LS coupling. Other types of coupling can also occur, such as jj coupling in which the individual $\mathbf{j}$'s add together to produce a resultant $\mathbf{J}$. In general, LS coupling occurs in the lighter elements and jj coupling in the heavy elements.

In LS coupling, all three quantities $\mathbf{L}$, $\mathbf{S}$, and $\mathbf{J}$ are quantized. Their magnitudes are given by

$$|\mathbf{L}| = \hbar \sqrt{L(L+1)}, \ |\mathbf{S}| = \hbar \sqrt{S(S+1)}, \ |\mathbf{J}| = \hbar \sqrt{J(J+1)}$$

where L, S, and J are quantum numbers with the following properties.

The quantum number L is always a positive integer, or zero. The spin quantum number S is either integral or half integral, depending on whether the number of electrons is even or odd, respectively. Consequently, the total angular-momentum quantum number J is integral, or half integral, depending on whether there is an even or odd number of electrons, respectively.

The total energy of a given state depends on the way the various angular momenta add together to produce the resultant total angular momentum. Hence, for given values of L and S, the various values of J correspond to different energies. This, in turn, results in the fine structure of the spectral lines.

The spectroscopic designation of a state having given values of L, S, and J is the following:

$$^{2S+1}L_J$$

Here the quantity $2S + 1$ is known as the *multiplicity*. It is the number of different values that J can assume for a given value of L, provided $L \gg S$, namely,

$$L + S, L + S - 1, L + S - 2, \cdots L - S$$

If $L < S$, then there are only $2L + 1$ different J values, namely

$$L + S, L + S - 1, L + S - 2, \cdots |L - S|$$

This is known as incomplete multiplicity.

If $S = 0$, the multiplicity is unity. The state is then said to be a singlet. Similarly, for $S = 1/2$, the multiplicity is two, and the state is a doublet. Table 7.3 lists the spin, multiplicity, and names of the first few types of states:

Table 7.3. MULTIPLICITIES OF STATES

S	MULTIPLICITY $(2S + 1)$	NAME
0	1	Singlet
1/2	2	Doublet
1	3	Triplet
3/2	4	Quartet
2	5	Quintet
5/2	6	Sextet

For one-electron atoms, only one value of S is possible, namely 1/2. Hence all states of one-electron atoms are doublet states. In the case of two electrons, S can have either of the two values $1/2 + 1/2 = 1$ or $1/2 - 1/2 = 0$. Thus, for two-electron atoms, there are two sets of states, triplets and singlets.

In addition to the naming of states according to multiplicity, a letter is used to designate the value of the total orbital angular momentum L. This designation is given in Table 7.4 below.

Table 7.4. DESIGNATION OF STATES ACCORDING TO ORBITAL ANGULAR MOMENTUM

L:	0	1	2	3	4	5	6	7	8	·	·
Designation	S	P	D	F	G	H	I	K	M	·	·

The letter S, designating states for $L = 0$, is not the spin quantum number, although it is the same letter. This is confusing, but it is accepted convention.

Let us consider, as an example, the case of two electrons. Let one electron be a p electron ($l_1 = 1$) and the other be a d electron ($l_2 = 2$). The possible values of L are $l_1 + l_2$, $|l_1 - l_2|$, and all integral values between. Thus $L = 1, 2$, or 3, which means that we have P states, D states, and F states. Since S can be 0 or 1, then there are both singlets and triplets for each L value. The complete list of possible states for the combination of a p and a d electron is the following:

SINGLETS		TRIPLETS	
$^1P_1$	$^3P_0$	$^3P_1$	$^3P_2$
$^1D_2$	$^3D_1$	$^3D_2$	$^3D_3$
$^1F_3$	$^3F_2$	$^3F_3$	$^3F_4$

Selection Rules In the case of LS coupling, the selection rules that govern allowed transition for dipole radiation are the following:

$$\Delta L = 0, \pm 1$$

$$\Delta S = 0$$

$$\Delta J = 0, \pm 1, (J = 0 \rightarrow J = 0 \text{ forbidden})$$

In all cases, the symbol Δ means the difference between the corresponding quantum numbers of the initial and final states of the transition.

Parity In addition to the above selection rules, there is another important rule involving a concept known as *parity*. The parity of an atomic state can be even or odd. This is determined by the sum of the l-values of the individual electrons. If the sum is even (odd), the parity is even (odd). For example, consider the states of a two-electron atom. If one electron is an s electron ($l_1 = 0$) and the other is a p electron ($l_2 = 1$), then $l_1 + l_2 = 1$, hence all sp states are of odd parity. Similarly, all sd states are of even parity, and so forth. The following selection rule holds for electric dipole radiation from transitions between two states:

$$\text{even} \leftrightarrows \text{odd (allowed)} \qquad \left. \begin{array}{l} \text{odd} \rightarrow \text{odd} \\ \\ \text{even} \rightarrow \text{even} \end{array} \right\} \text{(forbidden)}$$

In other words the parity of the final state must be different from the parity of the initial state.

It is possible for an excited state to be such that it cannot undergo a transition, by dipole radiation, to any lower state. In this case, the state is said to be *metastable*. If an atom is in a metastable state, it must return to the ground state either by emission of radiation other than dipole radiation, for example, quadrupole, and so forth, or it may return via collisions with other atoms.

7.9 Molecular Spectra

Molecules, like atoms, are found to exhibit discrete frequency spectra when appropriately excited in the vapor state. This indicates that the energy states of molecules are quantized and that a molecule may emit or absorb a photon upon changing from one energy state to another.

For purposes of spectroscopy, the energy of a molecule may be expressed as the sum of three kinds of energy. These are rotational energy E_{rot}, vibrational energy E_{vib}, and electronic energy E_{el}. Thus

$$E = E_{rot} + E_{vib} + E_{el}$$

Of the three, E_{rot} is generally the smallest, typically a few hundredths of an electron volt. Vibrational energies are of the order of tenths of an electron volt, while the largest energies are of the electronic type that are generally a few electron volts. Each of the three types of energy is quantized in a different way and accordingly, each is associated with a different set of quantum numbers.

It is possible for transitions to take place that involve the rotational energy levels only. The resulting spectrum, called the *pure rotation spectrum*, usually lies in the far infrared or the microwave region. If vibrational changes also occur in the transition but no electronic changes, we have the *rotation-vibration spectrum*. The rotation-vibration lines are generally found in the near infrared. Finally, transitions that involve electronic-energy changes are the most energetic. Lines of the *electronic spectra* of molecules occur typically in the visible and ultraviolet regions.

Rotational Energy Levels   The rotational energy, E_{rot}, is the kinetic energy of rotation of the molecule as a whole. The quantization of the rotational energy is expressed in terms of rotational quantum numbers. How many of these rotational quantum numbers are needed to specify a given rotational state depends on the particular molecular geometry. There are four basic molecular types. These are:

(1) Linear molecules,
(2) Spherical-top molecules,
(3) Symmetrical-top molecules, and
(4) Asymmetrical-top molecules.

The four types are illustrated in Figure 7.13.

In the case of linear molecules and spherical-top molecules, only one quantum number J is needed to specify the rotational state. As with atomic states, the quantity $\hbar \sqrt{J(J+1)}$ is the magnitude of the rotational angular momentum. The rotational energy is given by the quantum equivalent of the classical value, namely

$$E_{rot} = \frac{(\frac{1}{2})[\hbar \sqrt{J(J+1)}]^2}{I} = J(J+1)\, Bhc \quad (J = 0,1,2, \cdots) \quad (7.52)$$

where

$$B = \frac{h}{8\pi^2 cI} \quad (7.53)$$

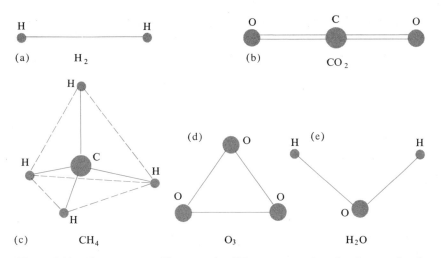

Figure 7.13. Some cases to illustrate the different types of molecular rotational symmetry. (a), (b) Linear molecules: $I_a = I_b$, $I_c = 0$. (c) Spherical top: $I_a = I_b = I_c$. (d) Symmetrical top: $I_a = I_b \neq I_c$. (e) Asymetrical top: $I_a \neq I_b \neq I_c$.

Here I is the moment of inertia of the molecule about the axis of rotation. (For a symmetrical diatomic molecule consisting of two atoms of mass $M/2$ separated by a distance $2b$, the moment of inertia is given by the classical expression $I = Mb^2$.) An energy-level diagram showing the rotational levels of a linear molecule is shown in Figure 7.14.

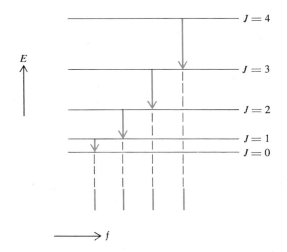

Figure 7.14. Transition diagram for a pure rotational spectrum.

In the case of symmetrical-top molecules, two quantum numbers are needed to specify the rotational states. These are customarily written as J and K where, again, $\hbar\sqrt{J(J + 1)}$ is the total rotational angular momentum. The quantum number K is the component, in units of $\hbar$, of the rotational angular momentum about the symmetry axis. For a given value of K, J can assume any of the values K, $K + 1$, $K + 2$, and so forth. The rotational energy levels are then given by the formula

$$E_{\text{rot}} = J(J + 1) Bhc + K^2(C - B)hc \tag{7.54}$$

In the above formula, the quantities B and C are related to the two principal moments of inertia of the molecule,

$$B = \frac{h}{8\pi^2 c I_b} \qquad C = \frac{h}{8\pi^2 c I_c} \tag{7.55}$$

Here I_c is the moment of inertia about the symmetry axis, and I_b is the moment about the perpendicular axis.

In the case of the asymetric-top molecule, there are three different moments of inertia, and three rotational quantum numbers are involved. The theory is quite complicated in this case, and there is no simple formula for the energies of the quantized states [23].

Rotational transition rules are governed by the general selection rules

$$\begin{aligned} \Delta J &= 0, \pm 1 \\ \Delta K &= \pm 1 \end{aligned} \tag{7.56}$$

In addition to the above rules, there are other selection rules involving the symmetry of the rotational states. We shall not go into a discussion of these.

Vibrational Energy Levels If a molecule contains N atoms, there are $3N$ modes of motion. Of these, 3 correspond to translation of the molecule, and 3 to rotation (or 2 for a linear molecule). The remaining $3N - 6$ (or $3N - 5$) correspond to the normal vibrational modes.

Theory shows that the quantizing of each vibrational mode can be expressed in terms of a single associated quantum number. The normal frequencies are designated $f_1, f_2, \cdots$ and so forth, and the associated vibrational quantum numbers are $v_1, v_2, \cdots$ and so on. The vibrational energy is then given by

$$E_{\text{vib}} = (v_1 + 1/2)hf_1 + (v_2 + 1/2)hf_2 + \cdots \tag{7.57}$$

The above formula is valid if the vibrational displacements are small enough so that the motion is essentially harmonic in character. It indicates that the energy levels associated with a given normal mode are

(1) equally spaced, and (2) the energy of the lowest vibrational state ($v_1 = 0$, $v_2 = 0$, $\cdots$) is *not zero*, but has a finite value: $(\frac{1}{2})hf_1 + (\frac{1}{2})hf_2 + \cdots$. This energy is called the *zero-point energy*. It is present even at the absolute zero of temperature.

The selection rule for vibration transitions is

$$\Delta v = \pm 1 \tag{7.58}$$

This rule is strictly adhered to only if the motion is absolutely harmonic. Such is never actually the case. Transitions in which $\Delta v = \pm 2, \pm 3$, and so forth, also occur. These *overtone transitions* are generally much weaker than the fundamental transitions in which $\Delta v = \pm 1$.

A homonuclear diatomic molecule does not exhibit a pure rotation spectrum nor does it show a rotation-vibration spectrum. This is because homonuclear molecules have no permanent electric dipole moment. Consequently neither rotational nor vibrational transitions produce an oscillating dipole moment. Thus there is no associated dipole radiation.

On the other hand, heteronuclear diatomic molecules, such as HC1, do exhibit strong rotation-vibration spectra.

A transition diagram illustrating the vibrational energy levels of a diatomic molecule, with rotational energy levels superimposed, is shown in Figure 7.15. The J-selection rule for rotation-vibration transitions is

$$\Delta J = 0, \pm 1 \tag{7.59}$$

The spectrum is divided into three branches known as the P, Q, and R branches. They are determined by the value of ΔJ as follows:

$$\Delta J = -1 \qquad P\text{-branch}$$
$$\Delta J = 0 \qquad Q\text{-branch}$$
$$\Delta J = +1 \qquad R\text{-branch}$$

Electronic Energy States in Molecules   The following discussion is restricted largely to the case of diatomic molecules, although many of the general principles apply to other molecules as well.

In molecules, the orbital angular momenta and spins of the electrons couple together in much the same manner that they do in atoms. In diatomic molecules, an important quantum number is one designating the sum of the projections of the orbital angular momenta on the line connecting the two atoms. This quantum number is denoted by the symbol Λ. The various electronic states corresponding to different values of Λ are designated by capital greek letters as follows:

$$\Lambda : 0, 1, 2, 3, \cdots$$
$$\text{Electronic State} : \Sigma, \Pi, \Delta, \Phi, \cdots$$

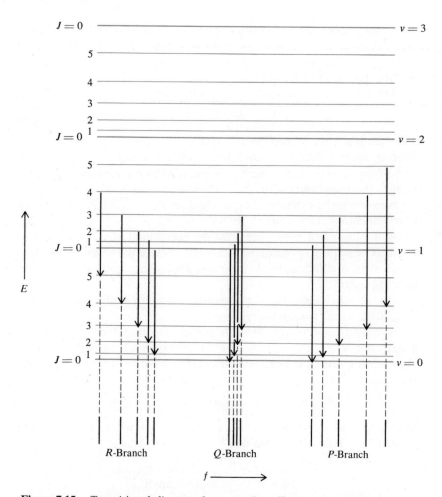

Figure 7.15. Transitional diagram for a rotation-vibration spectrum.

For a given value of Λ, the rotational quantum number J can have any of the values Λ, $\Lambda + 1$, $\Lambda + 2$, and so forth.

As in the case of atoms, the total spin S determines the multiplicity of an electronic state. This multiplicity is $2S + 1$. It is the number of sublevels for a given value of J. Thus there are singlet states ($S = 0$):

$$^1\Sigma, \; ^1\Pi, \; ^1\Delta, \; \cdots$$

doublet states ($S = 1/2$):

$$^2\Sigma, \; ^2\Pi, \; ^2\Delta, \; \cdots$$

and so on. It is also true, as with atoms, that the multiplicity is always odd (even) if the total number of electrons is even (odd).

The selection rules governing electronic transitions are

$$\Delta\Lambda = 0, \pm 1 \tag{7.60}$$

$$\Delta S = 0 \tag{7.61}$$

The following are examples of allowed electronic transitions:

$$^1\Sigma \to {}^1\Pi, \ {}^2\Pi \to {}^2\Delta, \ {}^3\Pi \to {}^3\Sigma$$

Since the electronic energies in molecules have the rotational and vibrational energies superimposed on them, electronic transitions may be accompanied by vibrational and rotational transitions. This results in a very large number of lines for each electronic transition and gives rise to the vibration-rotation structure in the electronic spectra of molecules. A partial energy-level diagram of the nitrogen molecule N_2 is shown in Figure 7.16 as an example.

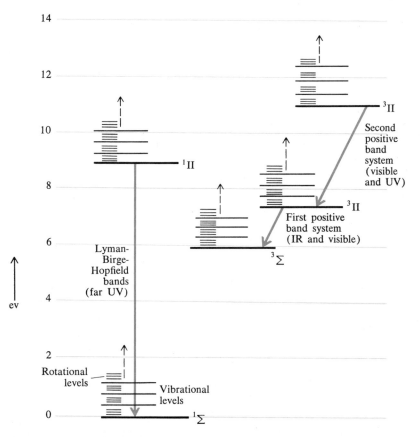

Figure 7.16. Partial energy level diagram of the nitrogen molecule N_2. Electronic transitions of some of the important band systems are indicated. The rotational and vibrational energy levels are not drawn to scale.

7.10   Atomic-Energy Levels in Solids

Consider an atom that is embedded in a solid, either as a part of the structure or as an impurity. One or more of the electrons may be shared by the solid as a whole, and thus are not associated with any particular atom.

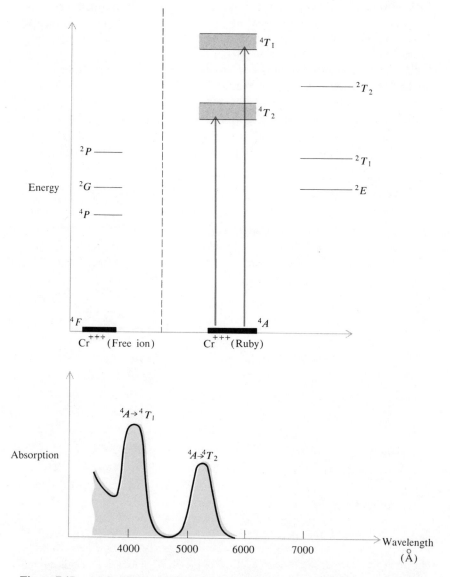

Figure 7.17.   (a) Energy level diagram of the Cr+++ ion in the free state and in ruby. (b) Absorption of the Cr+++ ion in ruby.

The energy levels of these electrons become smeared out into bands —the valence and conduction bands—of the solid. The atom in question then becomes an ion. The bound electrons associated with the ion may have various quantized states available to them, and therefore various energy levels. This gives rise to a characteristic ionic absorption spectrum.

In the case of the rare earth ions, the unfilled shells involve deep-lying $4f$ electrons. These electrons are well shielded by the outer electrons, and the energy levels of the free ion are essentially unchanged when the ion is embedded in a solid. The levels are quantized according to angular momentum and are designated in the same way as the regular atomic energy levels discussed in Section 7.2.

For the transition metals, such as Fe, Cr, and so forth, the $3d$ shell is unfilled. This shell is not as well shielded as the $4f$ shell in the rare earths. The result is that the energy levels of transition metal ions are profoundly changed when the ion is placed in a solid. Rather than angular momentum, it is the *symmetry* of the wave function that is important in the determination of the energy levels, in this case, particularly if the ion is in a crystal lattice. The quantization of the energy is then largely dictated by the symmetry of the field due to the surrounding ions.

It is beyond the scope of this book to develop the theory of atomic-energy levels in crystals. The subject is very involved. An extensive, rapidly growing literature already exists. However, as an illustration of the energy-level scheme of a typical case, the levels of the Cr+++ ion are shown in Figure 7.17. At the left are shown the levels of the free ion, while at the right are the levels of the Cr+++ ion in ruby. The symbols A, E, and T refer to different types of symmetry. The ruby crystal consists of Al_2O_3 (corundum) in which part of the Al atoms have been replaced with Cr. The red color of ruby is due to the absorption of green and blue light corresponding to transitions from the ground state, ^4A, to the excited states $^4T_1$ and $^4T_2$, as indicated.

For further reading in atomic, molecular, and solid-state spectroscopy, references [18] [19] [23] [24] [30] and [39] are recommended.

PROBLEMS

7.1. If R is the Rydberg constant for a nucleus of infinite mass, Equation (7.10), show that the Rydberg constant for a nucleus of mass M is given approximately by $R_M \approx R - (m/M)R$.

7.2. Calculate the difference between the frequencies of the Balmer $-\alpha$ lines of hydrogen and deuterium.

7.3. Calculate the frequency of the hydrogen transition $n = 101 \rightarrow n = 100$.

7.4. Show that the energy of the 2s state of atomic hydrogen (Table 7.2) is $-(1/4)R$ by substitution in the radial Schrödinger equation (7.36).

7.5. Consider a hydrogen atom in the ground state and imagine a sphere of radius r centered at the nucleus. Derive a formula for the probability that the electron is located inside the sphere. (a) What is the probability for $r = a_H$? (b) For what value of r is the probability equal to 99 percent?

7.6. Determine all of the states of a pf configuration of two electrons in LS coupling.

7.7. Find all of the allowed dipole transitions between a pd and a pf configuration.

7.8. Calculate the lifetime of the 2p state of atomic hydrogen by assuming that the magnitude of the dipole moment of the transition to the 1s state is approximately equal to ea_H.

7.9. Find the frequency of the radiation emitted by the pure rotational transition $J = 1 \rightarrow J = 0$ in HCl. The distance between the H atom and the Cl atom is 1.3 Å.

CHAPTER 8

Amplification of Light. Lasers

8.1 Introduction

Few developments have produced an impact on any established field of science compared to the effect of the laser or optical maser[1] on the field of optics. Vacuum-tube oscillators that generate coherent electromagnetic radiation at frequencies up to about 10^9 Hz have been known for many years. In 1954 the maser[1] was developed [13]. The maser generates microwaves (10^9 to 10^{11} Hz). The practical feasibility using the maser principle for the amplification of light ($\sim 10^{14}$ Hz) was studied in 1958 by Schawlow and Townes who laid down the basic theoretical groundwork. The first working laser, made of synthetic ruby crystal, was produced in 1960 at the Hughes Research Laboratories. It was followed in a few months by the helium-neon gas laser developed at the Bell Telephone Laboratories. The ruby laser generates visible red light. The helium-neon laser generates both visible red light and infrared radiation. Since their introduction, numerous types of lasers have been produced that generate radiation at various optical frequencies extending from the far infrared to the ultraviolet region of the spectrum [25].

A laser is essentially an optical oscillator. It consists basically of an amplifying medium placed inside a suitable optical resonator or cavity. The medium is made to amplify by means of some kind of external excitation. The laser oscillation is essentially a standing wave in the cavity. The output consists of an intense beam of highly monochromatic radiation.

Conventional light sources (arcs, filaments, discharges) provide luminous intensities corresponding to thermal radiation at temperatures of no more than about 10^4 °K. With lasers, intensities corresponding to

---

[1] The word *laser* is an acronym for "light amplification by stimulated emission of radiation." Lasers were developed several years after *masers* (microwave amplifiers). For this reason the first lasers were called *optical masers,* but the single word laser is now the generally accepted usage.

10^{20} to 10^{30} degrees are readily attained. Such enormous intensities make possible the investigation of new optical phenomena such as nonlinear optical effects, optical beating, long-distance interference, and many others that were previously considered out of the question. Practical applications of the laser include long-distance communications, optical radar, microwelding, and eye surgery, to mention only a few.

8.2 Stimulated Emission and Thermal Radiation

Einstein in 1917 first introduced the concept of stimulated or induced emission of radiation by atomic systems. He showed that in order to describe completely the interaction of matter and radiation, it is necessary to include that process in which an excited atom may be induced, by the presence of radiation, to emit a photon, and thereby decay to a lower energy state.

Consider a quantized atomic system in which there are levels labelled 1,2,3, $\cdots$, with energies E_1, E_2, E_3, and so forth. The populations, that is, the number of atoms per unit volume, in the various levels, are N_1, N_2, N_3, and so forth. If the atomic system is in equilibrium with thermal radiation at a given temperature T, then the relative populations of any two levels, say 1 and 2, are given by Boltzmann's equation

$$\frac{N_2}{N_1} = \frac{e^{-E_2/kT}}{e^{-E_1/kT}} \tag{8.1}$$

where k is Boltzmann's constant. If we assume, for definiteness, that $E_2 > E_1$, then $N_2 < N_1$.

An atom in level 2 can decay to level 1 by emission of a photon. Let us call A_{21} the transition probability per unit time for spontaneous emission from level 2 to level 1. Then the number of *spontaneous* decays per second is $N_2 A_{21}$.

In addition to these spontaneous transitions, there will be *induced* or *stimulated* transitions. The total rate of these induced transitions between level 2 and level 1 is proportional to the density u_f of the radiation of frequency f, where

$$f = \frac{(E_2 - E_1)}{h} \tag{8.2}$$

Let B_{21} and B_{12} denote the proportionality constants for stimulated emission. Then the number of stimulated downward transitions (emissions) per second is

$$N_2 B_{21} u_f$$

Similarly, the number of stimulated upward transitions (absorptions) per second is

$$N_1 B_{12} u_f$$

The proportionality constants in the above expressions are known as the Einstein A and B coefficients.

Under equilibrium conditions the net rate of downward transitions must be equal to that of upward transitions, namely,

$$N_2 A_{21} + N_2 B_{21} u_f = N_1 B_{12} u_f \qquad (8.3)$$

By solving for u_f, we obtain

$$u_f = \frac{N_2 A_{21}}{N_1 B_{12} - N_2 B_{21}}$$

Further, in view of Equation (8.1), we can write

$$u_f = \frac{A_{21}}{B_{21}} \frac{1}{(B_{12}/B_{21}) \, e^{hf/kT} - 1} \qquad (8.4)$$

In order for this to agree with the Planck radiation formula, the following equations must hold:

$$B_{12} = B_{21} \qquad (8.5)$$

$$\frac{A_{21}}{B_{21}} = \frac{8\pi h f^3}{c^3} \qquad (8.6)$$

Thus for atoms in equilibrium with thermal radiation, the ratio of stimulated emission rate to spontaneous emission rate is given by the formula

$$\frac{\text{Stimulated emission}}{\text{Spontaneous emission}} = \frac{B_{21} u_f}{A_{21}} = \frac{1}{e^{hf/kT} - 1} \qquad (8.7)$$

We recall, from Chapter 6, Section 5, that this is precisely the same as the number of photons per mode, that is, the occupation index.

According to the above result, the rate of induced emission is extremely small in the visible region of the spectrum with ordinary optical sources ($T \sim 10^3 \, °K$). Hence, in such sources, most of the radiation is emitted through spontaneous transitions. Since these transitions occur in a random manner, ordinary sources of visible radiation are incoherent.

On the other hand, in a laser the radiation density for certain preferred modes builds up to such a large value that induced transitions become completely dominant. One result is that the emitted radiation is highly coherent. Another is that the spectral intensity at the operating frequency of the laser is vastly greater than the spectral intensities of ordinary light sources.

8.3 Amplification in a Medium

Consider an optical medium through which radiation is passing. Suppose that the medium contains atoms in various energy levels E_1, E_2, E_3, and so forth. Let us fix our attention on two levels, say E_1 and E_2, where $E_1 < E_2$. We have already seen that the rates of stimulated emission and absorption involving these two levels are proportional to $N_2 B_{21}$ and $N_1 B_{12}$, respectively. Since $B_{21} = B_{12}$, the rate of stimulated downward transitions will exceed that of upward transitions if

$$N_2 > N_1$$

that is, if the population of the upper state is greater than that of the lower state.

Such a condition is contrary to the thermal equilibrium distribution given by the Boltzmann formula (8.1). It is called a *population inversion,* Figure 8.1. If a population inversion exists, then a light beam will in-

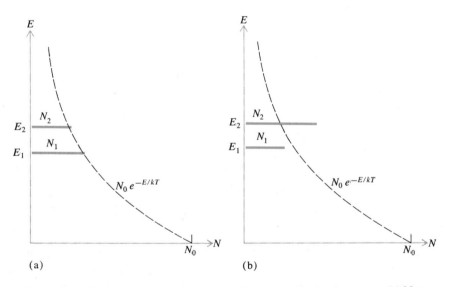

Figure 8.1. . Graphs of the population densities of two levels of a system. (a) Normal or Boltzmann distribution. (b) Inverted distribution.

crease in intensity, or in other words, it will be amplified as it passes through the medium. This is because the gain due to the induced emission exceeds the loss due to absorption.

Theory shows that the induced radiation is emitted in the same direction as the primary beam and that it also has a definite phase relationship, that is, it is coherent with the primary radiation.

In order to determine quantitatively the amount of amplification in a medium, we must take a closer look at the details of emission and absorption. Suppose a parallel beam of light propagates through a medium in which there is a population inversion. For a collimated beam, the spectral energy density u_f is related to the intensity I_f in the frequency interval f to $f + \Delta f$ by the formula

$$u_f \Delta f = \frac{I_f \Delta f}{c} \tag{8.8}$$

Due to the Doppler effect, and other line-broadening effects, not all of the atoms in a given energy level are effective for emission or absorption in a specified frequency interval. Rather, a certain number, say ΔN_1, of the N_1 atoms in level 1 are available for absorption. Similarly, of the N_2 atoms in level 2, the number ΔN_2 are available for emission. Consequently, the rate of upward transitions is

$$B_{12} u_f \, \Delta N_1 = B_{12}(I_f/c)\Delta N_1$$

and the rate of induced downward transitions is

$$B_{21} u_f \, \Delta N_2 = B_{21}(I_f/c) \, \Delta N_2$$

Now each upward transition subtracts a quantum of energy hf from the beam. Similarly, each downward transition adds the same amount. Therefore, the net time rate of change of the spectral energy density in the interval Δf is given by

$$\frac{d}{dt}(u_f \Delta f) = hf(B_{21}\Delta N_2 - B_{12}\Delta N_1)u_f \tag{8.9}$$

In time dt the wave travels a distance $dx = c \, dt$. Hence, in view of Equation (8.8) we can write

$$\frac{dI_f}{dx} = \frac{hf}{c}\left(\frac{\Delta N_2}{\Delta f} - \frac{\Delta N_1}{\Delta f}\right) B_{21} \, I_f \tag{8.10}$$

giving the rate of growth of the beam intensity in the direction of propagation.

The above differential equation can be integrated to give

$$I_f = I_{0f} \, e^{\alpha_f x} \tag{8.11}$$

in which α_f is the gain constant at frequency f. It is given by

$$\alpha_f = \frac{hf}{c}\left(\frac{\Delta N_2}{\Delta f} - \frac{\Delta N_1}{\Delta f}\right) B_{12} \tag{8.12}$$

An approximate expression for the gain constant at the center of a spectral line is obtained by taking Δf to be the linewidth. The ΔN's are then set equal to the N's. The result, which is correct except for a numerical constant of the order of unity, is

$$\alpha_{max} \simeq \frac{hf}{c\Delta f}(N_2 - N_1)B_{12} = \frac{c^2}{8\pi f^2 \Delta f}(N_2 - N_1)A_{12} \qquad (8.13)$$

The last step follows from the relation between the Einstein A and B coefficients, Equation (8.6).

A more exact analysis is as follows. In the case of broadening due to thermal motion, elementary kinetic theory [31] gives the fraction of atoms whose x-component of velocity lies between v_x and $v_x + \Delta v_x$ as

$$\sqrt{\frac{m}{2\pi kT}} \exp\left(\frac{-mv_x^2}{2kt}\right)\Delta v_x$$

where m is the atomic mass, k is Boltzmann's constant, and T is the absolute temperature. Due to the Doppler effect, these atoms will emit or absorb radiation propagating in the x direction, of frequency

$$f = f_0\left(1 + \frac{v_x}{c}\right)$$

where f_0 is the frequency of the line center. It follows that the fraction of atoms in a given level that can absorb or emit in the frequency range f to $f+\Delta f$ is given by

$$\sqrt{\frac{m}{2\pi kT}} \exp\left[\frac{-mc^2}{2kT}\left(\frac{f - f_0}{f_0}\right)^2\right]\frac{c}{f_0}\Delta f$$

Accordingly, we can express the gain constant at frequency f as

$$\alpha_f = \sqrt{\frac{m}{2k\pi T}}\, e^{-\beta(f - f_0)^2}(N_2 - N_1)hB_{21} \qquad (8.14)$$

in which $\beta = mc^2/(2kTf_0^2)$. The gain thus varies with frequency according to the Gaussian function $e^{-\beta(f - f_0)^2}$ centered at frequency f_0, Figure 8.2. This curve also represents the shape of a Doppler-broadened spectral line. The maximum gain occurs at the line center and is given by

$$\alpha_{max} = \sqrt{\frac{m}{2\pi kT}}(N_2 - N_1)hB_{21} \qquad (8.15)$$

or, equivalently,

$$\alpha_{max} = \sqrt{\frac{m}{2\pi kT}}(N_2 - N_1)\frac{c^3}{8\pi f^3}A_{21} \qquad (8.16)$$

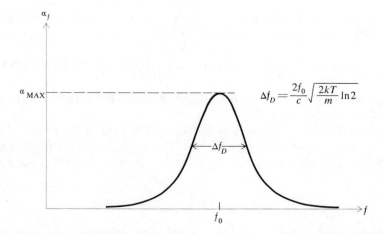

Figure 8.2.   Amplification coefficient for a Doppler broadened spectral line.

We see that α is positive if $N_2 > N_1$, which is the condition for amplification. Otherwise, if $N_2 < N_1$ (which is the normal equilibrium condition) then α is negative, and we have absorption.[2] Methods for producing population inversions in optical media will be discussed in the following section.

8.4   Methods of Producing a Population Inversion

There are several methods for producing the population inversions necessary for optical amplification to take place. Some of the most commonly used are:

(1) Optical pumping or photon excitation,
(2) Electron excitation,
(3) Inelastic atom-atom collisions.

In the case of optical pumping, an external light source is employed to produce a high population of some particular energy level in the laser medium by selective optical absorption, Figure 8.3(a). This is the method of excitation used in the solid-state lasers of which the ruby laser is the prototype.

Direct electron excitation in a gaseous discharge may be used to

---

[2] If the energy levels of the system are *degenerate*, that is, if there are several sublevels belonging to a given energy, then the gain formulas must be modified as follows. The quantity N_1 is to be replaced by $(g_2/g_1) N_1$. The degeneracy parameters g_1 and g_2 are the numbers of sublevels in level 1 and level 2, respectively. The condition for amplification then becomes $N_2 > (g_2/g_1) N_1$.

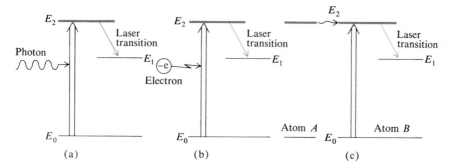

Figure 8.3. Diagrams showing three processes for producing a population inversion. (a) Optical pumping. (b) Direct electron excitation. (c) Inelastic atom-atom collisions.

produce the desired inversion, Figure 8.3(b). This method is used in some of the gaseous ion lasers such as the argon laser. With this type of excitation, the laser medium itself carries the discharge current. Under suitable conditions of pressure and current, the electrons in the discharge may directly excite the active atoms to produce a higher population in certain levels compared to lower levels. The relevant factors are the electron excitation cross-section and the lifetimes of the various levels.

In the third method, an electrical discharge is also employed. Here a suitable combination of gases is employed such that two different types of atoms, say A and B, each have some excited states, A^* and B^*, that coincide, or nearly coincide. In this case transfer of excitation may occur between the two atoms as follows

$$A^* + B \rightarrow A + B^*$$

If the excited state of one of the atoms, say A^*, is metastable, then the presence of gas B will serve as an outlet for the excitation. As a consequence, it is possible that the excited level E_{B^*} may become more highly populated than some lower level to which the atom B^* can decay by radiation, Figure 8.3(c). This is the case with the helium-neon laser. A neon atom receives its excitation from an excited helium atom. The laser transition then occurs in the neon atom.

8.5 Laser Oscillation

The optical cavity or resonator of a laser usually consists of two mirrors, curved or plane, between which the amplifying medium is located, Figure 8.4. If a sufficient population inversion exists in the medium, then the electromagnetic radiation builds up and becomes established

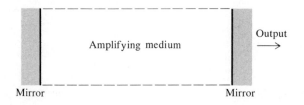

Figure 8.4. Basic laser setup.

as a standing wave between the mirrors. The energy is usually coupled from the resonator by having one or both of the mirrors partially transmitting.

In the case of plane reflectors, the optical cavity actually constitutes a conventional Fabry-Perot interferometer. The longitudinal modes of the Fabry-Perot resonator occur at an infinite number of equally spaced frequencies

$$\cdots, f_n, f_{n+1}, f_{n+2}, \cdots$$

They differ by the free spectral range

$$f_{n+1} - f_n = \frac{c}{2d}$$

where c is the speed of light and d is the spacing of the reflectors, as shown in Section 3.11.

Oscillation may occur at one or more of these resonant frequencies, depending on the width of the gain curve in relation to the mode spacing, Figure 8.5. Most lasers oscillate on several longitudinal modes at once.

However, if extremely high spectral purity is needed, it is possible to obtain oscillation on one mode by suitable selection of laser parameters. The inherent linewidth in this case is determined mainly by the Q of the laser cavity. Cavity linewidths are typically of the order of a few hertz. However, in practice, linewidths of the order of 10^3 Hz are obtained. The limitation is determined largely by mechanical and thermal stability.

Threshold Condition for Oscillation   We have seen that the intensity of a parallel beam in an amplifying medium grows according to the equation

$$I_f = I_{0f} e^{\alpha_f x}$$

Suppose a wave in a laser cavity starts out at some point and travels back and forth between the cavity mirrors. Upon its return the wave will lose a certain fraction δ of its energy by scattering, reflection loss,

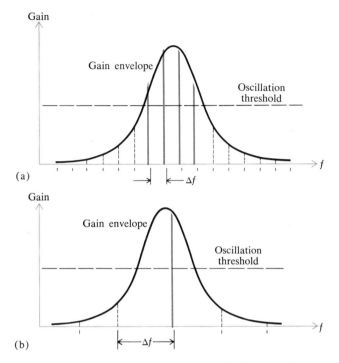

Figure 8.5. Oscillation frequencies in a laser. (a) Four longitudinal modes. (b) One mode.

and so forth. In order for the laser to oscillate, the gain must equal or exceed the loss, that is

$$I_f - I_{0f} \geq \delta I_f$$

or equivalently

$$e^{\alpha_f 2L} - 1 \geq \delta \qquad (8.17)$$

Here L is the active length of the amplifying medium. If $\alpha_f 2L \ll 1$, then the condition for oscillation can be written

$$\alpha_f 2L \geq \delta \qquad (8.18)$$

If, at a given frequency, the gain exceeds the loss, the ensuing oscillation grows until an equilibrium condition is attained. The fractional loss δ is essentially constant and independent of the amplitude of the oscillation. Hence, a depletion of the medium occurs that diminishes the population difference $N_2 - N_1$. The gain then drops until

$$\alpha_f 2L = \delta \qquad (8.19)$$

The depletion occurs only at the oscillating frequency and is called *hole burning*. Hole burning results in a modification of the gain curve as shown in Figure 8.6.

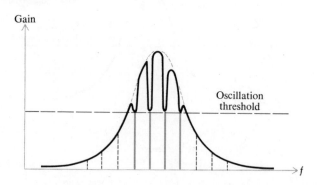

Figure 8.6.   Hole burning of the gain envelope in a laser.

8.6   Optical-Resonator Theory

In our derivation of the intensity distribution of the fringe patterns of the Fabry-Perot interferometer, Section 3.11, we neglected diffraction effects arising from the finite size of the mirrors. These effects result in diffraction losses, and a careful examination of such losses is necessary in laser applications. This is especially important for low-gain systems such as the helium-neon laser in which the amplification per pass is typically only a few percent.

To illustrate the mathematical problem involved in the study of the optical resonator, we show in Figure 8.7 the resonator mirrors with aperture coordinates x,y and x',y', respectively. The case is equivalent to diffraction with multiple apertures, as shown. If $U(x,y)$ and $U'(x',y')$ represent the complex amplitudes of the radiation over the mirror surfaces, then by applying the Fresnel-Kirchhoff diffraction theory, Section 4.2, we can write

$$U'(x',y') = \frac{-ik}{4\pi} \iint U(x,y) \frac{e^{ikr}}{r} (1 + \cos \theta) dx \, dy \qquad \textbf{(8.20)}$$

in which

$$r = [d^2 + (x'^2 - x^2) + (y'^2 - y^2)]^{1/2}$$
$$\cos \theta = \frac{d}{r}$$

If the mirrors are identical, which is typical, then for the steady-state condition, that is, after the radiation has been reflected back and forth

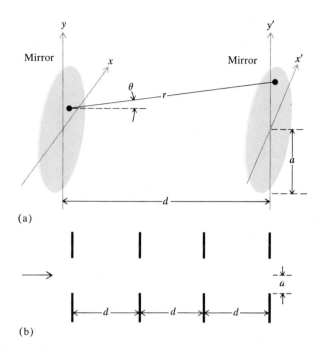

Figure 8.7. (a) Geometry of a Fabry-Perot laser cavity. (b) Equivalent multiple diffraction problem.

many times, the two functions U and U' will become identical, except for a constant factor γ. In this case

$$\gamma U(x',y') = \iint U(x,y)\, K(x,y,x',y')dx\, dy \tag{8.21}$$

where

$$K(x,y,x',y') = \frac{-ik}{4\pi}(1 + \cos\theta)\frac{e^{ikr}}{r} \tag{8.22}$$

Equation (8.21) is an integral equation in the unknown function U. The function K is called the kernel of the equation, and γ is known as the eigenvalue. There is an infinite number of solutions $U_n,\, n = 1,2,\cdots$, each with an associated eigenvalue γ_n. The various solutions correspond to the normal modes of the resonator. Expressing the γ_n as

$$\gamma_n = |\gamma_n|\, e^{i\phi_n} \tag{8.23}$$

we see that $|\gamma_n|$ specifies the ratio of the amplitude, and ϕ_n gives the phase shift associated with a given mode. The quantity $1 - |\gamma_n|^2$ is the relative energy loss per transit due to diffraction. (This is in addition to losses caused by absorption by the mirrors.)

Fox and Li were among the first to study the integral equation (8.21) for the Fabry-Perot resonator [9]. They employed an electronic digital computer to find numerical solutions and associated eigenvalues. Boyd and Gordon found analytical solutions [6]. The types of optical resonators studied included both plane-parallel mirrors and curved mirrors.

There are several combinations of curved and plane mirrors that can be used for laser cavities. A few of these are shown in Figure 8.8.

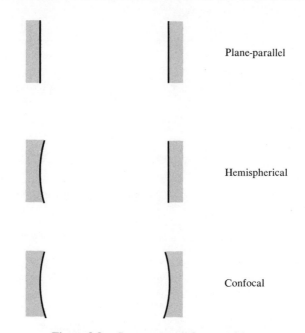

Figure 8.8.   Some common laser cavities.

One of the most commonly used cavity configurations is the *confocal* type. This configuration consists of identical spherical mirrors separated by a distance equal to the radius of curvature.

The confocal cavity is very much easier to align than the plane-parallel type. The latter requires an adjustment accuracy of something like one arc second, whereas the confocal type, being somewhat self-aligning, needs a setting accuracy of only about a quarter of a degree.

In addition to the longitudinal or axial modes already mentioned in Section 6.5, laser oscillation can occur on transverse modes even though the cavity may be open-sided. Since the electric and magnetic fields of a Fabry-Perot-type cavity are perpendicular, or very nearly perpendicular, to the cavity axis, the modes are usually designated as

TEM_{pq} (transverse electromagnetic) modes. The letters p and q stand for the number of transverse nodal lines at the cavity ends as illustrated in Figure 8.9.

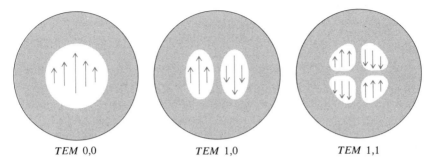

TEM 0,0   TEM 1,0   TEM 1,1

Figure 8.9.   Field distributions at the mirrors for some low-order modes.

The diffraction loss for some of the low-order modes in plane-parallel and in confocal resonators is plotted in Figure 8.10. The loss is plotted as a function of the *Fresnel number* $N = a^2/\lambda d$ where a is the mirror radius and d is the mirror separation. With confocal spherical mirrors, the diffraction losses of low-order modes are negligibly small when $N > 1$. A comparison of the losses for the plane parallel resonator and the confocal resonator shows that the latter is definitely superior.

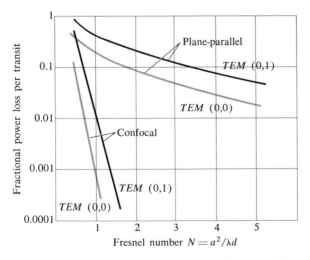

Figure 8.10.   Loss curves for the first two modes in plane-parallel and confocal laser cavities.

Field Distribution. In optical resonators employing curved mirrors, the radiation field is concentrated near the longitudinal axis and falls off smoothly away from the axis. In the case of the confocal resonator, the lateral extent of the field is smallest at the midpoint between the two mirrors. In particular, for the lowest mode ($TEM_{0,0}$), theory shows that the lateral distribution is approximately Gaussian. The amplitude is proportional to the quantity

$$\exp\left[\frac{-2\pi\rho^2 d}{\lambda(d^2 + 4z^2)}\right]$$

Here ρ is the lateral distance from the axis, and z is the distance from the midpoint. The reflectors are located at $z = \pm(1/2)d$. The amplitude drops to $1/e$ in a lateral distance

$$\rho_s = \sqrt{\frac{\lambda(d^2 + 4z^2)}{2\pi d}} \tag{8.24}$$

This is called the *spot size*. At the center ($z = 0$) the spot size is $\sqrt{\lambda d/2\pi}$, whereas at either mirror ($z = \pm(\frac{1}{2})d$), it is $\sqrt{\lambda d/\pi}$. The situation is illustrated in Figure 8.11.

Figure 8.11. Standing wave pattern and lateral distribution of the $TEM_{0,0}$ mode of a confocal laser cavity.

8.7   Gas Lasers

Figure 8.12 shows a typical physical arrangement of a gas laser. The optical cavity is provided by external mirrors. The mirrors are coated with multilayer dielectric films in order to obtain high reflectance at the desired wavelength. Spherical mirrors arranged in the confocal configuration are used because of the low loss and ease of adjustment of this type of cavity.

The laser tube is fitted with Brewster end windows in order to obtain the maximum possible transparency. When Brewster windows are used, the output of the laser is linearly polarized. The reason is that the win-

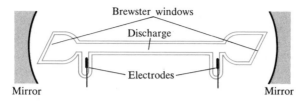

Figure 8.12.   Typical design of a gas laser.

dows are highly transparent for one preferred direction of polarization —the *TM* polarization—as discussed in Section 2.8. Consequently, laser oscillation at this favored polarization builds up and becomes dominant over the orthogonal *TE* polarization.

External electrical excitation may be provided in any of the following ways:

(1) Direct current discharge,
(2) Alternating current discharge,
(3) Electrodeless high frequency discharge.

Methods (1) and (2) are commonly employed in commerical gas lasers. The dc discharge (1) is advantageous if the laser is to be used for such things as optical heterodyning, communications, and so forth. The ac discharge (2) is simplest because the power source need be only an ordinary high-voltage transformer connected to cold metal electrodes in the tube. The electrodeless rf discharge (3) was used in the first gas laser—the helium-neon laser—developed at the Bell Telephone Laboratories by Javan, Bennett, and Herriott [21].

The Helium-Neon Laser   Figure 8.13 shows an energy-level diagram of the helium-neon laser system. Helium atoms are excited by electron impact in the discharge. The populations of the metastable states ^3S and ^1S of helium builds up because there are no optically allowed transitions to lower levels. It is seen from the figure that the neon levels labeled $2s$ and $3s$ lie close to the metastable helium levels. There is, therefore, a high probability of energy transfer when a metastable helium atom collides with an unexcited neon atom. These energy transfers are:

$$He(^3S) + Ne \rightarrow He + Ne(2s)$$
$$He(^1S) + Ne \rightarrow He + Ne(3s)$$

Under suitable discharge conditions a population inversion of the

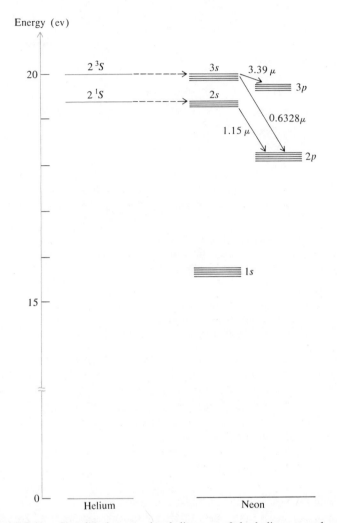

Figure 8.13. Simplified energy level diagram of the helium-neon laser.

Ne(2s) and Ne(3s) levels can take place. The optimum value of total pressure is about 1 torr, and the most favorable ratio of helium to neon is found to be about 7 to 1.

The main laser action in the helium-neon system corresponds to the following transitions in the neon atom:

$$3s_2 \rightarrow 2p_4 \ 6328 \ \text{Å}$$
$$2s_2 \rightarrow 2p_4 \ 11,523 \ \text{Å}$$
$$3s_2 \rightarrow 3p_4 \ 3.39 \ \mu\text{m}$$

In addition to these, many weaker transitions in neon have been made to undergo laser oscillation [25].

Other Gas Lasers   Electrical discharges in pure gases and in various mixtures have produced laser action at a large number of different wavelengths from the far infrared to the ultraviolet. All of the noble gases He, Ne, A, Kr, and Xe exhibit laser transitions in the pure gas. The argon ion laser, for example, generates visible light at several wavelengths in the blue region. Pulsed discharges in metal vapors have been

Table 8.1.   SOME GAS LASERS

Gas or Gas Mixture	Active Ion, Atom or Molecule	Principal Laser Wavelengths μ	Remarks
He – Ne	Ne	0.6328, 1.15, 3.39, (−)	cw
He	He	2.060, 1.954	cw
Ne	Ne	1.15, 2.10, 5.40, (−)	cw
Ne	Ne+	0.3323, 0.3378, 0.3392, (−)	pulsed
A	A	1.69, 2.06 (−)	cw
A	A+	0.4579, 0.4764, 0.4879, 0.4965, (−)	pulsed and cw
Kr	Kr	2.11, 2.19 (−)	cw
Kr	Kr+	0.4619, 0.4680, 0.5681, (−)	pulsed and cw
Xe – He	Xe	2.026, 3.507, (−)	cw, high gain
Xe	Xe+	0.4603, 0.5419, 0.5971, (−)	pulsed and cw
Ne – O_2, A – O_2	O	0.8446	cw
O_2	O+, O++	0.4414, 0.5592, (−)	pulsed
He – NO, Ne – NO	N	1.358, 1.454	cw
N_2	N_2	1.04–1.05, 0.88–0.89, 0.334, (−)	pulsed
Air, N_2	N+	0.5679, (−)	pulsed
He – Cl_2	Cl	1.97, 2.02	cw
He – Cl_2	Cl+	0.5217, (−)	pulsed or cw
A – Br_2	Br	0.8447	cw
He – I_2	I	3.23, 3.43	cw
He – I_2	I+	0.5407, 0.5760, 0.6127, (−)	pulsed
SF_6	S	1.045, 1.063	cw
He – S	S+	0.5320, 0.5432, 0.5454, 0.5640 (−)	pulsed and cw
He – P	P+	0.6024, 0.6043	pulsed
He – Zn	Zn+	0.4924, (−)	pulsed
He – Cd	Cd+	0.5378, (−)	pulsed
He – Hg	Hg	1.529, 1.813, 3.93, (−)	cw
He – Hg	Hg+	0.5677, 0.6149, (−)	pulsed
CO	CO	0.52, 0.56, (−)	pulsed
CO_2 – He	CO_2	9.4, 10.4	cw (high efficiency)
H_2O	H_2O	27.9, (−)	pulsed

Data is taken from [25] and [37].
(−) indicates that there are other important laser transitions.

used to obtain laser action in Zn, Cd, Hg, Pb, Sn, and other metals [4] [8] [37]. The halogens Cl, Br, and I similarly yield laser transitions under pulsed conditions [22]. Discharges in molecular gases have yielded population inversions on transitions in various molecules. Notable among these are the molecular nitrogen laser (N_2) that produces infrared and ultraviolet radiation, and the CO_2 laser that oscillates in the 10 μm region. Table 8.1 summarizes some of the common gas lasers.

8.8 Optically Pumped Solid-State Lasers

In solid-state lasers, of which ruby is the prototype, the active atoms of the laser medium are embedded in a solid. Both crystals and glasses have been used as the supporting matrices for this application. The crystal or glass is usually made in the form of a cylindrical rod whose ends are optically ground and polished to a high degree of parallelism and flatness. The laser rod may be made to constitute its own optical cavity by coating the ends, or external mirrors may be employed.

Optical pumping of the active atoms is accomplished by means of an external light source. This source may be either pulsed or continuous. High intensity lamps, such as xenon flashlamps or high-pressure mercury discharge lamps, are generally used for this purpose.

Figure 8.14 shows two typical arrangements of optically pumped

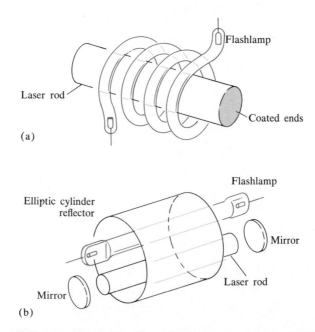

Figure 8.14. Typical designs for optically pumped solid-state lasers.

solid-state lasers. In (a) a helical flashlamp is used with the laser rod placed inside the helix. The rod ends are coated so that the complete laser is very simple and compact. A more elaborate system is shown in (b). The laser rod is placed at one focus of an elliptical reflector, and the pumping lamp is placed at the other focus. External mirrors are used for the optical cavity.

The Ruby Laser The rod of a ruby laser is made of synthetic saphire (Al_2O_3), which is doped with approximately 0.05 percent by weight of Cr_2O_3. This concentration produces a pink-colored material. The color is due to the presence of Cr+++ ions, which replace Al in the crystal lattice.

An energy-level diagram of Cr+++ in ruby is shown in Figure 7.17. In operation of the laser, the pumping light is absorbed by the Cr+++ ions raising them from the ground state ^4A to either of the excited states $^4T_1$ or $^4T_2$. From these levels, a rapid radiationless transition to the level ^2E takes place. Decay from ^2E is relatively slow, so that with sufficient excitation a population inversion between ^2E and the ground state ^4A can occur. When this condition attains, amplification occurs at the wavelength 6934 Å, corresponding to the transition $^2E \rightarrow {}^4A$. The resultant output is an intense pulse of light at this wavelength.

Other Solid-State Laser Materials Besides ruby, a number of other crystals, when doped with impurity atoms containing incomplete sub-shells, have been found to exhibit stimulated emission. Neodymium, for example, has a laser transition at about 1.06 μm. Various host solids have been used with neodymium, including crystals of calcium fluoride (CaF_2) and calcium tungstate ($CaWO_4$), as well as glass. Table 8.2 lists a number of examples of solid-state laser materials.

8.9   Miscellaneous Lasers

In addition to gas lasers and optically pumped solid-state lasers, there are several other types. One is the liquid laser that employs a solvent as the support for the lasing atom or molecule. The list of liquid laser transitions is not extensive. Successful liquid lasers have incorporated the rare earth chelates. For example, in europium tribenzolacetonate dissolved in ethyl alcohol, laser oscillation at 6130 Å can be obtained. This wavelength corresponds to a transition of the Eu++ ion in the chelate.

Another type of laser is the semiconductor junction laser. Here the relevant energy levels are those of the electrons in the conduction and valence bands of the solid semiconductor. A population inversion can be obtained by driving a large current ($\sim 10^4$ A/cm²) through a $p - n$ junction. A common semiconductor used for this purpose is

Table 8.2. SOME SOLID-STATE LASER MATERIALS

Laser Ion	Host Material	Wavelength μ	Remarks
Cr+++	Al_2O_3	0.6943	Operates at room temp. High Power
Pr+++	$CaWO_4$	1.04	liquid air temp.
	LaF_3	0.5985	
Nd+++	BaF_2	1.060	
	SrF_2	1.043	liquid air temp.
	CaF_2	1.046	
	$CaMoO_4$	1.067	
	$CaWO_4$	1.06	
	Gd_2O_3	1.079	room temp.
	LaF_3	1.063	
	Glass	1.06	
Sm++	CaF_2	0.7085	liquid helium temp.
	SrF_2	0.6969	
Eu+++	Y_2O_3	0.6113	room temp.
Gd+++	Glass	0.3125	liquid air temp.
Ho+++	CaF_2	2.09	
	$CaWO_4$	2.05	liquid air temp.
	Glass	2.04	
Er+++	CaF_2	1.617	liquid air temp.
	$CaWO_4$	1.612	
Tm+++	SrF_2	1.972	liquid air temp.
	$CaWO_4$	1.911	
Yb+++	Glass	1.015	liquid air temp.
U+++	BaF_2	2.55	liquid air temp.
	CaF_2	2.51–2.61	room temp.
	SrF_2	2.40	liquid air temp.

gallium arsenide, which exhibits laser action at about 8380 to 8390 Å. The semiconductor laser is relatively compact and simple. One drawback is the large linewidth, typically several angstroms. This limits the semiconductor laser to applications not requiring high spectral purity.

8.10 The Ring Laser

The ring laser is a good example of a technological application of lasers. It is a device designed to measure rotation by means of counter-rotating coherent light beams and was developed in 1963 at the Sperry-Rand Corporation. The device is the laser analogue of the Sagnac experiment (Section 1.7).

The basic design is shown in Figure 8.15. The optical cavity of the

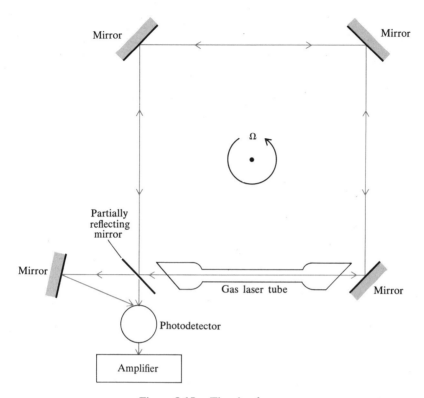

Figure 8.15. The ring laser.

laser consists of four mirrors arranged in a square. One or more laser tubes are inserted into the cavity to provide amplification. Oscillation occurs at those resonance frequencies

$$f_n = n\frac{c}{L} \tag{8.25}$$

which lie within the amplification curve of the laser medium. Here L is the effective length of the complete loop and n is an integer.

If the system is rotating about an axis perpendicular to the plane of the loop, the effective path lengths for the clockwise and the counterclockwise beams are different. This results in a difference Δf between the frequencies of the laser oscillation of the two beams. The difference is

$$\Delta f = f\frac{4A}{c}\Omega \tag{8.26}$$

where f is the frequency of the laser when it is not rotating, A is the loop area, and Ω is the angular speed of rotation.

In the operation of the ring laser, the method of optical heterodyning is used. The two output beams of the laser are brought together and fed to a photodetector as shown. The output of the photodetector consists of a beat signal whose frequency is equal to the difference Δf. This, in turn, is proportional to the angular speed of rotation.

PROBLEMS

8.1. The first line of the principal series of sodium is the "D" line at 5890 Å. This corresponds to a transition from the first excited state ($3p$) to the ground state ($3s$). What is the energy in ev of the first excited state?

8.2. What fraction of sodium atoms are in the first excited state in a sodium vapor lamp at a temperature of 250° C.

8.3. What is the ratio of stimulated emission to spontaneous emission at a temperature of 250° C for the sodium "D" line.

8.4. Calculate the approximate gain constant of a ruby laser with 0.05 percent Cr_2O_3 in Al_2O_3. The laser wavelength is 6934 Å, and the linewidth is 1 Å. Assume that 50 percent of the Cr^{+++} ions are in the first excited state and 40 percent are in the ground state.

8.5. Calculate the inversion density $N_2 - N_1 (g_2/g_1)$ for a helium-neon laser operating at 6328 Å. The gain constant is 2 percent per meter, and the temperature of the discharge is 100° C. The lifetime of the upper state against spontaneous emission to the lower state is 10^{-7} s.

8.6. If the spot size at the mirrors of a helium-neon laser is 0.5 mm, what is the length of the laser cavity? The cavity is of the confocal-type, and the wavelength is 6328 Å. What is the spot size of the 3.39-μm transition in the same cavity?

8.7. Limiting apertures are placed at the mirrors of a confocal cavity in order to suppress the higher modes. If the cavity is one meter in length, what should the diameter of the apertures be in order that the loss for the *TEM* 0,1 mode be 1 percent? What is the corresponding loss for the *TEM* 0,0 mode? (See Figure 8.10.) The wavelength is 6238 Å.

8.8. Prove Equation (8.26) giving the difference frequency of the ring laser.

APPENDIX I

The Ray Velocity Surface of a Crystal

In order to find the equation of the ray velocity surface, it is convenient to express the wave equation (5.91) in terms of the vector $\mathbf{D} = \mathfrak{D}/\varepsilon_0$ where $\mathfrak{D}$ is the displacement vector. We have therefore, for plane harmonic waves in a crystal,

$$\mathbf{k} \times (\mathbf{k} \times \mathbf{E}) = -\frac{\omega^2}{c^2}\mathbf{D} \tag{I.1}$$

This shows that $\mathbf{D}$ is perpendicular to the wave vector $\mathbf{k}$. Expanding the triple cross product gives

$$\mathbf{k}(\mathbf{k} \cdot \mathbf{E}) - k^2\mathbf{E} = -\frac{\omega^2}{c^2}\mathbf{D} \tag{I.2}$$

Next, take the dot product with $\mathbf{D}$. Since $\mathbf{k} \cdot \mathbf{D} = 0$, we find

$$k^2\mathbf{E} \cdot \mathbf{D} = \frac{\omega^2}{c^2}\mathbf{D} \cdot \mathbf{D} \tag{I.3}$$

or, in view of the fact that $v = \omega/k$,

$$\mathbf{E} \cdot \mathbf{D} = ED \cos\theta = \frac{v^2}{c^2}D^2 \tag{I.4}$$

Now the angle θ between $\mathbf{E}$ and $\mathbf{D}$ is the same as that between the phase velocity $\mathbf{v}$ and the ray velocity $\mathbf{u}$, because $\mathbf{k} \perp \mathbf{D}$. Hence, $v = u \cos\theta$, and Equation (I.4) yields

$$\frac{D}{E}\cos\theta = \frac{c^2}{u^2} \tag{I.5}$$

Let us express $\mathbf{D}$ in terms of its projections along $\mathbf{E}$ and $\mathbf{u}$. Thus

$$\mathbf{D} = \mathbf{E}\frac{D}{E}\cos\theta + \mathbf{u}\frac{\mathbf{u} \cdot \mathbf{D}}{u^2} \tag{I.6}$$

which, from (I.5), becomes

$$\mathbf{D} = \mathbf{E}\frac{c^2}{u^2} + \mathbf{u}\frac{\mathbf{u} \cdot \mathbf{D}}{u^2} \tag{I.7}$$

If the coordinate axes are principal axes of the crystal, the components of $\mathbf{E}$ are related to those of $\mathbf{D}$ by $E_x = D_x/\varepsilon_{11} = D_x/n_1^2$, and so forth. Thus, upon taking components and rearranging terms, Equation (I.7) is equivalent to the following three scalar equations:

$$D_x \left(\frac{c^2}{n_1{}^2} - u_y{}^2 - u_z{}^2 \right) + D_y \, u_x \, u_y + D_z \, u_x \, u_z = 0$$

$$D_x \, u_y \, u_x + D_y \left(\frac{c^2}{n_2{}^2} - u_x{}^2 - u_z{}^2 \right) + D_z \, u_y \, u_z = 0 \qquad \text{(I.8)}$$

$$D_x \, u_z \, u_x + D_y \, u_y \, u_z + D_z \left(\frac{c^2}{n_3{}^2} - u_x{}^2 - u_y{}^2 \right) = 0$$

The determinant of the coefficients must vanish in order that a non-trivial solution exists. This gives the equation of the ray-velocity surface, Equation (5.107).

APPENDIX II

Lens Formulas

THIN LENS

If s is the object distance, s' is the image distance, and f is the focal length, then

$$\frac{1}{s} + \frac{1}{s'} = \frac{1}{f} \qquad \text{(II.1)}$$

When the lens consists of a single component of index n with radii of curvature r_1 and r_2, then the focal length in air is given by

$$\frac{1}{f} = (n - 1) \left(\frac{1}{r_1} + \frac{1}{r_2} \right) \qquad \text{(II.2)}$$

known as the *lens maker's formula*.

A radius is considered positive if the surface is convex and negative if the surface is concave. In a double convex lens, like that shown in Figure II.1, both radii are positive.

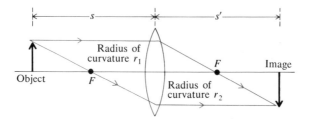

Figure II.1. Formation of an image by a thin lens. The distance from the center of the lens to either of the points marked F is equal to the focal length f.

COMBINATIONS OF THIN LENSES

The combined focal length f of any number of thin lenses placed close together (in contact) is expressible as

$$\frac{1}{f} = \frac{1}{f_1} + \frac{1}{f_2} + \frac{1}{f_3} + \cdots \qquad \text{(II.3)}$$

where $f_1, f_2, \cdots$ are the focal lengths of the individual lenses. For two lenses not in contact, but separated by a distance d, the effective focal length of the combination is given by the expression

$$\frac{1}{f} = \frac{1}{f_1} + \frac{1}{f_2} - \frac{d}{f_1 f_2} \tag{II.4}$$

THICK LENS

For a single thick lens in air, Equation (II.1) applies where, however, the object and image distance are measured from the *principal planes*,

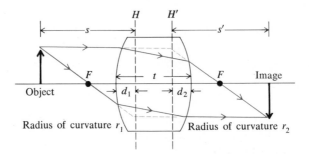

Figure II.2.   Formation of an image by a thick lens. The focal length f, given by Eq. (II.5), is the distance from either principal plane to the points marked F.

H and H' Figure II.2. The focal length f is calculated from the equation

$$\frac{1}{f} = (n - 1) \left(\frac{1}{r_1} + \frac{1}{r_2} - \frac{(n - 1)^2 t}{n r_1 r_2} \right) \tag{II.5}$$

where t is the lens thickness. The positions of the principal planes are given by

$$d_1 = ft \left(\frac{1 - n}{r_2} \right)$$

$$d_2 = ft \left(\frac{1 - n}{r_1} \right) \tag{II.6}$$

CHROMATIC ABERRATION

Due to dispersion, the focal length of a simple lens, Equation (II.2), varies with the wavelength. This variation, called *chromatic aberration,* can be reduced substantially by means of a lens combination in which the component lenses are made of glasses having different dispersions. An *achromatic* combination of focal length f for two thin lenses in contact is obtained if the focal lengths of the component lenses are

$$f_1 = f\left(1 - \frac{\delta_1}{\delta_2}\right) \qquad f_2 = f\left(1 - \frac{\delta_2}{\delta_1}\right) \qquad \text{(II.7)}$$

where $\qquad \delta_1 = \frac{1}{n_1 - 1}\frac{dn_1}{d\lambda} \qquad \delta_2 = \frac{1}{n_2 - 1}\frac{dn_2}{d\lambda} \qquad$ (II.8)

Since $dn/d\lambda$ also varies with wavelength, a lens can be achromatized over a limited wavelength interval only.

Spherical Aberration

In the case of a simple lens, the effective focal length varies with the distance h at which the incident rays enter the lens, Figure II.3. This

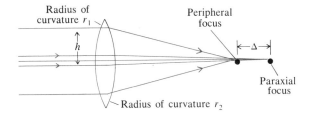

Figure II.3.   Illustrating spherical aberration.

variation is called *spherical aberration*. For *paraxial* rays ($h \approx 0$) formula (II.2) applies. The difference Δ between the focal length f for paraxial rays and the focal length for rays entering the lens a distance h from the axis is approximately proportional to h^2. It can be expressed

$$\Delta = (\tfrac{1}{2})Kh^2 \qquad \text{(II.9)}$$

in which K is given by the rather complicated expression

$$K = \frac{f^2(n-1)}{n^2}\left[\frac{1}{r_1{}^3} + \left(\frac{1}{f} + \frac{1}{r_2}\right)^2\left(\frac{n+1}{f} + \frac{1}{r_2}\right)\right] \qquad \text{(II.10)}$$

This is minimum when the ratio of the radii is

$$\frac{r_1}{r_2} = \frac{n + 4 - 2n^2}{n + 2n^2} \qquad \text{(II.11)}$$

The above formula giving the shape of a simple lens for minimum spherical aberration holds only if the object is at an infinite distance. For derivations of the above equations and additional reading, the student should consult textbooks in lens design such as *Applied Optics and Optical Design* by A. E. Conrady.

REFERENCES

1. Beran, M. J., and G. B. Parrent, Jr., *Theory of Partial Coherence*. Englewood Cliffs, N. J.: Prentice- Hall, 1964.
2. Besancon, R. M., ed., *The Encyclopedia of Physics*. New York: Reinhold, 1966.
3. Bloembergen, N., *Nonlinear Optics*. New York: W. A. Benjamin, 1965.
4. Bloom, A. L., W. E. Bell, and F. O. Lopez, *Phys. Rev.*, **135**, A578 (1964).
5. Born, M., and E. Wolf, *Principles of Optics*. New York: Macmillan, 1964.
6. Boyd, G. D., and J. P. Gordon, *Bell System Tech. J.*, **40**, 489 (1961).
7. Candler, C., *Modern Interferometers*. London: Hilger and Watts, Ltd., 1951.
8. Fowles, G. R., and W. T. Silfvast, *J. Quantum Electronics*, **QE-1**, 131 (1965).
9. Fox, A. G., and T. Li, *Bell System Tech. J.*, **40**, 453 (1961).
10. Francon, M., *Modern Applications of Physical Optics*. New York: Interscience, 1963.
11. Frauenfelder, H., *The Mössbauer Effect*. New York: W. A. Benjamin, 1962.
12. Gabor, D., *Nature*, **161**, 777 (1948).
13. Gordon, J. P., H. Z. Zeiger, and C. H. Townes, *Phys. Rev.*, **95**, 282 (1954).
14. Gray, D. E. ed., *American Institute of Physics Handbook*. New York: McGraw-Hill, 1957.
15. Hanbury-Brown, R., and R. Q. Twiss, *Proc. Roy. Soc.* (*London*) **A243**, 291 (1957).
16. Harnwell, G. P., *Principles of Electricity and Electromagnetism*. New York: McGraw-Hill, 1938.
17. Harrison, G. R., R. C. Lord, and J. R. Loofbourow, *Practical Spectroscopy*. Englewood Cliffs, N. J.: Prentice-Hall, 1948.
18. Herzberg, G., *Atomic Spectra and Atomic Structure*. New York: Dover, 1950.
19. ———, *Molecular Spectra and Molecular Structure*. Princeton, N. J.: Van Nostrand, 1950.
20. Ives, H. E., and G. R. Stilwell, *J. Opt. Soc. Am.*, **31**, 369 (1941).
21. Javan, A., W. R. Bennet, Jr., and D. R. Herriott, *Phys. Rev. Letters*, **6**, 106 (1961).
22. Jensen, R. C., and G. R. Fowles, *Proc. IEEE*, **52**, 1350 (1964).
23. King, G. W., *Spectroscopy and Molecular Structure*. New York: Holt, Rinehart and Winston, 1964.

24. Kuhn, H. G., *Atomic Spectra*. New York: Academic Press, 1962.
25. Lengyel, B. A., *Introduction to Laser Physics*. New York: Wiley, 1966.
26. Lilley, A. E., *et al.*, *Nature*, **209**, 468 (1966).
27. Mathews, J., and R. L. Walker, *Mathematical Methods of Physics*. New York: W. A. Benjamin, 1964.
28. Nicols, E. F., and G. F. Hull, *Phys. Rev.*, **13**, 307 (1901).
29. Pearson, J. M., *A Theory of Waves*. Boston: Allyn and Bacon, 1966.
30. Prather, J. L., *Atomic Energy Levels in Crystals*. Washington, D.C.: Nat. Bur. Stand. Monograph 19, U. S. Govt. Printing Office, 1961.
31. Present, R. D., *Kinetic Theory of Gases*. New York: McGraw-Hill, 1958.
32. Rindler, W., *Special Relativity*. London: Olives & Boyd, 1960.
33. Rosa, E. B., and N. E. Dorsey, *A New Determination of the Ratio of the Electromagnetic to the Electrostatic Unit of Electricity*. Washington, D.C.: U. S. Bureau of Standards, Reprint No. 65, 1907.
34. Rossi, B., *Optics*. Reading, Mass.: Addison-Wesley, 1957.
35. Sawyer, R. A., *Experimental Spectroscopy*. Englewood Cliffs, N. J.: Prentice-Hall, 1944.
36. Shurcliff, W. A., and S. S. Ballard, *Polarized Light*. Princeton, N. J.: Van Nostrand, 1964.
37. Silfvast, W. T., G. R. Fowles, and B. H. Hopkins, *Appl. Phys. Letters*, **8**, 318 (1966).
38. West, C. D., and R. C. Jones, *J. Opt. Soc. Am.*, **41**, 975 (1951).
39. White, H. E., *Introduction to Atomic Spectra*. New York: McGraw-Hill, 1934.
40. Williams, W. E., *Applications of Interferometry*, 4th ed. New York: Wiley, 1950.

ADDITIONAL REFERENCES

Ditchburn, R. W., *Light,* 2d ed. New York: Interscience, 1963.

Garbuny, M., *Optical Physics.* New York: Academic Press, 1965.

Jenkins, F. A., and H. E. White, *Fundamentals of Optics,* 3d ed. New York: McGraw-Hill, 1957.

O'Neill, E. L., *Introduction to Statistical Optics.* Reading, Mass.: Addison-Wesley, 1963.

Stone, J. M., *Radiation and Optics.* New York: McGraw-Hill, 1963.

Strong, J., *Concepts of Classical Optics.* San Francisco: W. H. Freeman and Company, 1958.

Wolf, E., ed., *Progress in Optics,* Vols. I–V. New York: Interscience, 1961–1966.

ANSWERS TO SELECTED
ODD-NUMBERED PROBLEMS

Chapter 1

1.7 $v = c/1.5,\quad u = c/1.7$
1.9 $n = \lambda/(a + b\lambda^2)$ where a and b are constants.
1.17 (a) 6.2 Å   (b) 0.003 Å
1.21 $\Delta f = 8.5 \times 10^8$ Hz $\Delta\lambda = 0.1$ Å

Chapter 2

2.3 39.8 W/m^2
2.5 (a) $E_0[2\hat{\mathbf{i}} + \hat{\mathbf{j}}(1 + i)]$
    (b) $E_0(\hat{\mathbf{i}} - 2i\hat{\mathbf{j}})$
    (c) $E_0[\hat{\mathbf{i}} - \hat{\mathbf{j}}(1 + i)2]$
2.7 (a) $E_0(\sqrt{3}\hat{\mathbf{j}} + \hat{\mathbf{k}})\exp i(kx - \omega t)$
    (b) $E_0(\hat{\mathbf{i}} - 2i\hat{\mathbf{k}})\exp i(ky - \omega t)$
    (c) $E_0\hat{\mathbf{k}}\exp i[k(x + y)/2 - \omega t]$
2.9 (a) $\begin{bmatrix}1\\2\end{bmatrix}$ linearly polarized 63.4 degrees from x axis.

        $\begin{bmatrix}1\\2i\end{bmatrix}$ left elliptically polarized with major axis of ellipse along y axis.

        $\begin{bmatrix}1\\1+i\end{bmatrix}$ left elliptically polarized with major axis of ellipse inclined 58 degrees from x axis.

    (b) $\begin{bmatrix}2\\-1\end{bmatrix}$ linearly polarized -26.6 degrees from x axis.

        $\begin{bmatrix}-2\\i\end{bmatrix}$ right elliptically polarized with major axis of ellipse along x axis.

        $\begin{bmatrix}-2\\1+i\end{bmatrix}$ right elliptically polarized with major axis of ellipse inclined -32 degrees from x axis.

2.13 Linearly polarized 18.4 degrees from horizontal axis.
2.15 (a) Critical angle = 48.6 degrees, Brewster angle = 53 degrees.
     (b) Critical angle = 34.8 degrees, Brewster angle = 60.25 degrees.
2.21 (a) 0.00023 mm   (b) $10^{-3,800}$

Chapter 3

3.1 $2\mathbf{E}_1 \cdot \mathbf{E}_2 \cos \theta_{12} + 2\mathbf{E}_1 \cdot \mathbf{E}_3 \cos \theta_{13} + 2\mathbf{E}_2 \cdot \mathbf{E}_3 \cos \theta_{23}$

3.3 $I/I_0 = 3 + 4 \cos \theta + 2 \cos 2\theta$ where $\theta = kyh/x$

3.5   83 cm

3.7   0.017 mm

3.11 2.1×10^{-12} s,   0.062 mm

3.13   0.08 mm

3.15 $G(\omega) = (A/4\pi)^2 [(\omega - \omega_0)^2 + \gamma^2]^{-1}$

3.17 $|\gamma(t)| = e^{-\gamma t}$

3.19 $\lambda - \lambda' = 0.22 (\lambda^2/d) (1 - R)R^{-1/2}$,
$f - f' = 0.22 (c/d) (1 - R)R^{-1/2}$

3.21 $I_T/I_0 = (1 - R)^2/[(1 - R)^2 + 4R \sin^2 (2\pi nd/\lambda)]$
where $R = [(n - 1)/(n + 1)]^2$
(a) $I_T/I_0 = 1$ (b) $I_T/I_0 = 0.85$

3.23   (a) $I_T (\max)/I_T (\min) = $ fringe contrast $= 2.35$
(b) R.P. = 86,000

3.25   (a) 40 cm   (b) 4 mm

Chapter 4

4.1   (a) Fresnel   (b) Fresnel   (c) Fraunhofer

4.3   0.0025

4.5   56 cm

4.9   0.05 (approximately independent of number of lines)

4.11   105 cm

4.13 $I/I_0 = 4$ (Open part of aperture contains exactly three Fresnel zones)

4.17   (c) 44 cm from slit

4.19 $g(y') = 2 \, \text{Si}[2\pi b/(b - 2y')] + 2 \, \text{Si}[2\pi b/(b + 2y')]$

where Si is the *sine integral*, $\text{Si}(u) = \int_0^u (\sin u/u)du$.

Chapter 5

5.9 $R = 30.69$ $\alpha = 364{,}000$ cm^{-1} $\varphi = 39$ degrees

5.13   40.25 degrees

5.15   0.014 degrees

5.17   2.6 degrees

Chapter 6

6.1   (a) 3.4×10^5 (b) 4×10^{13}
6.3 2.4×10^{14}
6.5 $3.2 \times 10^7 T^3 V$
6.7 $I_\lambda = 2\pi hc\lambda^{-5}/(e^{hc/\lambda Kt} - 1)$
6.9   (a) 3.2×10^{15} (b) 4.7×10^9
6.11 $35,600°K$

Chapter 7

7.3 6.58×10^9 Hz
7.5   (a) 0.33   (b) approximately $4a_H$
7.9 3×10^{12} Hz

Chapter 8

8.1   2.1 eV
8.3 1.6×10^{-25}
8.5 0.9×10^{22} m^{-3}
8.7   1.5 mm

Index